Short Stories

FOR STUDY AND ENJOYMENT

Revised Edition

TO THE MEMORY OF MY PARENTS

CHARLES T. EATON *and* EMMIE J. EATON

THIS BOOK IS AFFECTIONATELY DEDICATED

Short Stories

FOR STUDY
and
ENJOYMENT

Edited by HAROLD T. EATON

Revised Edition

NEW YORK

THE ODYSSEY PRESS · INC ·

Copyright 1929, 1934, and 1959
By The Odyssey Press, Inc.
All Rights Reserved
Printed in the United States

Second Printing of the Revised Edition

Preface

WHEN *Short Stories for Study and Enjoyment* was first being planned, it was then the opinion of both the editor and the publisher that there was a place for an anthology of carefully selected, class-tested stories — a collection to provide a very definite plan for the study of the short story as a type of literature. The revised edition is still based on that time-tested opinion. The introductory chapters of the book offer a text for studying the development of the short story and also its contemporary form. Part I, the bulk of the text, contains modern short stories for study. About one-quarter of this section is devoted to nineteenth-century authors, two-fifths (actually over forty per cent) to writers of our twentieth century, and slightly less than one-third to authors whose work was done in both periods. Each selection is preceded by a brief introduction containing important information about the author and his work; each selection is followed by a set of questions designed to help the student to learn and to think as well as to test his factual knowledge, an assignment in vocabulary building, and a problem developing some particular aspect of short-story form. The problems in Part I are arranged in an order following as closely as possible the order in the introductory technical discussion of the short story. These problems present a point-by-point method for studying the short story and contain provision for reviewing points already studied. For those students who are interested in creative writing, there is a brief section on writing the short story which is followed by a few carefully selected suggestions.

Part II of the text contains examples of those earlier forms of short fiction that are of some importance to students who are interested in the complete history of the short story. The fable, the parable, the essay-parable, the tale, and the early short story are all represented. Each of these earlier forms is accompanied by a brief explanatory note, an assignment in vocabulary building, and questions designed to show the purpose of the particular form under discussion and its relation to the modern short story.

The selections in this book have all been chosen expressly to provide a collection which contains worthwhile, interesting short stories for both study and enjoyment and which has little or no duplication with other short-story anthologies. Practically all of the stories were scientifically class-tested for student interest; and of the many selections tried out in the classroom, no story was finally included if it failed to appeal to at least the majority of the students.

Adequate provision has been made for the chronological study of the stories if such a procedure seems advantageous. The stories may also be studied as types for those who care to use this classification, although, of course, many stories may be correctly classified in more than one category. For example, a sea story may also be a war story, a story of character, a story of local color, or a story of action. Thus minute classification is not always either logical or particularly successful.

Because the work of vocabulary building is of great importance in all fields of learning, the student will find a definite assignment in each selection, since it is obvious that frequent additions to any individual's stock of words will aid both expression and understanding.

It is the sincere hope of the editor that the various study helps will simplify to some degree the teaching of the short story as a type of literature, for even in our radio-television age, there is still time left for reading for *both* study and enjoyment.

As no textbook is the product of one person, the editor thankfully acknowledges the advice and assistance of many people who contributed something to this book. He is indeed greatly indebted to his former associates in the teaching of English in Brockton, Mass. since almost every member of the department class-tested a number of short stories. He is also most grateful to the staff of the Brockton Public Library and to Miss Edith Blanchard of the John Hay Library, Brown University. In preparing this revised edition of the book, he acknowledges with gratitude the coöperation of Mrs. J. F. Colson of the staff of the Frederick Eugene Lykes, Junior, Memorial County Library of Brooksville, Florida.

Most of all, the editor is greatly indebted to his wife, Ruth Y. Eaton, who spent countless hours in proof-reading, translated two stories from the French, and made many helpful suggestions.

H. T. E.

Ridge Manor, Florida

Contents

Part II: Earlier Types of Fiction

Chronological Arrangement of Stories

Suggestions for Study

THE BEST reason for reading short stories is, of course, that we enjoy them. We like the breathless action of some stories, the clever character drawing of others, the presentation of special places and conditions of still others. Unfortunately, however, we do not always know why we like the stories — do not always recognize the action, the character-drawing, or the presentation of scene, as the thing that attracts us to them. We are vaguely conscious that one story differs from another and that we like some stories better than we do others, but we seldom understand why we prefer them or what makes them different from each other. This lack of understanding of the *whys* and *wherefores* of the short story leaves our impressions dulled and our appreciations faulty. It is only when we have learned the differences in construction and in quality of the many stories we read that we enjoy them fully and select them by the standards of good taste.

The purpose of this book is twofold, then: to give you enjoyment and to develop your understanding of the short story. To insure enjoyment, the stories have been chosen for their universal appeal. To insure a profitable study of the short story, the book has been equipped with enough informative material to provide a basis of knowledge for the study of individual stories, and with an organized set of provocative questions to establish a method for the course.

The introduction of the book contains an account of how short stories grew out of man's love of fiction, an explanation of the forms and construction of the modern short story, and some suggestions that should help you write stories of your own. Whenever, in your study, you find difficulty in understanding the discussion of technique, read the story named in parenthesis to learn how the point under discussion is applied in an actual story.

When you come to read the stories in the book, read them first as rapidly as you like, simply to enjoy them. Don't worry about the problem or the general questions until you are through. Then read the introduction to the story to learn something about the author and his methods. Then study the story. Use the suggestive questions, which are designed to help your understanding of the story and to keep you reminded of what you have already learned, and the problems, which are designed to teach new facts about short stories. Use the parenthetical references to the introduction whenever you need them. They are put in to help you find the information you need in the introduction.

It is possible to study this book in the order of the historical development of the short story. This order may be adopted without losing the benefit of the special problems if the class has studied both parts of the introduction, and if the cross references are used in studying the problems. A chronological table of contents is supplied for this use. The book has been organized, however, to teach what the modern story *is* before trying to teach what it came from. The best way to follow the plan of the book is to study Part I, and then Part II, and to finish by reviewing all the stories in the order of the chronological table and the historical introduction.

There are certain facts that should be known and remembered about each individual story. The following questions supply a means of determining whether you have learned these facts:

General Questions and Topics for the Study of Any Short Story

1. Note the title carefully. How is it connected with the story? Is it unusual and does it excite the reader's curiosity? Explain.

2. To what type does the story belong? If it is difficult to classify the story, mention the most important elements.

3. Is the theme of the story important? State it in a single sentence. Do you think the author was conscious of having any theme at all or did he write his story primarily to amuse? Explain.

4. Study the introduction. What information does it give the reader?

5. Is the setting important? Could the story have occurred anywhere else?

6. What is the initial incident that arouses the curiosity of the reader? State the problem or struggle.

7. What are the chief incidents of the story? Does each one contribute something to the outcome? Explain. Do you find any irrelevant material?

8. What is the climax? Prove that everything in the story leads up to the climax.

9. What information is given the reader in the conclusion?

10. How is the style of the writer individual? Would it be possible to recognize another story of this author by style alone?

11. Give your opinion of the story and be prepared to state your reasons for liking or disliking it.

If the class is doing notebook work in English, a brief entry made for each story will serve as a reminder of the characteristics of the story. The following form is suggested for the entries.

TITLE

AUTHOR

TYPE

THEME

Chief Characters	Setting	Problem	Climax	Opinion of Story (Give reasons)

Sometimes your understanding of the plot will be aided by making a diagram to show the development of the plot. The accompanying diagram of one of the stories in this book may be used as a model for the making of diagrams. (See "The Whirligig of Life," page 340.)

DIAGRAM OF "The Whirligig of Life"

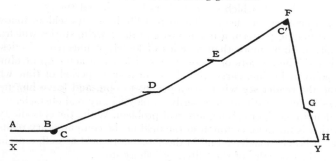

X–Y: *Base line*
A–B: *Introduction* — Time, place, characters
   C: *Problem* — What will be the outcome of the divorce suit?
   D: *Incident* — The demand for alimony
   E: *Incident* — The robbery of the Justice
   F: *Climax* — The decision to return together

C': *Problem solved*
F–G: *Falling action*
G: *Incident* — The remarriage
G–H: *Conclusion*

To diagram a short story: Estimate the length of the story in pages. Draw a line to represent that length. Estimate the length of introduction, of the incidents that make up the rising action, and of the falling action. Mark off lightly the lengths estimated so that the line is divided in the same proportions as is the story. Using this line as a base, draw the diagram, representing the introduction by a horizontal line, the rising action by a rising line, and the falling action by a falling line. The point at which the rising and falling lines join is, of course, the climax. The separate incidents that make up the action are indicated on the rising and falling lines; they are placed directly above the space allotted to them on the base line. The angle at which the action line rises is determined by the swiftness of the action.

THE EPISODIC SHORT STORY

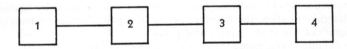

While most short stories are climactic in construction, and the plot builds up to a definite turning point or climax, there is also a much less common form which some authors have termed the *episodic short story*. Accepting the theory that in real life incidents seldom follow a truly climactic pattern, a few realistic authors write stories which are actually nothing more than a series of loosely connected episodes or incidents. The authors of these stories pick a character up at almost any point in his life, carry him along for a short period of time while letting the reader see what is happening to him, and leave him more or less abruptly without necessarily employing any real obstacle, using any definite goal, or solving any real problem. While the episodic type of fiction is far more common in the field of the contemporary realistic novel, it is occasionally found in the short-story field as well, especially among the examples of the "literary" short story.

THE SHORT STORY

The Development of the Short Story

When we try to find the real beginning of short narrative, we find ourselves following back through the ages until we go beyond all history — all written records — and come to the point where knowledge ends and supposition begins. We can only suppose that narrative and man's love of narrative had a beginning almost as long ago as had man's speech. We can only guess that primitive man, like the uncivilized tribes of today, told tales of great deeds, of sorcery and witchcraft, and of the doings of gods and demons.

TALES OF THE ANCIENTS

Our positive knowledge of early narrative begins, much later, with ancient inscriptions telling of the glorious deeds of kings, and with old manuscripts that have by chance come down to us. One such manuscript, the oldest of them, marks the real beginning of our study of the short story. This manuscript, found in Egypt, is called *Tales of the Magicians*, and is supposed to have been written some three thousand years or more before the birth of Christ. The stories it contains are much more like the folk tales of primitive peoples than like modern short stories: they are short but rambling; they lack that orderly arrangement of incidents that we call plot; they make no attempt to present believable situations or convincing characters; and they deal with the miraculous adventures of noblemen and the simple magic of sorcerers. The *Tales of the Magicians* are plainly made on the same pattern as the oral tales that were their immediate ancestors.

The next known step in the development of the short story goes forward two thousand years to classic Greece. There we find the *Iliad* and the *Odyssey* of the blind poet Homer. (If you do not know the stories of the *Iliad* and the *Odyssey*, and something about the theories of their authorship, look them

3

up in the encyclopedia.) These finished poems are a far cry indeed from the simple little anecdotes in the Egyptian manuscript. In these great chronicles are many short incidents, stories in themselves, that must be considered a part of short-story development. In Greece, even the historians were not above incorporating an occasional tale in their narratives. One of them, Herodotus (fifth century B.C.) is more renowned today for the interest of the stories he told about historical characters than he is for accuracy as a historian.

In Greece, too, the fables began, those direct ancestors of our tales and short stories. Æsop, a lame Greek slave, is said to have told them first in the sixth century B.C., and to have given them their form. Unfortunately, Æsop was not a writer, and we can prove nothing positive about him. The fables accredited to him, however, were written down by later Greeks and come to us as having had wide currency for years at the time of their writing.

The Romans did very little to advance the development of the short story. Their historians wrote history, and their poets, poetry. Virgil's *Aeneid*, however, contains some story-like incidents, as did Homer's poems before it. The stories of "Androcles and the Lion" and "Cupid and Psyche" were written in Rome; but, on the whole, the years of Roman supremacy formed a barren period in short-story development.

THE BIBLE

During all this time, however, another people, the Jews, had built up a great book from the writings of many different men. The Old Testament of the Bible contains many short narratives that can be detached from the books in which they occur, and at least two books, Esther and Ruth, that are unified stories in themselves. The New Testament has even clearer examples of a special type of story, the parables. So clear is the connection between these concentrated, well-written narratives and the modern short story that two of them are included in Part II of this book, to show the development of the short-story form.

TALES OF THE MIDDLE AGES *p. 45b*

After these early times, civilization was upset for generations by barbarian invasions of the centers of culture and by
the consequent readjustments of race and language that took
place. It was then that the vocal narrative flourished again.
The wandering minstrel and the troubadour sang narratives
in verse, and the old custom of passing on stories by word of
mouth, a custom that had never been near a real end, grew
stronger than ever.

Out of the oral tradition of the Dark Ages the written
story started up once more. Tales told to illustrate the teach-
ings of the Church were written by the monks; each one contained a little bit of narrative introducing, and giving point
to, a long moral discourse, or *exemplum*. The *Gesta Romanorum*
(deeds of the Romans) is a collection of such narratives. Oddly
enough, the stories of the *Gesta Romanorum* are not about
Romans at all. The *Contes Devots* (tales of piety) were another
religious form of about the same period.

More secular stories developed, too. The tales of the bards
and minstrels were collected, in France, into the *Chansons de*
Gestes (songs of great deeds). Some of these poems are known
to us now — the *Chanson de Roland*, about Charlemagne and
his followers, and the Arthurian cycle of legends that grew up
in Brittany and was written in English as *Le Mort d'Arthur* by
Sir Thomas Malory. *Fabliaux*, like the fables, as their name
implies, were written during the same period. A Frenchwoman,
Marie de France, who lived at the English Court of Henry II
in the twelfth century, made a collection of *lais*, short fairy
tales and mystical stories, that were popular in their time.
Good examples of many of these forms are found in the *Canter-*
bury Tales of Geoffrey Chaucer, the earliest of our great
English writers.

BOCCACCIO AND CHAUCER

Before Chaucer in the development of the short story should
come Giovanni Boccaccio of Naples and Florence. Boccaccio

wrote a book that is one of the most important in the development of the modern novel and the modern short story. This book, the *Decameron* (published in 1353 or 1358), contains one hundred short tales of all kinds bound together by a "frame" of narrative that explains the circumstances in which the stories were told. Many of the stories and poems of that time had grown up in groups and cycles — poems or stories about the same events, or the same characters, or the same court, forming the cycle or the group. The *Decameron* contained stories that were not related in any of these ways. They were held together only by the running narrative that accounted for the narrator, the place, and the circumstances of the narration. Chaucer, in England a few years later, used a similar device in the *Canterbury Tales*.

The *Canterbury Tales* were probably influenced in form and content by the Italian collection. Although they were written in verse, there is in them a close similarity to the stories of the *Decameron*. Chaucer's book contains the best examples of early short narrative to be found in the English language. Many collections were built on the "frame" plan in England, in France, and in Italy, but these two, the *Decameron* and the *Canterbury Tales*, are undoubtedly the best of them.

THE ARABIAN NIGHTS ENTERTAINMENTS

At about the same time (during the fourteenth century), some unknown writer in Egypt was compiling a collection of oriental tales, some of them already very old and some written during that century by contemporary authors. These tales were grouped on a plan which had long been familiar to the East and were called *The Thousand and One Nights* or *The Arabian Nights Entertainments*. Indeed, the well-known story of the oriental princess, Scheherazade, who told her husband a story every night and left it unfinished to insure her life for the following day, is too familiar to most readers to need more than mere mention. How old the idea of the book and some of the stories in it were at that time is impossible to state. According to ancient records, however, there was in 987 B.C.

a Persian writer who mentioned such a collection under the title, *A Thousand Nights and a Night*, although the oldest definitely-known date for an actual manuscript of *The Arabian Nights* is 1548 A.D. In fact, the first translation into English was made a little over a century ago, and the well-known scholarly translation by Sir Richard Burton came out during 1885–1888 in an edition of sixteen volumes.

THE PERIOD OF NEGLECT

During the sixteenth and the seventeenth centuries, short prose fiction was for a time rather neglected. In England, the chief reason for this neglect seems to have been the great popularity of the drama, which in the Age of Shakespeare overshadowed almost every other type of literary production, with the possible exception of poetry. In some of the longer prose books of the period, however, we find numbers of short episodes which might in a more favorable time have been good short-story material. When Oliver Cromwell came into power in the Puritan Age, he closed the theaters, as the Puritans were opposed to all plays and playwriting. Indeed, the only type of writing to find public favor was religious in theme. In fact, until the Restoration of Charles II in 1660, the chief type of approved writing was religious. The Puritan Age was the period which sponsored books like the immortal *Pilgrim's Progress* and *Paradise Lost*, even though both books were given to the world shortly after the Puritan influence had waned and Charles II had been restored to the English throne.

During the eighteenth century, sometimes called the Age of Classicism or the Age of Reason, writers of prose narratives, both long and short, were again popular, and prose itself became more graceful, simple, and understandable. Foremost among the writers of a type of literature which could have been classified as "almost short stories" were the essayists Joseph Addison, Richard Steele, and Eustace Budgell — all three of whom collaborated to produce *The Tatler* and *The Spectator Papers*. Many of the individual essays in the series were simple narratives which really are not too dissimilar in form and content from the short stories of today. It was during the eighteenth century that the novel was created when — in 1740 — Samuel Richardson wrote *Pamela*. Three other novelists of the period — Judge Henry Fielding, first of the realists, Laurence Sterne, and Tobias Smollett — also helped to develop this popular type of literature, and in several of the early novels there are to be found various episodes — each complete in itself — which are not unlike the short stories of today.

WASHINGTON IRVING

In the nineteenth century the writing of the true short story began. In this century also, American writers first appear in our discussion. Washington Irving is the first of them. He wrote essays, sketches, and tales, many of which approached the short-story form. Irving's tales, among them *The Legend of Sleepy Hollow* and *Rip Van Winkle*, differ from short stories only in that they are less closely confined to one effect, and in that they take us where the writer's interest lies instead of staying close to the imaginary line of single effect or writer's aim. His tales are stories about people and localities and action all at once. They are genial and loosely connected; sometimes they ramble a bit, but always they are real stories, not to be mistaken for fables, parables, essays, or other forms of literature.

EDGAR ALLAN POE AND NATHANIEL HAWTHORNE

It was after Washington Irving, however, that a technique for the present-day short story was developed. To Edgar Allan Poe must be given credit for formulating the principles that have guided other writers, and for exemplifying the principles he had formulated. Nathaniel Hawthorne, another important American writer, had just published his collection of short stories, *Twice Told Tales*. Poe reviewed the book and, in his review, gave his explanation of the method of the short story. He said, among other things:

I prefer commencing with the consideration of an *effect*. Keeping originality in view ... I say to myself, in the first place, "Of the innumerable effects, or impressions, of which the heart, the intellect, or (more generally) the soul is susceptible, which one shall I, on the present occasion, select?" Having chosen a novel first, and secondly a vivid effect, I consider whether it can be best wrought by incident or tone ... afterward looking about me (or rather within) for such combinations of events, or tone, as shall best aid me in the construction of the effect.

Poe followed his own method in his stories. All of them are marvels of compact unity, with the single effect — frequently one of horror — carefully developed. Hawthorne's method was similar, but his stories are more loosely constructed, less intense, and more complex in theme. Hawthorne, even in his short tales, was primarily concerned with moral values; Poe was not.

To Poe we owe also most of our stories of detectives and of the solving of mysteries. He created C. Auguste Dupin, the first amateur detective of fiction, and in "The Gold Bug" gave a clear example of an ingenious system of cryptic writing which has since served as a model for many writers of detective stories.

After the success of these three — Irving, Poe, and Hawthorne — many American writers adopted the short story. So many of them were there, and so well was their work done, that we have not space here for a full discussion of them. For the most part, they followed the example and technique of Hawthorne and Poe rather than the manner of Washington Irving or the earlier writers.

LATER WRITERS OF THE NINETEENTH CENTURY

These newer writers, however, did not all follow Hawthorne and Poe in their choice of mood and effect. They discarded non-essential material and limited the effects to be produced in their stories, but they did not limit themselves to detective stories, or horror stories, or moral stories. Each of them chose his own field. One or two stories by each of the following writers will give you some idea of the diverse methods and materials of the period: Fitz-James O'Brien, Ambrose Bierce, Bayard

Taylor, George William Curtis, Edward Everett Hale, Harriet Beecher Stowe, Frank Stockton, Francis Bret Harte, Thomas Bailey Aldrich, George W. Cable, Joel Chandler Harris.

New influences determined the tone of many of the stories of the time. Mark Twain, who wrote a few humorous short stories — "The Notorious Jumping Frog of Calaveras County" is the best known of them — was an appreciable influence on many of his contemporaries. Frank Stockton and H. C. Bunner were humorists, too, and clever handlers of story material. Thomas Bailey Aldrich also could be amusing; he wrote "Marjorie Daw," one of the most ingenious of surprise-ending stories.

BRET HARTE AND THE LOCAL COLORISTS

During the last third of the nineteenth century, Francis Bret Harte (1839–1902) was a strong influence in the short-story field, as he did much to make popular the regional or provincial short story — more commonly called the story of local color. Harte is best remembered today for his highly emotional, sentimental, dramatic stories featuring California mining camps and early towns during the Gold Rush Days, which began in 1849 and lasted for about a decade. It was Harte's story, "The Luck of Roaring Camp," which helped to make him known both in England and in the United States. In the regional or local-color stories, the authors emphasize the local customs, manners, speech, dress, and general surroundings; indeed, the reader can learn much from these stories about how the inhabitants of a particular section actually live.

Harte's contemporaries and successors wrote many colorful stories about different sections of our United States. For example, Mark Twain wrote about the Mississippi and his Missouri home town as he remembered it from the days of his boyhood; Mary E. Wilkins Freeman and Sarah Orne Jewett wrote about a few small Massachusetts villages; while Hamlin Garland wrote stories of the farming communities of our Middle West. Jack London and Rex Beach wrote colorful stories of Alaska and other parts of the frozen North. In brief there is scarcely an important area in our entire country which has not produced its own story teller; and today stories of local color are still fairly popular even though they are not so common as they were in the days when Bret Harte and his contemporaries were featuring them.

HENRY JAMES

During the late nineteenth and the early twentieth centuries, more authors became interested in portraying character skillfully, vividly, and accurately. Henry James (1843-1916), best remembered today as a late Victorian novelist, wrote stories in which he achieved superlative character drawing. It is to James, then, as well as to William Dean Howells (1837-1920), the author of *The Rise of Silas Lapham* and other fine American novels, that our contemporary short story is indebted for much of its sound character delineation and modern realism.

O. HENRY AND THE MAGAZINE METHOD

Another important influence in the short-story field was William Sydney Porter (1862-1910), better known to readers as O. Henry. At the height of his fame, this popular short-story writer probably had more imitators and far more readers than any other author of his day; and even now, about five full decades after his death, he is still influencing authors and — through them — thousands of readers. Particularly original in creating clever plots, most of them with his trademark, the surprise ending, O. Henry wrote of life in New York City at the turn of the century, of outlaws, of derelicts, of confidence men, of shop girls and "Of Cabbages and Kings" as the author himself expressed it when he selected this quotation from Lewis Carrol as the title for one of his short-story collections:

> "The time has come," the Walrus said,
> "To talk of many things:
>
> Of shoes — and ships — and sealing wax —
> Of cabbages — and kings."

THE CONTEMPORARY SHORT STORY IN OTHER COUNTRIES

Nineteenth- and twentieth-century developments of the short story as a type of literature have not, of course, been confined to the United States. In an age of quick communication and speedy travel, our American writers have influenced those of other countries and in turn have themselves been influenced by these same foreign authors.

This is especially true of the writers of Great Britain and a few of the writers of France. Indeed, a small group of authors has even been classified as Anglo-American because the various members have close ties with each country and are completely familiar with both ways of life. Roald Dahl and the late Eric Knight and Canadian Stephen Leacock could be mentioned as excellent examples of this group. Today, some of the well-known British writers have lived and written here in the United States, and a few from our country have lived and written in Great Britain. Indeed, the American influence in England really began about a century and a half ago with Washington Irving, a close friend of Sir Walter Scott and other British writers of the earliest years of the Age of Romanticism. Many critics, however, believe that the British development of the modern short story dates from Robert Louis Stevenson — poet, essayist, novelist, short-story writer, and above all else explorer and lover of adventure. Rudyard Kipling, too, has had a decided influence upon the development of the modern short story, for it was in this field that he won much of his early fame with his excellent short stories about India.

Our own twentieth century has witnessed the passing of many well-known British authors — Arnold Bennett, Gilbert K. Chesterton, Joseph Conrad, Walter De la Mare, Sir Arthur Conan Doyle, John Galsworthy, Thomas Hardy, W. W. Jacobs — one of the very few short-story specialists — Rudyard Kipling, Stephen Leacock, Katherine Mansfield, H. G. Wells, to list a few of them. On the other hand, some of the twentieth-century writers are carrying on — for example, Nadine Gordimer, who writes interestingly about South Africa and Frank O'Connor, who writes realistically and competently about Ireland and the Irish. Then, in addition to these, there are a number of young authors who are writing original short stories, many of which differ materially from the short-story patterns of Poe, De Maupassant, and O. Henry. Some short-story experimentalists in Britain are trying new forms and new methods so that it is probably true that the short stories of the British Empire today show more variety than do our contemporary American short stories.

In France at the present time, the technique of the short story, with its unified treatment of a simple idea and the carefully planned elimination of all non-essentials, has probably reached a higher point of development than it has here in the United States. The great French master of the short story, Guy de Maupassant, has influenced the writing of many authors in many different nations. In fact, some literary historians assert that he, even more than Poe, was the real originator of the modern short story. Then, too, magazines like *Transition* and *The Paris Review* have undoubtedly influenced the literary short stories of both France and the United States. Quite naturally, the entire literature of France has been altered materially by the effects of World War I and World War II, since practically all authors in any literary field whatever have been and are greatly influenced by all the important changes in their own land and their own way of life.

In Communist Russia, the short story — once somber in tone and realistic both in treatment and theme — has become a type of propaganda devoted almost exclusively to singing the praises of the government and all contemporary government policies. Today, we read stories about the struggle of a group of factory workers to meet their quota, stories about the great efforts of agricultural coöperative workers to harvest all of the grain before the coming of the killing frost, and stories of the exploits of a loyal party worker in unmasking a foreign spy and turning him over to the police. To the non-communist reader at least, most of these selections seem stilted, artificial, and uninteresting.

THE MODERN AMERICAN SHORT STORY

During the past third of a century, there have naturally been some important developments in the American short-story field. In the first place, reading — important as it still is — has met with powerful competitors — motion pictures, radio, and (perhaps the most important of all) television. One editor wrote recently that it is not encouraging to note that there were fewer books published in 1957 than there were in 1910, while within that period our population had practically doubled and tens of millions of Americans had more money to spend and leisure to enjoy. On the other hand, it is encouraging to note the millions of copies of paperback books which have been bought and read during the past two or three decades.

So far as the short story itself is concerned, it has today to compete with very well-written interesting nonfiction; and contemporary articles seem to be much more numerous and popular than are contemporary short stories. Indeed, with many magazine editorial staffs, the policy today is to have fewer stories in each issue and more nonfiction. (This statement does not, of course, apply to our relatively few remaining all-fiction publications.) During the years of World War II, the paper shortage reduced the length of all kinds of writing. While the *number* of selections in each magazine remained practically the same in many cases, the *length* of each selection was materially reduced. As a reduction in length had already been inaugurated by the increasingly popular pocket-sized magazines like the *Reader's Digest*, it is not at all surprising to find that — on the whole — both stories and articles are today briefer, more compact, and better organized so that there is little space open to the leisurely tale, the rambling short story, and the slow-moving personal essay of forty or fifty years ago.

There is now a sharper division, perhaps, between the so-called "commercial" short story, found in the large circulation magazines and the "literary" stories found chiefly in the issues of the "little magazine" group. Today, love stories — perhaps most popular of all — westerns, action stories, and detective fiction still entertain thousands of readers. In addition to these types, there has been a big increase in the number of stories of phantasy and science fiction; in fact, over a dozen magazines devoted entirely to this particular field attest the popularity of these two varieties. Of course, these amazing highly imaginative tales are true descendants of the stories written a generation before by Jules Verne and, a little later, by the prolific H. G. Wells, whose work is still popular. Some of today's unusually weird horror tales stem almost directly from Mary Shelley's *Frankenstein* and Bram Stoker's horror-novel, *Dracula*.

The years of depression here in the United States — commencing with the stock-market crash in the fall of 1929 and extending well into the late thirties — influenced all fields of literature — both fiction and nonfiction. There were (and still are) short stories which show a similar outlook and emphasis to John Steinbeck's *The Grapes of Wrath*, a realistic novel devoted to the social problems of the dispossessed farmers during the worst of the long depression. (A generation before Steinbeck, Hamlin Garland — 1860–1940 — had dealt with somewhat similar material in his *Main-Traveled Roads*, published in 1890.) Other authors have recently written about similar social problems — poverty, injustice, unemployment, illness, and death. These somber stories — a few of which are still being written today — have reflected the viewpoint of a generation which found it difficult sometimes to make even a bare living. Along with the realistic fiction, there have been some good historical short stories written, although most authors of historical fiction have preferred to write novels. Indeed, many of our best short-story writers of today are much better known as novelists. The reason for this is not hard to find: novels are frequently popular; collections of short stories (with the exception of a few anthologies) are not.

It is not surprising, then, that more and more of our writers of fiction choose the novel as their vehicle of expression, especially since our modern novelists are able to write what they like, as they like it. There are today few writers like O. Henry, whose literary reputation is based almost exclusively on his work in the short-story field.

During the past two or three decades, many of our well-known American authors have died — Rex Beach, Stephen Vincent Benét, Ellis Parker Butler, Irvin S. Cobb, Mary E. Wilkins Freeman, Dorothy Canfield Fisher, John Fox Junior, Hamlin Garland, William Dean Howells, Ring Lardner, Jack London, Christopher Morley, Marjorie K. Rawlings, Mary Roberts Rinehart, Morgan Robertson, Booth Tarkington, Albert Payson Terhune, and Henry Van Dyke, to list some of them. With many of these authors, the short story was decidedly a secondary field. Other novelists and short-story writers are still active (William Faulkner, Paul Gallico, Dorothy Parker, Conrad Richter, and John Steinbeck, to name only a few), and there are many of the younger generation of authors now in their twenties and early thirties, some of whom will undoubtedly become the leading authors of tomorrow. For example Ray Bradbury, born in Illinois in 1920, has already published more than two hundred short stories and his work has appeared in more than eighty anthologies.

What the short story of the future will be like is something for the prophets to predict. It is enough to attempt to evaluate the past and the present. It is obvious, however, that short stories will change with the times even though the truly gifted teller-of-tales will doubtless find an audience in any country and age.

QUESTIONS

1. Try to develop a theory to account for the beginning of narrative. Do you believe the primitive men told tales of their own adventures? Do you believe that they repeated accounts of their fathers' and grandfathers' deeds? Would such tales help to make a beginning of narrative?

2. Give a brief account of the oldest story manuscript that has come down to us.

3. What are the *Iliad* and the *Odyssey?*

4. Which made the greater contribution to the development of the short story — the Greeks or the Romans? Explain.

5. Name some of the varieties of short narrative that were written during the Middle Ages.

6. Who wrote the *Decameron?* The *Canterbury Tales?* Why are these books important to us?

7. With the aid of an encyclopedia, trace the probable history of the *The Arabian Nights Entertainments.*

8. Tell what each of the following contributed to the development of the short story: Geoffrey Chaucer, Edgar Allan Poe, Guy de Maupassant, Francis Bret Harte, Sir Arthur Conan Doyle, O. Henry, Robert Louis Stevenson.

9. What are the characteristics of the French short story? The Russian? The English?

The Technique of the Short Story

VARIETIES OF SHORT FICTION

We have seen that the short story has developed gradually from other kinds of short fiction. Among its ancestors we have numbered the fable, the parable, the essay-parable, and the tale. Not one of these is the true short story, although individual short stories may closely resemble one or another of them; and all of them may be found — if only occasionally — in the writing of today.

The *fable* is a short narrative — usually a very short narrative — told for the express purpose of teaching a moral, which is drawn directly from the wise or foolish actions of the characters. The characters in the fable may be birds, beasts, or fishes, as well as men. (See "The Old Man, His Son, and Their Donkey," page 403, and "The Shepherd Boy," page 401.)

The *parable* also is a brief narrative intended to teach a moral or ethical idea. In the parable, however, the idea is taught less directly than in the fable, and it is taught as an idea, and not as a rule to govern conduct. (See "The Good Samaritan," page 405, and "The Prodigal Son," page 407.)

The *essay-parable* is a combination, as its name implies. The essay portion of it describes a social abuse, and the parable following shows in story form the author's idea of the way to correct it. (See "The Story of an Heir," page 415.)

The *tale* is more nearly like the short story than any of the other forms. Like most short stories, it has for a purpose to put before the reader an interesting story, interesting scenes, and interesting persons. Unlike the short story, it may take all the time needed fully to present all three of the story elements. The story part of the tale may wander along, turning aside as the writer's interest turns to include descriptions, character sketches, and interesting bits of narrative about persons or scenes. The tale may, and frequently does, contain

18

a story within a story. (See "The Three Rings," page 411.) It is nowhere marked by the compression, the devotion to one idea, and the elimination of all unnecessary details that are the distinguishing marks of the short story. (See "The Belated Travelers," page 422.)

The *short story* usually contrives to leave behind a single impression or effect. It is usually, though not always, built about one character, one place, one idea, or one act. It makes no attempt to present the number of ideas, scenes, and persons that may be found in the tale. (See "The Tell-Tale Heart," page 448.)

A good short story must have a proper balance of plot, setting, and character — the elements that make a story. It must be believable on the basis of its own evidence or of our common knowledge. It must create some definite impression on our minds. And it must give the effect of getting somewhere, either in deeds accomplished, struggles ended, puzzles solved, or points proved.

PLOT

Of the three elements of the short story, the first to be considered is plot. The plot of a story is simply the action that takes place in it. A plot is properly made up of a series of connected happenings, or *incidents*, and their result.

These incidents must be interesting in themselves, and they must lead logically up to a high point of interest and to a real result. In the story of Little Red Riding Hood, for instance, the little girl's departure for her grandmother's is one incident; her meeting the Wolf in the woods is another; the Wolf's encounter with the grandmother is a third; the meeting of Red Riding Hood and the Wolf in the grandmother's cottage is a fourth (which contains the high point of interest for the reader); the killing of the Wolf by the woodcutter is the final incident; and the Wolf's death in this incident is the result of all that has gone before.

In order to have a result, the action must contain a *conflict*, a struggle between opposing forces. The conflict gives rise to the *problem* of the story, the question to be answered by the result of the struggle.

Several different kinds of conflict are used in short stories: the struggle of man with man, in which two men or two groups of men are opposed to each other; the struggle of man with animals; the struggle of man with the forces of nature; the struggle of man with the supernatural; and the struggle of man with himself, in which one aspect of the man's character is shown in sharp conflict with another. In "The Adventure of the Three Garridebs," the conflict lies between man and and man, detective and criminal. In "Little Red Riding Hood," the conflict lies between man and animal. In "Children of Loneliness," the conflict lies within the mind of the chief character; two sides of her nature are shown warring against each other. A conflict of some sort occurs in every story that you read.

The incidents of the plot, then, must follow each other logically, and must show a struggle leading to a result which shall solve the problem of the story. The high point of interest in the story, at which the result of the conflict begins to be decided, is the *climax*.

PARTS OF THE SHORT STORY

The short story may easily be divided into parts by tracing out the pattern of the plot. The first part, the *introduction*, contains such information as the reader must have to understand the story. Usually, the introduction tells who is in the story, where it takes place, and what has led up to the situation with which the story opens. Because so much antecedent material (material describing what has happened before the story opens) slows up the action of the story at the very beginning, many writers begin at once with the action and work in the introductory material as the opportunity arises. Whether it is lumped at the beginning or presented gradually in the story, the introduction must be smoothly written, interesting, and as brief as possible in order not to interfere with the reader's interest.

After the introduction comes the body of the story. It begins with the *initial incident* which indicates what the problem is, and what struggle is to come. From this incident follow the other events that make up the *rising action*, leading to the *climax*.

After the climax, there is only enough action to finish the solution of the problem. The *falling action*, therefore, is usually brief, and is followed by a *conclusion* that has for its purpose the answering of any questions remaining in the reader's mind. In the conclusion, anything unexplained in the story is accounted for, the picture in the reader's mind is clarified; and any loose ends of the story are picked up and fastened together. (See "The Siege of Berlin," page 40.)

THE STORY OF PLOT

If you will ask yourself what you like best about some story you have read recently, you will probably find that the "what-happened" element interested you more than anything else. In most of the stories in our current magazines, action (the plot) is the most important element of the stories. The chief interest of the story featuring plot lies in the action itself — the adventure, the mystery, or the surprising twist to the outcome. The story that depends for its effect upon such an interest is called a *story of plot*. (See "A Service of Love," page 48.)

SUSPENSE

Up to the climax of the story, the reader's interest is held by a feeling of suspense, an uncertainty of the outcome of the struggle. This feeling, present in some quantity in every story, is deliberately intensified in some stories by the author's handling of his materials. The writer may hint of impending doom by the very words he uses; he may involve his hero in great danger, and deliberately turn aside from him to tell about something else; or he may use the device known as retardation, suddenly becoming detailed in his description of every act, every object in the setting, every thought in the characters' minds, while the reader becomes more and more alarmed over the outcome of the situation. Real suspense must arise from the situation, but it may be very much heightened by a clever writer. (See "The Siege of Berlin" page 40.)

THE SURPRISE ENDING

There are several particular effects to be had by special handling of the details of a plot. Here, we shall consider only one of the most important of them. The method of arranging the discoveries in a detective story is one example of this effect. In the best kind of detective story, the evidence used by the detective in solving the mystery is put before the reader bit by bit, but usually in such a manner that a careless reader will ignore important details. By this method, the triumph of the detective has an unexpected or surprising twist to it.

There is another kind of story, the *surprise-ending story*, that uses a closely similar method for its special effect. The surprise-ending story is a story in which the reader is allowed, and even encouraged, to misinterpret events up to the last moment of the story; then, suddenly set right, he finds that the outcome of the story is quite different from what he has been led to expect. The outcome of the story must, however, be made to appear reasonable. There is, plainly, one good way to accomplish such an end. At the same time that the reader is being led astray by one set of details, there must be another set, more or less hidden in the story, that could lead him in the right direction if he were sharp enough to see them. Thus, he usually overlooks the second set of details until the outcome is revealed to him; then, by looking back through the story, he can find a logical explanation for the ending.

All this amounts to saying that the surprise ending must be carefully planned — that if the author is fair to his readers, he must have in the story information pointing to the ending. By reading one or two surprise-ending stories, any one can see how they are made. (See "The Commutation Chophouse," page 69, and "A Service of Love," page 48.)

SETTING

Setting is another of the three short-story elements. The setting is the background against which the incidents in the story take place. Setting is not merely place; it includes place where, time when, and conditions under which the story moves. Setting includes also the atmosphere of the story, and thus helps to determine its general tone or feeling — cheerful, gloomy, hopeful, despairing, weird. If, for instance, the place of a story is a feudal castle on a hill in Central Europe and the time is the middle of a stormy night in the thirteenth century, the atmosphere is fairly well prepared for any story of medieval danger, terror, or mystery that we could invent.

Setting is not, however, of invariable importance. Every story has a setting, but sometimes it is so sketchily indicated as to pass almost unobserved. The old tales that began "Once upon a time, an old woodcutter lived in a little hut on the edge of a great forest" were not very definite about their settings, but they had them. The setting of a story may often be its least important element; but some kind of setting is always either indicated or implied. On the other hand, in certain types of stories, setting becomes enormously important, so that the story could fit only into the particular scene described for it. Such a story, in which action and character depend upon time, place, and condition, is called a *story of setting*. (See "North of Fifty-Three," page 81.)

Many stories (Bret Harte's, for example) are written rather to present a picture of a definite region at a definite time than to show action interesting in itself or to offer a study of character. These stories, depending for interest upon the peculiarities of a locality, are called *local color* stories, and they, also, are stories of setting. In any story, the presentation of the special characteristics of the region or locality in which the story takes place is local color. (See "How Santa Claus Came to Simpson's Bar," page 138.)

CHARACTER

The third element in the short story, character, has always some importance in the story. The plot may be almost negligible; the setting may be barely indicated; but there must be living beings that think or act to keep the story going. These living beings are generally, but not always, human. They may be presented fully, so that we know what they think and feel and are, or they may be shown to us simply as things that act; but they must always seem natural and alive, and capable of doing what the author makes them do.

The principal characters are not always human. The lover of wild-animal stories will think at once of tales in which no man appears. There are even a few stories in which the characters are inanimate objects personified — made to speak and think as persons do. (Hans Christian Andersen wrote some stories about brooms, mops, pans, pots, clocks, and toys, in which no humans appeared. Lord Dunsany, in his *Dreamer's Tales*, has written others.) Whatever they are, the characters in the story must seem to be living and feeling individuals if they are to gain our sympathies.

There are several ways of making the characters in a story seem real to us as readers. Authors present them to us by the same methods that we use to form our opinions of real people. The characters are shown behaving as people behave, are made to act, think, feel, and speak as the people about us do. Sometimes we are told what the characters say or think about each other, or the author tells us directly what his opinion of them is. The four usual methods of presenting a character consist of showing the reader (1) actions or thoughts of the character, (2) conversation of the character, (3) conversation of other characters about him, and (4) the author's own opinion. Any one or all of these methods may be used in any story. (See "A Village Singer," page 95, and "The Grudge," page 112.)

Like plot and setting, character may be the most important element in a story. *Stories of character* may show us persons whose fortunes are determined by peculiarities of temperament; they may be stories of mental struggle; they may be studies of particular sides of man's character, or of personal struggles of any kind.

DIALOGUE

To all three of the elements, dialogue (the conversation of characters in the story) is important. Dialogue helps to advance the plot by presenting antecedent material, by explaining the action as it takes place, and by preparing the reader for incidents to come. It offers a natural means of explaining the setting. It is clearly very important in at least two of the usual means of presenting character.

In addition to these uses, dialogue adds to the reader's interest in the story by breaking the monotony of the telling and by adding life and action to the incidents. It serves, too, to add to the humor of a funny story, and to make clearer the peculiarities shown in a local-color story.

To serve any of these purposes, dialogue must be well-written and interesting. Above all else, it must be natural. No reader must be allowed to feel that the character speaking would not have said the things the writer says he said, or that he would not have said them in the manner indicated by the dialogue.

POINT OF VIEW

An important factor in the construction of a short story is the *point of view*. Point of view is usually explained as a position that the writer chooses from which to show the reader what happens in the story. More simply, point of view is a way of telling a story.

The author, of course, writes the story, but he does not always put his own personality into it. Usually he tells the tale through one of several assumed personalities. He may tell it (with no reference to himself as a person) as if it were something he saw and heard. Thus he limits himself to telling what a witness might have seen, or heard, had there been one.

This manner of telling is called the *objective* point of view. (See "How Santa Claus Came to Simpson's Bar," page 138.)

The author may write as one who knows all about the characters in the story — their relations with each other, their thoughts, their feelings. He may assume that he knows more about them than anybody possibly could if they were real persons. If he does assume such knowledge, the point of view is *omniscient*, or all-knowing. (See "Where Love Is, There God Is Also," page 217.) Both the omniscient and the objective are third-person points of view. When he uses them to tell his story, the author writes in the third person, speaking of each of the characters as *he* or *she*.

Sometimes an author lets one of the characters tell the story. If he does, he can choose a minor character and let him tell what he heard and saw and thought, or he can let the main character tell his own story. In the use of either one of these methods, the story is told from the first-person point of view, in which the character speaks of himself as "I" and relates the story as one of the actors.

In a good story, the point of view is usually chosen for some real reason. If it is necessary to show what the characters think and feel, the author may choose the omniscient point of view. If he wishes to let the reader see the action of the story without entering into the minds of the characters, he may use the objective point of view. If, for some reason, the story is hard to believe, the author frequently adopts the first person to let the reader feel that a real person is saying to him, "I was there, and I saw this strange thing. Therefore, it really happened." Thus, many stories of adventure are told by major or minor characters, and supernatural stories frequently use the same device. There are other reasons just as good as these for choosing one point of view or another. You will be able, if you try, to find the reason for the point of view in most of the stories you read. Many a detective story, for example, is told by a minor character, who is able to tell the story as a witness without being able to give away the secret, which he does not know. (See "The Adventure of the Three Garridebs," page 181.)

Often several points of view are used in the same story, but when they are the author must make the changes in point of view seem natural to the reader. When you have read "The Poison Ship" and "The Damned Thing," you will see how the point of view may logically be changed.

TONE OR ATMOSPHERE

In both "The Poison Ship" and "The Damned Thing" the changing point of view contributes to the atmosphere or tone of the narrative. Atmosphere has already been mentioned in the discussion of setting. It is the general feeling of the story as determined by the setting, the attitudes of the characters, and the style of the author. O. Henry, in some of his stories, writes of pathetic, and sometimes even tragic, happenings, but the tone of his narrative is sprightly and gay. Poe's stories are frequently gloomy in tone and are written for the purpose of creating a solemn or terrible atmosphere around his characters. The tone of a story and the final impression it makes upon a reader are usually closely related. (See "The Damned Thing," page 200.)

THEME

The atmosphere of a story must be suited to its theme. Theme is the idea behind the story. Frequently, the theme is not apparent in the story, and is too slight to be detected. This is especially true in stories written merely to amuse the reader. In some stories, however, the theme is the most important thing in the story. In such stories, the narrative is written chiefly to illustrate the theme. The parables and the fables are theme stories of two special kinds.

Theme is not the same thing as moral. The theme of a dog story might be the idea that a faithful collie will return to the wild to avenge the death of another dog he loves; but that theme is not a moral. If the story were written merely to prove that one must never kill a dog that has a faithful collie for a playmate, there would be a moral. Theme is an underlying general idea on which the story is based. Moral is a lesson that the reader learns from reading the story. Most stories do not have morals at all, but all stories have themes, however slight they may be. (See "The Pack," page 211.)

ROMANCE AND REALISM

Whether the most important element in the story is plot, setting, character, or theme, there is another kind of impression that it may make upon us. This impression depends upon all the elements discussed before. If the characters are presented as persons of the kind that we know in the world, doing things that real people ordinarily do, among scenes that are familiar to us through experience or report — if the story seems extremely probable, and the happenings in it might really take place — we may call the story realistic. If, on the other hand, the characters are presented as persons without the common faults of mankind, doing great deeds of heroism in strange settings — if the story appears to our common sense as improbable or impossible in the common scheme of things — we say that the story is romantic.

Realism deals with the difficulties common to mankind or to some certain class among men. Romance deals with unusual situations, commonly exaggerated somewhat for effect. The aim of the first is to show us what really happens in the world; of the second, to show us something interesting or exciting either in the world or out of it. The probable story is likely to be realistic; the improbable or impossible story is almost certainly romantic. (See "The Bottle Imp," page 251, and "Children of Loneliness," page 299.)

HUMOR

There is another important quality in many stories — *humor*. Humor in the short story is often used merely as an aid to the light or the ironic tone of the story. Frequently, however, it is itself the effect that the author is seeking.

Written humor is obtained by several different methods: by an unexpected contrast, by an amusing situation, by exaggeration, and by funny dialogue. In a humorous story, written simply to keep the reader laughing, all these different methods will probably be used for variety. (See "Pigs Is Pigs," page 317, and "Keeping Up Appearances," page 329.)

THE CLASSIFICATION OF SHORT STORIES

In the discussion of the technique of the short story, several different types of stories have been mentioned. The three usual classes of the modern short story are *story of plot*, *story of setting*, and *story of character*. To these we should add *story of theme*.

Some students, however, are not satisfied with these broad classes. They divide stories into groups according to the kinds of settings, plots, and character they contain. Thus, the "detective story" is really a story of plot; the "sea story" is commonly a story of setting or of plot; the "problem story" is a story in which the "problem" is most important, a story of theme. It is frequently impossible to classify a story accurately in any one of these groups. For example, a "sea story" may be also an "adventure story"; a "character story" may be also a "local-color story." If the reader desires to classify a story as belonging to two types instead of one, there is no reason why he should not; for an author practically never sits down to write a story expressly to fit one class or another. The usual types of the modern short story follow:

1. Story of Adventure	10. Story of Character
2. Story of Romantic Adventure	11. Story of Local Color
3. Love Story	12. Sea Story
4. Detective Story	13. Story of the Supernatural
5. Mystery Story	14. Psychological Story
6. Problem Story (Apologue)	15. Story of Terror
7. Story of Dramatic Incident	16. Story of Humor
8. Story of Youth	17. Animal Story
9. Story of Fantasy	18. Burlesque

QUESTIONS

1. Name four common varieties of short fiction. Compare the tale and the short story.
2. What is the plot of a story? Why is a conflict necessary to the plot of a story?
3. What is suspense? How is it heightened in a story?
4. Why should a surprise-ending story be difficult to construct?
5. What is the setting of a story? How important to the story is its setting?
6. What are the four usual ways of presenting character in the story?
7. Explain the uses of dialogue in the story. Try to think of other uses of dialogue.
8. What is third-person point of view? What is first-person point of view? How does the point of view make a difference in the story?
9. What determines the atmosphere of a story?
10. Explain the difference in a short story between theme and moral. Which is essential to the story?
11. What is romance? What is realism? What determines whether a story is romantic or realistic?
12. What means do writers use to achieve humor in fiction? Try to think of examples.
13. How are short stories classified?

Writing Short Stories

The student who really desires to understand how short stories are written can do nothing better than to write some of his own. If he will write a few stories, and write them conscientiously, he will find that he quickens his appreciation of the work of other writers at the same time that he gains for himself valuable experience in the use of literary materials. If you as a student are willing to try the writing experiment, the following suggestions may be of use to you.

CHOICE OF MATERIALS

Before you can begin to write a story, you must know definitely what you are going to write about. Choose situations that you understand as material for your story. You will probably do best if you write about political intrigue in a high-school student government, a situation in a family like your own or a friend's, something that might happen in your town or in some other place that you know well. Perhaps some man you know is a war veteran who has told you stories. If his adventures are perfectly familiar to you, there is no reason that you should not make them the basis of a story. Be careful, however, that you really know what you are writing about. Don't try to tell a story of intrigue in the Court of Spain, of adventure in the deserts of Australia, or of life on the plains of South America, unless you know something about Spanish court life, or Australian deserts, or South American plains.

The plots of your stories need not, however, be limited to your own experiences and the experiences of your friends. Plot material may be purely imaginative or it may be derived from your reading or from some other source. Newspaper stories, for example, are good sources of plot material. Many writers search the daily news for human-interest stories and reports of unusual incidents. The story of an old woman who disinherited two sons and left her money to a foundling cat hospital might yield the idea for a plot; so might the story of three sisters who were living in the poorhouse, but who owned property and bank balances worth forty thousand dollars. Such material contains ideas for plot; it does not generally contain the full plot that the writer finally uses. For that he must depend upon his imagination, upon his understanding of men and events, and upon his ability to keep a reasonable balance between his imagination and his common sense.

When you have chosen something that you understand to write about, look it over carefully to be sure that it is really something to write about, and not just one of the old, old tricks that have been used by amateur writers everywhere. The story of the strange adventure that turns out to be a dream is such a trick. The story of the substitute football player who goes into the big game of the year during the last five minutes of play and saves the day for dear old Mugwump, is another. The story of the hero who leaves his aged parents to run the farm while he goes off to seek his fortune, which he finds just in time to rush home and stop foreclosure of the family mortgage, is a third. It is perfectly true, of course, that people sometimes have interesting nightmares, that substitutes have occasionally made winning touchdowns, and that a few wandering boys have probably turned up on the old farm at the critical moment, but the number of stories that have been written about these and similar events is already out of all proportion to their importance in our lives. They are hackneyed plots and are to be avoided.

PLANNING THE STORY

When you have decided what you are to write about, you are ready to decide what you are to write about it. Be sure that your story has a plot — that it contains action leading to a result, that the action is shown in a series of incidents related to each other and leading to a climax. Be sure, too, that there are enough incidents in the plot to make the development of the story clear to the reader, and that all the material in the story has a relation to the story itself. Don't tell your readers that your hero is hideously ugly unless his ugliness has something to do with the story. If, however, his ugliness *has* something to do with the story, don't neglect to include some incident in which the importance of his ugliness is shown.

Plan your story, and be sure it is well-planned, before you begin to write. Know what you are going to do about plot, setting, characters, theme, and point of view. Decide how much introductory information the reader must have to understand the story, and give it to him. Then you may begin to write with some assurance; your worst troubles are over before you start.

WRITING THE STORY

Write the story as naturally as you can. Try to make your characters act and speak as real people would. Do not waste your time and your readers' by indulging in "fine writing," but try to make every word and every sentence count.

You will probably find when you have finished that parts of your story do not satisfy you. If they do not, study them carefully to find what is wrong, then rewrite them. For many stories, the rewriting is even more important than the first writing.

TESTING YOUR STORY

Before you may consider your story finished, you must study it as a whole. Is it well written? Does it conform to the technical requirements for a short story? Is the plot strong enough to support it? Is the story reasonable? Are the characters real? Is the setting clearly indicated? Have you changed your point of view anywhere? If you have, is the change a reasonable one? Test your story by these and other questions. If the answer to each of them is satisfactory, you have written a good story. If it is not, try again.

I. Introduction
  1. Write the introduction for a story of the supernatural. Select a suitable setting and give the tone or atmosphere of your story.
  2. Write the introduction for a sport story in which the central interest lies in a game between the rival schools. Try to avoid a trite, hackneyed plot.

II. Plot
  1. Write a brief summary of the plot of a story you have read.
  2. Write an original plot.
  3. Develop plots from the following materials:
     (a) Holyoke "Dead" Man Returns after Wife Spent Insurance. — Police unable to advise frantic woman who identified wrong man as to proper etiquette. (Boston *Herald*, Aug. 10, 1928)
     (b) Aged Spinster Leaves Fortune to Boy Who Saved Pet Cat from Drowning.
     (c) Millionaire Disowns Only Son.
     (d) Politics Sever Life-long Friendship — Confederate Veterans Quarrel over Presidential Elections.
     (e) Football Hero Wins Scholarship — Had Hoped for College Education.

III. Dialogue
  1. Two students are discussing a member of the football team. One is a friend of the player in question while the other is distinctly hostile to him. Reproduce their conversation.
  2. Two girls are discussing the coming senior prom. What do they say?
  3. Three friends have met for the first time after their summer vacation. One has been working all summer; the second has been at the seashore; and the third has spent six weeks at a camp in the Adirondacks. They compare notes. Give an account of the conversation.
  4. The scene is a soda water fountain; the time, the present. The characters are the clerk, two "teen-agers," a college boy, an elderly gentleman, and a matronly woman who evidently disapproves of the younger generation. Reproduce the general conversation.

IV. Description of Character
  1. Describe the heroine of one of your own stories

    (a) by direct description. "She was tall — etc."
    (b) by showing her speech, manners, actions.
  2. Apply the same two methods to
    (a) the most unusual character you know
    (b) the captain of one of the school teams
    (c) the teacher you like best.

V. Write a short story, from 1,500 to 2,000 words long, suitable for
   publication in your school magazine. Write a clear summary of
   the plot and examine it carefully to see that it is correctly constructed as well as unique and interesting. Avoid direct description
   of characters; instead, let them reveal themselves through their
   speech and actions. Be sure that your conversations are natural
   and that the speech of each character is true to type. After you
   have written the first draft of the story, revise it carefully and ask
   your teacher to criticize it for you. Keeping in mind all construc-
   tive criticisms, write the final manuscript.

PART I
MODERN SHORT STORIES

The Siege of Berlin *

Alphonse Daudet (1840–1897)

The Daudet family lived at Nîmes, in the south of France, where the younger son Alphonse was born in 1840. The father, Vincent Daudet, had been a prosperous silk manufacturer, but had failed in business and had become, for a time, a commercial traveler. After a brief schooling, Alphonse Daudet obtained a position as usher in one of the French schools — a position in which he was generally despised by the teachers and hated by the students. He was rescued from his disagreeable situation by his older brother, Ernest, who had found work on one of the Paris papers. After a few years in Paris, Alphonse Daudet wrote his first book — a collection of poems — and succeeded in finding a publisher who had faith enough in him to publish it.

Sometime later, the Empress, impressed by one of Daudet's best pieces, "Les Prunes," commanded the powerful Duc de Morny to do something for the author. De Morny found an easy governmental position which gave Daudet an assured income.

In 1867 Daudet married Mademoiselle Julia Allard, who proved to be a wonderful influence upon her husband's work. It is a tribute to her that all of her husband's great books were published after his marriage. The illness of Daudet's later years racked his body but left his mind clear and his vigor undiminished. He died in 1897.

Daudet is noted for his novels, short stories, and plays. A close observer of human nature, he wrote of people with directness and clarity. Although some of his characters are exaggerated and resemble somewhat the caricatures of Dickens, Daudet displayed originality, true psychological insight, and a genuine sympathy for his characters.

"The Siege of Berlin" has been classed by some editors as a story of dramatic incident. While the setting is important and

---

* Translated by Ruth Young Eaton.

39

the characters themselves are well drawn, the entire action hinges about one dramatic crisis — the entrance of the Prussians into the city of Paris. The style, clear and vivid, shows the simplicity of genius.

The reader will have less difficulty in appreciating the story if he considers for a moment the condition of France during the Franco-Prussian War (1870–1871). Napoleon III (1852–1870), Emperor of France, fearing the growing power of the Hohenzollern family, had declared war on Prussia. The French were defeated at Wissembourg on August 4, and at Sedan on September 1, where Napoleon was taken prisoner. Immediately following the defeat, a revolution took place in Paris, and a republic was declared. The Prussians captured Metz and Strassburg, and laid siege to Paris, which fell only when the inhabitants had been reduced almost to starvation.

WE WERE going down the Avenue des Champs-Élysées with Dr. V. when he stopped and, pointing out to me one of the large houses grouped around the Arc-de-Triomphe, said:

"Do you see those four closed windows up there on the balcony? During the first days of the month of August, that terrible month of August in the year '70, I was called there to treat a case of apoplexy. It was at the home of Colonel Jouve, a cavalry officer of the First Empire, who at the beginning of the war had come to live on the Champs-Élysées, in an apartment opening on the balcony. Do you know why? To be present at the triumphal return of our troops! Poor old man! The news of Wissembourg had reached him as he was getting up from the table. When he read the name of Napoleon at the bottom of that bulletin of defeat, he had fallen smitten with apoplexy.

"I found the old gentleman stretched his full length on the carpet of his bed chamber, his face bloody and lifeless as if he had received a blow with a club on his head. Standing, he would have seemed very tall; lying down, he appeared to be immense. He had fine features, superb teeth, white hair rather curly, and was eighty years old, although he appeared to be sixty. Near him his granddaughter, who looked very like him, knelt in tears.

"The sweetness of the child touched me. Daughter and granddaughter of a soldier, she had a father on the staff of MacMahon, and the sight of this grand old man stretched out before her brought to her mind another image not less terrible. I reassured her to the best of my ability; but deep down in my heart I despaired somewhat, for at eighty one seldom recovers from apoplexy.

"For three days, in fact, the patient remained in the same lifeless stupor. In the meantime, the news of Reichshofen arrived in Paris. You remember the strange way in which it came. Up till evening we believed it a great victory, twenty thousand Prussians killed, and the crown-prince a prisoner. I do not know what miracle, what magnetic current it was; perhaps it was an echo of that national joy that reached our poor sick patient. However, that evening, when I approached his bed, I no longer found the same man there. His eyes were almost clear, and his speech was less thick. He had strength to smile at me and stammer twice, 'Vic-to-ry!'

"'Yes, colonel, a great victory,' I replied.

"And, as I gave him the details of the wonderful success of MacMahon, I saw his features relax and his face light up.

"When I left the room, I found the young girl very pale waiting for me outside the door. She was weeping.

"'Why, he is saved!' I said to her, taking both her hands.

"The unhappy child scarcely had courage enough to reply to me. They had just given out the true report of Reichshofen — MacMahon in flight and the entire army scattered. We looked at each other in dismay. She was grieving at the thought of her father; I was trembling at the thought of the old man. Certainly, he could not withstand this new shock. But what was to be done! Leave him his joy, the illusions which had brought him back to life? If that, then it would be necessary to lie!

"'Yes, indeed, I will lie!' the heroic girl said to me, quickly brushing aside her tears, and radiantly she went back into her grandfather's room.

"It was a hard task she had taken upon herself. The old fellow's head was cloudy, and he allowed himself to be deceived like a child. But with returning health, his ideas began to be more clear. We had to tell him of the daily movements of the armies, and draw up military bulletins for him. It was truly a pitiful sight to see that beautiful child night and day leaning over the map of Germany, and sticking in tiny flags, trying to contrive a whole glorious campaign. She used to ask my aid for all that, and I would help her as best I could, but it was really the grandfather who helped us most in this imaginary invasion. He had conquered Germany so many times under the First Empire! He knew all the strategy of the advance: 'Now that's where they are going to go — That's what they are going to do' — and his prophecies were always realized, a fact which made him very proud.

"Unfortunately, in vain we took cities, won battles; we never went fast enough for him. Each day when I arrived I learned of a new feat of arms.

"'Doctor, we have taken Mayence,' the young girl would say, coming up to me with a sad smile, and through the door I would hear a happy voice calling to me.

"'They are on the march! They are on the march! In eight days we shall enter Berlin.'

"At that very moment the Prussians were not more than eight days from Paris. We asked ourselves first if it would not be better to take him into the country; but once outside, he would have learned the true state of France, and I still found him very weak, too weak from his great shock to allow him to hear the truth. We finally decided to remain in Paris.

"On the first day of the blockade, I went upstairs very much perturbed, with that feeling of anxiety in my heart which a battle under one's very walls gives one. I found the old fellow jubilant and proud.

"'Well,' he said, 'the siege has begun!'

"I looked at him dumbfounded. 'Why, colonel, how do you know?'

"His granddaughter turned toward me and said:

"'O! yes, doctor. It's great news. The siege of Berlin has begun!'

"She said it while plying her needle with a calm air. How could he doubt anything! The cannons at the fort, he could not hear them. Unhappy Paris, sad and distracted, he could not see that! What he did see from his bed was a part of the Arc-de-Triomphe, and in his room all about him mementos of the First Empire helped indeed to create the delusion.

"From that day on, our military operations became simplified indeed. Taking Berlin was no more than a matter of patience. From time to time, when the old man became bored too much, we read him a letter from his son, an imaginary letter, of course, since nothing came into Paris any more, and since MacMahon's aide-de-camp had been sent off to a fortress in Germany after Sedan. Imagine the despair of that poor child, without news of her father, knowing him to be a prisoner, deprived of everything, perhaps ill, and yet obliged to make him talk in those happy letters. Sometimes strength failed her; weeks went by without news. But then the old man would become restless; he would not sleep any. Suddenly a letter would come from Germany which, kneeling beside his bed, she would read to him in a gay tone, holding back her tears. The colonel would listen religiously, smile understandingly, approve, criticize, and explain the slightly troublesome passages to us. But where he was especially fine was in the replies he sent his son. 'Never forget that you are a Frenchman,' he would tell him. 'Be generous to those poor people. Don't make them fear the invasion too much.' Along with these bits of advice he would also offer some general ideas on politics, and the conditions of peace to be imposed upon the vanquished. Upon that point I ought to say he was not unreasonable.

"'Indemnity for the war, and nothing more. What good would it do to take their provinces from them? Can one make France out of Germany?'

"He dictated all that with a firm voice, and one felt so much candor in his words, such a beautiful patriotic faith, that it was impossible not to be moved while listening to him.

"During this time, the siege continued to progress, but not that of Berlin, alas! It was a time of intense cold, of bombardment, of epidemics, of famine. But thanks to our care, to our efforts, to the indefatigable tenderness which surrounded him, the serenity of the old man was not disturbed for a moment. Right up to the end I was able to procure white bread and fresh meat for him. There was only enough for him, of course; and you could not imagine anything more touching than those meals of the grandfather, the old man in his bed, fresh and laughing, his napkin under his chin, near him his granddaughter, rather pale from her privations, guiding his hands, making him drink, helping him to eat all those good forbidden things. Then, animated by the meal, in the comfort of his warm room, the cold winter wind shut out, snow hurling itself against the window panes, the old cavalry officer would recall his campaigns in the north, and retell us for the hundredth time of that awful retreat from Russia when they had eaten only frozen biscuits and horse meat.

"'Do you understand that, little girl? We ate horse meat!'

"I know she understood well. For two months she had been eating nothing else. From day to day, however, as the period of convalescence approached, our task with the sick man became more difficult. That numbness of his senses, of all his limbs, which had helped us so much up till now began to disappear. Two or three times already the terrific bombardment of the Maillot gate had made him start and prick up his ears like a dog in the hunt. We were obliged to invent a final victory near Berlin and salutes fired in honor of this at the Hotel des Invalides. Another day, when we had pushed his bed near the window, he saw very distinctly the national guard drawn up on the Avenue de le Grand-Armée.

"'What are those troops doing there?' the old fellow asked, and we heard him muttering between his teeth, 'Bad discipline! Bad discipline!'

"There was nothing to be done about it, but we understood

that henceforth we must take great precautions. Unfortunately, so far we hadn't taken enough.

"One evening the girl came to me very much disturbed. 'Tomorrow they enter,' she told me.

"Was the door of her grandfather's room open? The fact is that since, on thinking it over, I can recall that that evening he had an extraordinary expression on his face. It is probable that he had heard us. Only *we* were speaking of the Prussians, and the old fellow was thinking of the French in connection with this triumphal entry for which he had been waiting so long — MacMahon coming down the avenue amidst flowers and fanfares, *his* son at the side of the marshal, and he, the old man, on his balcony, saluting the tattered flags, and the black eagles in the dust.

"Poor father Jouve! He was, without doubt, imagining that we wished to prevent him from being present at the parade of our troops, in order to spare him too great an emotion. He was careful not to speak to anyone, but the next day at the very time when the Prussian battalions started timidly on the long avenue which leads from the Maillot gate to the Tuileries, the window up there opened softly and the colonel in full uniform appeared on the balcony with his helmet and his great sword. He was astonished to find the avenues so deserted, so silent, the window blinds of the houses shut, Paris gloomy as a great pest-house, flags everywhere, but so odd, all of them white with red crosses, and no one to go to greet our soldiers.

"For a moment he thought he had been deceived.

"But no! Down there behind the Arc-de-Triomphe there was a confused noise, a black line which was advancing in the dawn. Then, little by little, the points of the helmets glistened, the drums began to beat, and under the Arc-de-Triomphe burst forth the triumphal march of Schubert.

"There in the melancholy silence, one heard a cry, a terrible cry: 'To arms! — To arms! — the Prussians!' And the advance guard could see up there on the balcony a tall old man tottering, waving his arms, and falling.

"This time Colonel Jouve was really dead."

QUESTIONS

1. What is the meaning of the title? Can you think of a better title?
2. When did the doctor and the granddaughter first begin to deceive Colonel Jouve? Did they do so intentionally?
3. How could they carry out the deception? Did either of them know anything of military affairs?
4. Do you think they were justified in lying? Explain.
5. Why were the letters invented by the granddaughter?
6. What were the old man's remarks about just terms of peace? Why are they significant?
7. Who was MacMahon? Find out the causes and the result of the Franco-Prussian War.
8. What is the setting of this story? The atmosphere?
9. How much time does the story cover?
10. *Word Study.* — What do the following words mean as they are used in the story: *delusion, indemnity, apoplexy, strategy, perturbed, privation?*

Problem: PLOT
(See pages 19–20.)

1. What is the usual purpose of an introduction? Where does the introduction end? Should you like more or less introduction? Does the introduction do anything besides give necessary information?

2. What is the conflict that makes this story possible? Where is it first indicated? What complications make the story more interesting? Does your interest in the story rise steadily almost to the end?

3. What is the climax of the story? Were you prepared for it? Did it follow logically from preceding incidents?

4. What information does the author give you after the climax of the story? Was it sufficient for his purpose?

A Service of Love *

O. Henry (William Sydney Porter) (1862–1910)

William Sydney Porter, better known as O. Henry, was born in Greensboro, North Carolina, in 1862 and died in New York City, June 5, 1910. At different times during his life he was druggist, ranchman, editor, publisher, bank clerk, and author. He traveled all over the United States, and lived for a time in Central America.

In 1901 O. Henry came to New York City, where he spent the remaining nine years of his life. Here his work received real appreciation, and he became known, and probably is still known, as the most popular short-story writer in the United States. Personally, he was a shy, reserved, whimsical soul with practically no intimate friends.

O. Henry's stories are almost flawless in technique. He used extensively what is called the surprise ending. Very few of his stories end in the way that the reader expects; yet it is easy to see on a second reading that the ending is logical and carefully prepared for.

O. Henry has written stories of life in Central America, of life in the West during the latter part of the nineteenth century, of life in the Cumberland Mountains, and of life in New York City. He wrote about all kinds of people: gamblers, confidence men, shop girls, clubmen, country boys and girls, bankers, brokers, and a host of others. His sympathies were always with the poor and the oppressed. O. Henry's work has influenced a majority of contemporary short-story writers, and the number of his direct imitators is very large. Both the influence and the imitation are to be found in our popular fiction magazines.

"A Service of Love" is characteristic of the sympathetic, whimsical genius of O. Henry. The time is modern; the setting, New York City, the scene of many of the writer's famous stories. After

pretending to take for his theme "When one loves one's art no service seems too hard," the author reveals his real theme in the conclusion. Written in O. Henry's inimitable style, the story carries the reader along breezily and ends, like so many of this author's narratives, with a twist that catches the reader unaware.

WHEN one loves one's Art no service seems too hard. That is our premise. This story shall draw a conclusion from it, and show at the same time that the premise is incorrect. That will be a new thing in logic, and a feat in story-telling somewhat older than the great wall of China.

Joe Larrabee came out of the post-oak flats of the Middle West pulsing with a genius for pictorial art. At six he drew a picture of the town pump with a prominent citizen passing it hastily. This effort was framed and hung in the drug-store window by the side of the ear of corn with an uneven number of rows. At twenty he left for New York with a flowing neck-tie and a capital tied up somewhat closer.

Delia Caruthers did things in six octaves so promisingly in a pine-tree village in the South that her relatives chipped in enough in her chip hat for her to go "North" and "finish." They could not see her f—, but that is our story.

Joe and Delia met in an atelier where a number of art and music students had gathered, to discuss chiaroscuro, Wagner, music, Rembrandt's works, pictures, Waldteufel, wallpaper, Chopin, and Oolong.

Joe and Delia became enamored one of the other, or each of the other, as you please, and in a short time were married — for (see above) when one loves one's Art no service seems too hard.

Mr. and Mrs. Larrabee began housekeeping in a flat. It was a lonesome flat — something like the A sharp way down at the left-hand end of the keyboard. And they were happy, for they had their Art, and they had each other. And my advice to the rich young man would be — sell all thou hast, and give it to the poor — janitor for the privilege of living in a flat with your Art and your Delia.

Flat-dwellers shall indorse my dictum that theirs is the only true happiness. If a home is happy it cannot fit too close — let the dresser collapse and become a billiard table; let the mantel turn to a rowing machine, the escritoire to a spare bed-chamber, the washstand to an upright piano; let the four walls come together, if they will, so you and your Delia are between. But if home be the other kind, let it be wide and long — enter you at the Golden Gate, hang your hat on Hatteras, your cape on Cape Horn and go out by the Labrador.

Joe was painting in the class of the great Magister — you know his fame. His fees are high; his lessons are light — his high-lights have brought him renown. Delia was studying under Rosenstock — you know his repute as a disturber of the piano keys.

They were mighty happy as long as their money lasted. So is every —— But I will not be cynical. Their aims were very clear and defined. Joe was to become capable very soon of turning out pictures that old gentlemen with thin side-whiskers and thick pocketbooks would sandbag one another in his studio for the privilege of buying. Delia was to become familiar and then contemptuous with Music, so that when she saw the orchestra seats and boxes unsold she could have sore throat and lobster in a private dining-room and refuse to go on the stage.

But the best, in my opinion, was the home life in the little flat — the ardent, voluble chats after the day's study; the cozy dinners and fresh light breakfasts; the interchange of ambitions — ambitions interwoven each with the other's or else inconsiderable — the mutual help and inspiration; and — overlook my artlessness — stuffed olives and cheese sand-wiches at 11 P. M.

But after a while Art flagged. It sometimes does, even if some switchman doesn't flag it. Everything going out and nothing coming in, as the vulgarians say. Money was lacking to pay Mr. Magister and Herr Rosenstock their prices. When one loves one's Art no service seems too hard. So, Delia said she must give music lessons to keep the chafing dish bubbling.

For two or three days she went out canvassing for pupils. One evening she came home elated.

"Joe, dear," she said, gleefully, "I've a pupil. And oh, the loveliest people. General — General A. B. Pinkney's daughter — on Seventy-first street. Such a splendid house, Joe — you ought to see the front door! Byzantine, I think you would call it. And inside! Oh, Joe, I never saw anything like it before.

"My pupil is his daughter Clementina. I dearly love her already. She's a delicate thing — dresses always in white; and the sweetest, simplest manners! Only eighteen years old. I'm to give three lessons a week; and, just think, Joe! Five dollars a lesson. I don't mind it a bit; for when I get two or three more pupils I can resume my lessons with Herr Rosenstock. Now, smooth out that wrinkle between your brows, dear, and let's have a nice supper."

"That's all right for you, Dele," said Joe, attacking a can of peas with a carving knife and a hatchet, "but how about me? Do you think I'm going to let you hustle for wages while I philander in the regions of high art? Not by the bones of Benvenuto Cellini! I guess I can sell papers or lay cobble stones, and bring in a dollar or two."

Delia came and hung about his neck.

"Joe, dear, you are silly. You must keep on at your studies. It is not as if I had quit my music and gone to work at something else. While I teach I learn. I am always with my music. And we can live as happily as millionaires on fifteen dollars a week. You mustn't think of leaving Mr. Magister."

"All right," said Joe, reaching for the blue scalloped vegetable dish. "But I hate for you to be giving lessons. It isn't Art. But you're a trump and a dear to do it."

"When one loves one's Art no service seems too hard," said Delia.

"Magister praised the sky in that sketch I made in the park," said Joe. "And Tinkle gave me permission to hang two of them in his window. I may sell one if the right kind of a honeyed idiot sees them."

"I'm sure you will," said Delia, sweetly. "And now let's be thankful for General Pinkney and this veal roast."

During all of the next week the Larrabees had an early breakfast. Joe was enthusiastic about some morning-effect sketches he was doing in Central Park, and Delia packed him off breakfasted, coddled, praised, and kissed at seven o'clock. Art is an engaging mistress. It was most times seven o'clock when he returned in the evening.

At the end of the week Delia, sweetly proud but languid, triumphantly tossed three five-dollar bills on the eight by ten (inches) center table of the eight by ten (feet) flat parlor.

"Sometimes," she said, a little wearily, "Clementina tries me. I'm afraid she doesn't practice enough, and I have to tell her the same things so often. And then she always dresses entirely in white, and that does get monotonous. But General Pinkney is the dearest old man! I wish you could know him, Joe. He comes in sometimes when I am with Clementina at the piano — he is a widower, you know — and stands there pulling his white goatee. 'And how are the semiquavers and the demi-semiquavers progressing?' he always asks.

"I wish you could see the wainscoting in that drawing-room, Joe! And those Astrakhan rug portières. And Clementina has such a funny little cough. I hope she is stronger than she looks. Oh, I really am getting attached to her; she is so gentle and high bred. General Pinkney's brother was once Minister to Bolivia."

And then Joe, with the air of a Monte Cristo, drew forth a ten, a five, a two and a one — all legal tender notes — and laid them beside Delia's earnings.

"Sold that watercolor of the obelisk to a man from Peoria," he announced overwhelmingly.

"Don't joke with me," said Delia — "not from Peoria!"

"All the way. I wish you could see him, Dele. Fat man with a woolen muffler and a quill toothpick. He saw the sketch in Tinkle's window and thought it was a windmill at first. He was game, though, and bought it anyhow. He ordered another — an oil sketch of the Lackawanna freight depot — to take back with him. Music lessons! Oh, I guess Art is still in it."

"I'm so glad you've kept on," said Delia, heartily. "You're

bound to win, dear. Thirty-three dollars! We never had so much to spend before. We'll have oysters to-night."

"And filet mignon with champignons," said Joe. "Where is the olive fork?"

On the next Saturday evening Joe reached home first. He spread his eighteen dollars on the parlor table and washed what seemed to be a great deal of dark paint from his hands.

Half an hour later Delia arrived, her right hand tied up in a shapeless bundle of wraps and bandages.

"How is this?" asked Joe after the usual greetings. Delia laughed, but not very joyously.

"Clementina," she explained, "insisted upon a Welsh rabbit after her lesson. She is such a queer girl. Welsh rabbits at five in the afternoon. The General was there. You should have seen him run for the chafing dish, Joe, just as if there wasn't a servant in the house. I know Clementina isn't in good health; she is so nervous. In serving the rabbit she spilled a great lot of it, boiling hot, over my hand and wrist. It hurt awfully, Joe. And the dear girl was so sorry! But General Pinkney! — Joe, that old man nearly went distracted. He rushed downstairs and sent somebody — they said the furnace man or somebody in the basement — out to a drug store for some oil and things to bind it up with. It doesn't hurt so much now."

"What's this?" asked Joe, taking the hand tenderly and pulling at some white strands beneath the bandages.

"It's something soft," said Delia, "that had oil on it. Oh, Joe, did you sell another sketch?" She had seen the money on the table.

"Did I?" said Joe; "just ask the man from Peoria. He got his depot today, and he isn't sure but he thinks he wants another parkscape and a view on the Hudson. What time this afternoon did you burn your hand, Dele?"

"Five o'clock, I think," said Dele plaintively. "The iron — I mean the rabbit came off the fire about that time. You ought to have seen General Pinkney, Joe, when ——"

"Sit down here a moment, Dele," said Joe. He drew her to the couch, sat beside her and put his arm across her shoulders.

She braved it for a moment or two with an eye full of love and stubbornness, and murmured a phrase or two vaguely of General Pinkney; but at length down went her head and out came the truth and tears.

"I couldn't get any pupils," she confessed. "And I couldn't bear to have you give up your lessons; and I got a place ironing shirts in that big Twenty-fourth Street laundry. And I think I did very well to make up both General Pinkney and Clementina, don't you, Joe? And when a girl in the laundry set down a hot iron on my hand this afternoon I was all the way home making up that story about the Welsh rabbit. You're not angry, are you, Joe? And if I hadn't got the work you mightn't have sold your sketches to that man from Peoria."

"He wasn't from Peoria," said Joe, slowly.

"Well, it doesn't matter where he was from. How clever you are, Joe — and — kiss me, Joe — and what made you ever suspect that I wasn't giving lessons to Clementina?"

"I didn't," said Joe, "until tonight. And I wouldn't have then, only I sent up this cotton waste and oil from the engine room this afternoon for a girl upstairs who had her hand burned with a smoothing-iron. I've been firing the engine in that laundry for the last two weeks."

"And then you didn't ——"

"My purchaser from Peoria," said Joe, "and General Pinkney are both creations of the same art — but you wouldn't call it either painting or music."

And then they both laughed, and Joe began:

"When one loves one's Art, no service seems ——"

But Delia stopped him with her hand on his lips. "No," she said — "just 'When one loves.'"

QUESTIONS

. Did you expect the story to end as it does? Go back and try to find statements that might have made you suspicious.

. Is O. Henry's style like any other you have read? Explain.

3. Is there slang in the story?
4. Find places where the author uses contrast to be humorous. Find sentences in which the author plays on the meanings of words (puns).
5. Could this have been made a sad story? Do you think O. Henry could have made it a sad story?
6. Has the story a happy ending? Explain.
7. What do you like best about "A Service of Love"?
8. *Word Study.* — What do the following words mean as they are used in the story: *contemptuous, enamored, cynical, distracted, voluble, mutual?*

Problem: PLOT IN THE STORY
(See pages 19–21.)

1. What is the plot of this story?
2. What is the author trying to show you, an interesting setting, an interesting character, or an interesting series of actions?
3. Where does the real action of the story begin? Does the introduction give you a clear picture of Joe and Delia? Does it give you a clear statement of the situation from which the story develops?
4. Would Joe and Delia really talk as O. Henry makes them talk? Does the conversation in this story tell you anything about the chief characters? What does it do? About how much of the story is told by means of conversation?

The Symbol *

Jan Stransky (1913–   )

Born on December 3, 1913, into a prominent Czecho-slovakian family, at Brno — formerly called Brünn — Jan Stransky was brought up and educated in his native land — first at Brno, the capital of Moravia, an ancient city of more than a quarter of a million people, and later at Prague, the capital of Czechoslovakia, where he studied at Charles University and received the degree of Doctor of Laws. Dr. Stransky's grandfather had been a member of the first government in 1918 after Czecho-slovakia had won its independence, while his father had served as Deputy Prime Minister and Minister of Education. The author himself has served in many fields; for example he has been a journalist, a foreign correspondent, a novelist, an editor, and a diplomat. Escaping when Hitler seized Czechoslovakia, he returned at the close of World War II and was elected to serve as a member of Parliament. "After the Communist 'coup' in 1948," writes Dr. Stransky, "I escaped again from Czechoslo-vakia, where I was facing persecution for my anti-Communist writings." The author has had a busy adventurous life. "In 1951," he continues, "I became Deputy Desk Chief of the Czecho-slovak Desk of Radio Free Europe in Munich, until 1952, when I joined Free Europe Press, a division of Free Europe, Inc., in New York and Munich." In his present work, the author does a large amount of traveling. With two books to his credit, "Czecho-slovakia" and a novel, "East Wind Over Prague," he still man-ages to find a little time for free-lance writing. Dr. Stransky is married and the father of one child.

Jan Stransky's powerful story, "The Symbol," gives a grim but vivid, realistic picture of family life in any totalitarian slave state, where the government is everything and the individual is nothing, and where family peace, harmony, love, loyalty, and

* Reprinted from *This Week Magazine.* Copyright, 1953, by United Newspapers Magazine Corporation. Reprinted by permission of *This Week* and the author.

*coöperation are frequently forgotten in the service of the "Party"
and the "State." The story also provides some excellent examples
of two common propaganda devices — employing "halo words"
to get desired ideas accepted and using "horned words" to insure
the rejection of other ideas without thinking. The propagandist
wishing to make converts uses "good words" (People's democracy, true pioneer, socialist vigilance, class consciousness, and
bolshevist zeal) for his side and employs bad labels (old capitalist
régime, Western imperialists, atomic criminals, Nazi murderers,
reactionary, and aggressor) for the opposing side. These devices
(sometimes termed "glittering generality" and "name-calling")
can be tremendously effective. After all, "socialist vigilance" is
a much better sounding word than "spying" and "atomic criminals" calls forth a very unpleasant picture of the opposition.
Based on an actual trial which took place in Pilsen only a few
years ago, the story shows clearly to the reader what it is like to
live in any country where the chief democratic virtues and morals
are considered sentimental weaknesses and where family life as
we know it is frequently nonexistent. As the foreign correspondent,
Vincent Sheehan, wrote more than twenty years ago about the
Nazi government of Germany and the fascist government of Italy:
"No citizen of any democracy — even of the democracies that
are threatened in their existence — has the slightest cause to envy
the subjects of the 'Duce' and the 'Führer.'" That statement is
even more true today; and every citizen of any of our democratic
countries should thank God that he is a citizen and not a slave.*

WHEN the two girls, Anna and Zora, stepped out of
the overheated courtroom, the silent crowd in the anteroom
shifted and made room for them to pass.

Anna, who walked with an easy and self-assured stride, did
not mind the staring eyes of the people. They were reproachful
eyes, contemptuous eyes, even menacing eyes. She countered
with a bold, challenging look and, keeping her chin up, proudly
sailed toward the door.

Zora envied her. She was not as strong as her sister; she
was ashamed and frightened. She had not wanted to come.
She had not wanted to testify. But they made her. Now she

could feel all those cold eyes upon her, and she could feel her face growing red.

She must not cry — not here at any rate, not in front of Anna. Her head was swimming; her heart was pounding. The whole thing was like a bad dream, a horrible nightmare. Only it was not a dream: the courtroom was real; the policeman and the judges were real; the crowd was real.

She felt acutely miserable, more miserable than she had ever been before. Besides, the new pair of shoes which she had bought only yesterday were too small by half a size, and now her feet were in agony. *God!* she thought. *To get home, to lie down, to get some sleep, God! Shall we ever reach the door?*

In the street, Comrade Karel Holdos was waiting for them. Karel was the secretary of the local branch of the Party. He was also Anna's boy friend. He was smiling at her, making his way to them through the crowd.

"Congratulations, girls! Well done, very well done, indeed! You were splendid; you really were! You, Anna my dear, you were especially good."

Anna murmured something, but Karel did not let her speak.

"No, no, really, it was excellent. I am sure the press will speak well of you both. And — who knows? — there might even be a letter of appreciation from headquarters. I was very proud!"

Zora did not say anything. Anna pressed Karel's hand.

"Thank you, Karel, but it really is not worth speaking about. We have done the obvious thing — what else would you expect?"

"Ah, but that is just the point: certainly, it was the thing to do. Whether they were your parents or not, one's duty is one's duty. But how many people would have the same moral courage to get over family prejudices the way you did? Even among our comrades . . ." And he shook his head. "But you, girls, you are true pioneers. You see, we are the new generation. There is nothing we cannot achieve!"

They were on their way home, with Karel accompanying them and pouring out a continuous stream of familiar words

and slogans: socialist vigilance ... class consciousness ...
bolshevist zeal ... He was talking to both of them, but it
was really Anna alone, whom he was addressing — Anna, his
sweetheart, Anna, the clever one.

Zora knew it and was glad for not having to listen and to
think of the appropriate answer. She did not listen. She could
not.

She was still in the courtroom, still on the witness stand,
keeping her eyes glued to the prosecutor, terrified that she
would slip and let them wander further where she might
catch a glimpse of the two people there on the left — the
two defendants, flanked by policemen — her father and her
mother.

"Your father was an enemy of the régime," the prosecutor
was saying. "Did he attempt to indoctrinate you with his
reactionary ideas?"

"Yes, sir, he did."

"Did your father criticize the People's Government and
its representatives?"

"He did."

"Did he try to enlist your help in his own criminal activities?"

"Yes, he did."

"I can see, comrade, that you are an intelligent and pro-
gressive citizen. Now tell me please: Why, in your opinion,
did your father conceive such hatred against our People's
Democracy?"

Even now in the street, Zora once more could hear herself
reciting the words which she had previously learned by heart.

"My father used to belong," she said, "to the former
exploiting classes. He could not feel friendly toward our new
socialist régime because he did not want the working people
to become the masters in our factories and our offices ..."

"Did he hope for a change?"

"Yes, he did."

"How did he imagine that the People's Democracy could
be abolished and the old capitalist régime re-established?"

"My father knew that the Western imperialists were preparing an aggressive war against the great Soviet Union and its allies, and he hoped that the atomic criminals, together with the Nazi murderers of Western Germany would invade our country and once more enslave the working people."

"Which means," the prosecutor was saying with an eloquent glance toward the press gallery, "your father forgot just as all the other reactionaries do that our great Soviet Allies are invincible and that the aggressors will be annihilated."

If this remark was gratefully picked up by the reporters, it was utterly lost on Zora, for while she was reciting the well-memorized bit about the atomic criminals and Nazi murderers, she forgot to keep her eyes on the prosecutor — and then it happened. As if attracted by some magic power, she turned her head further to the left and saw her father and mother sitting there.

There they were, the two old people, and they knew that she was looking at them. Her father knew it first. His pale face became even a shade whiter; his lips contracted into two hard lines; and his eyes quickly shifted away. But her mother kept on looking, and there was no hatred in her eyes nor pleading but just the expression of a childish and puzzled incomprehension.

There she sat, a frightened lonely woman, and it was so obvious that she was unable to understand what this was all about; it was so obvious that she could not understand what had happened to her husband, her family, her people.

Suddenly Zora remembered with a shock that once before she had seen exactly the same expression on her mother's face. It was during the war, some six years ago. An air raid was in progress; they were all in the cellar, and a bomb exploded in the street and demolished the entrance to the shelter.

It took the rescue squad about an hour to dig their way into the cellar, and the people who knew that they were trapped were getting panicky. Now, in the courtroom, Zora saw her mother again as she looked then, six years ago —

silent, her hands shaking, asking again and again where she was and what it was all about.

Zora had been only eleven years old then, but wartime children were used to emergencies, so she put her arm around her mother's shoulders and talked to her quietly and succeeded in soothing her. But that was six years ago.

The same expression was on her mother's face now, and Zora felt a wave of tenderness surging in her heart; she desperately wanted to turn around and run to her mother and put her arm around her shoulders and soothe her again. But she knew that she would not dare, and that, even if she tried, they would not let her. And, anyway, had she not herself testified under oath that her father and mother were criminals?

Why did she do it? She was asking herself this question even before the trial, and she still was not able to find an answer. It all seemed so easy at the beginning — after the police came and arrested her parents. Karel came to the apartment, talked to her and explained that it was her duty to tell the truth. He talked about what the Party stood for, about the new world they were trying to build and the old people who were in the way obstructing the road towards a happier future. He let her understand, too, that the sentence would not be too heavy. And there was Anna, too, persuading her and pressing her — Anna, who had always been the more resolute of the two and the strong one.

But now things looked different. Zora's faith in the Party was shaken. The trial had been a travesty of justice. Everything seemed so false and unreal — everything except that expression on her mother's face. What had been her father's crime? They told her that he had been caught by the police in the very act of writing one of those "E's" on a wall. But now Zora could not quite silence a chilling and horrible thought, the thought that it was Anna who had denounced the old people so that she could get them out of the apartment and marry Karel. She told herself again and again that it could not be, that it was absurd. But the suspicion was there . . .

When they reached the house, Karel said good-by. No, he could not come up now — he had a meeting to attend — but he might drop in later, some time after dinner.

Zora was glad that he was gone. As soon as she reached the apartment, she took off her shoes and that, at least, was a relief. If only she could lie down for a while! But she knew that Anna would not let her — Anna would want to talk. There were some unspoken words which for the last few days were gradually coming to the surface, and Zora instinctively felt that her sister would want to speak out now. She was proven right.

"It was a pretty poor performance you gave in court," Anna said after a moment's silence.

"I know it was," Zora said, "but I had a headache. . . . And I was frightened . . . . I know it is silly, but I really was frightened."

"Frightened? In heaven's name why?" Anna asked.

"I . . . I don't know, really . . ."

"But I do," Anna said. "I do know and I am going to tell you. You see I happen to know that you were not frightened. You have got sloppy; that is what has heppened to you. I think you have started having feelings."

Zora did not answer, so Anna went on: "Yes, you started having feelings, and you got all sentimental. Don't think I don't know that you disapprove of me. You think that I am hard, don't you? A bad daughter, that's what you think I am. I know that you think that I am a swine. Why don't you say so?"

"But, Anna, I don't. You don't understand. . . ."

"All right, I *am* hard. And I have no feelings — not your kind of feelings. What difference does it make if one person is another person's father or mother? Did Father and Mother choose me, and did I choose them? The whole relation is surely accidental — even *you* must see it!"

"Anna, please," Zora said imploringly, "let's not discuss it — not now, please. You don't have to justify yourself in front of me."

"I'm not trying to justify myself! I want to explain. Aren't you a communist? Don't you see how wrong your tearful attitude is?

"Besides," Anna went on when no answer came from her sister, "I did warn them, didn't I? I have known for some time that Father was up to something idiotic. When I found those leaflets in the lining of his overcoat, I told him what I thought of his activities. And would he listen to me? Not for a moment!

"He just yelled at me and told me to mind my own business. And he said that he was my father. *My father!* Is that an argument? And just because he happens to be my father I should not mind that he is associating with reactionaries and criminals? Well, I am a communist and I have higher loyalties than that."

Will she ever stop? Zora thought. Higher loyalties . . . Yes, there certainly are higher loyalties — but on what scale shall I weigh them? There is the community of the people and the new world. But a child still loves its mother and father. And Zora suddenly remembered a sentence which she had read some time ago. She had read it in the letter from a girl she knew who had committed suicide: "I feel too cold in your new world," the letter said. "It is an icy world."

"And as for those 'E's' which he was writing on the walls," Anna was saying, "I ask you, how can a grown-up man go for such childish stuff? Just like the little boy who carves the initials of his sweetheart into his school desk — or draws dirty pictures on a wall. 'E' for Eisenhower . . . 'E' for Europe . . . I tell you what the 'E' really stands for: it is 'E' for atom bombs, 'E' for dollars!"

Anna stopped talking, and she was looking challengingly at her sister. But Zora remained silent. What was the good of arguing? Anna has had her say, so now, maybe, we will have some peace.

"All right," Anna said after a moment. "I can see that you have made up your mind — you want to be stupid. For all I care, you can be as idiotic as you wish. . . . All I ask you is to watch your step where the Party is concerned. You don't want to get into trouble, do you? And now let us forget about the whole business and start moving."

Moving? Zora thought. *What does she mean by that?* And she asked rather stupidly: "You want to move? But we have nowhere else to go."

"Honestly, Zora," Anna said impatiently, "you are like a child. *We* do not move anywhere. It is the old people's stuff that we must get rid of so that we can reorganize the apartment. I'll have a room for myself now at last, and so will you — aren't you thrilled? I will take Father and Mother's bedroom; you can stay where you are. Only we must collect all their bits and pieces and store them in the attic — I will need all the cupboards."

Zora was stunned. She felt the blood rushing to her face.

"Anna," she said, "must we? I mean must we do it now? It's only . . . only a few hours since —"

"And why not? What do you want to wait for? Come on, Zora, be sensible! The old people are gone; we have got the apartment to ourselves, so stop being sentimental and give me a hand. Come on; let's start with Father's cupboard."

So they started with the father's cupboard, taking out his suits and hats, his shoes, his shirts and underwear, the woollen scarf which Zora knitted for him for Christmas two years ago, his handkerchiefs with large initials which the mother used to embroider so painstakingly in the evenings.

"What are you doing?" Anna asked, seeing that her sister had started packing her father's things into one of the large trunks.

"Well . . . how else do you want to store it?" Zora asked.

"Oh, I do not think that it is any good storing Father's things. It is all right for Mother's stuff — she will be back in five years. But as for Father . . . I thought of telling Karel to pick out all that might come useful to him. As for the rest, we had better sell it. It is no good fussing. Father is not likely to need those things ever again — we'd better face it."

Yes, we'd better face it, Zora was thinking. Anna will bring Karel, and Karel will choose a few shirts and ties and possibly the woollen scarf I gave Daddy for Christmas. The rest will be sold.

No, he is not likely to need those things again — he is not a young man and he was sentenced to twenty years. All he will need is a convict's uniform, and that not for long, either. One does not live too long in a forced-labor camp — let us face it.

The girls were working in silence, emptying cupboards and drawers, piling up linen, dresses and underwear, selecting what was to be kept and what to be thrown away. The job was nearly done except for a few cardboard boxes down in the corner.

Zora knew what they contained and she was postponing the moment when she would have to untie the cords which held them together, and the moment had come. Whether she liked it or not, she had to attack them; she had to make the plunge — a plunge into the past.

For it was the past that those boxes contained — family photographs, picture postcards, newspaper clippings, a bunch of artificial flowers which Mother wore on her evening dress — the one she had made many years ago when Father took her to the civil servants' ball in the capital. And letters, hundreds of them, which Mother used to receive from her old school friends; and the letters which Grandma used to write three or four times a year; and the letters which Father used to write to her during their courtship, all neatly arranged and tied in pink ribbons.

And Zora's and Anna's school reports and the candle which Anna bought for her first communion and the first tooth Zora lost when she was five. . . . All sorts of souvenirs: ugly ashtrays from Venice, a framed picture of the Virgin which Mother brought from Lourdes, a cheap marble statuette of Cupid and Psyche — probably somebody's wedding present which the parents did not like but could not part with, and Father's army cap from the first war . . . all the junk which one keeps for the sake of memories which cling to it, all the junk which has no home except in the heart of its owner.

Zora opened another box. It was the box in which her mother used to keep all kinds of ornamental bits and pieces to be hung on the family Christmas tree — the large silver star, little glass bells, gold painted candle holders, long glistening silver chains, yards and yards of them. Zora let them run through her fingers, caressed them fondly with the palm of her hand.

And suddenly she saw the Christmas tree, the silver star on top, the long chains glittering in candlelight — the glowing Christmas tree, with two little girls standing underneath it and holding Daddy's and Mummy's hands. Two little girls, a little frightened but enchanted and so happy!

Was it the strain of the past few days — or the heat in the courtroom or the boxes with the family relics? Zora did not know. All she knew was that she had to speak, she had to or she would choke. She stood up, faced her sister.

"How could you!" she said. "How could you!"

"How could I what?" Anna asked, bent over a suitcase. But then she looked up and saw her sister's face. "What — what do you mean?"

"You devil!" Zora cried. "How could you do this to them? How could you do this to all of us? You are not human, you . . . you. . . . Did you see Mummy's face this morning? Did you see her expression? You and your Party!"

"Shut up, you fool!" Anna said menacingly. "What is the matter with you? Will you shut up?"

"I will not shut up! I won't! Do you think I don't know why you did it? It was *you* who denounced them — you and your Karel! You wanted another good mark on your Party record. And you wanted to get them out of the apartment so that Karel could move in. . . . You devil! You shameless devil!"

Anna came swiftly to her sister and slapped her across the face. She slapped her hard, again and again. Zora stopped shouting. She stood still, holding her face in her hands, still clutching one end of the long silver chain which lay on the floor like a glistening serpent. In a moment she let the chain drop. She gave a dry sob, turned around and rushed out — out of the apartment, out of the house, down the street.

She did not know how long she had been wandering through the streets. One hour — two, three? She was in the factory district now, walking beside a high brick wall. Someone had written his name on it; someone else drew a heart pierced by an arrow.

Zora stopped and looked around. She saw a lump of coal. She picked it up and started drawing a letter, a large letter "E" — "E" for Europe, "E" for Eisenhower, "E" for her father's convict's uniform, "E" for the look in her mother's eyes — "E" for all the misery around, all her lost happiness, all the hatred in her heart!

QUESTIONS

1. Explain the meaning of the title.
2. Compare and contrast the two sisters, Anna and Zora.
3. What small details in the story prove clearly that the two girls were despised and hated by their fellow countrymen?
4. What is the character, Karel Holdos, like?
5. What did he mean by "moral courage" and "getting over family prejudices"?
6. What did Holdos mean by congratulating the girls on being "true pioneers" and "the new generation"? What is your opinion of their conduct? Discuss.
7. Give a brief account of the trial. How did it differ from a trial in a democracy?
8. What was Zora's testimony?
9. When Zora glanced at her parents, what difference did she note between the look her father gave her and the expression on her mother's face? Under what circumstances had she seen this expression before?
10. Why had Zora testified against her parents? How much do you blame her personally? Discuss.
11. What did Zora finally suspect was the real reason why Anna wanted her parents out of the way?

12. After the two girls had returned home, why was Anna displeased with her younger sister and what excuses did Zora give?

13. What did Anna mean by having what she called "higher loyalties" and how does this point of view differ from that usually held in the democracies?

14. Describe the "moving."

15. Why did Anna decide to sell her father's things? What is your opinion of her and her attitude? Discuss.

16. Why did Zora finally rebel and why did Anna slap her sister?

17. What did Zora do after she had wandered about the streets? Why?

18 *Word Study.* — What do the following words mean as they are used in the story: *menacing, appreciation, slogan, socialist* (n. and adj.), *bolshevist* (n. and adj.), *régime, indoctrinate, exploit, democracy, capitalist, imperialist, reactionary* (n. and adj.), *invincible, annihilate, travesty, communist, Cupid, Psyche?*

Problem: MORAL OR LESSON

Stories of theme are written primarily to teach the reader a lesson, make him understand a problem, or explain the right solution. In a story based on an actual trial which took place in Pilsen, Czechoslovakia only a few years ago, Dr. Stransky paints a powerful picture of family disunity under a totalitarian régime.

1. What, in your opinion, are the chief differences between family life in a slave state as compared to that in any democracy?

2. In the story, what other differences do you notice between totalitarianism and democracy? Discuss.

3. What is the chief lesson that the story has taught you?

4. What other lessons have you learned through the reading of the story? Discuss.

The Commutation Chophouse *

Christopher Morley (1890–1957)

Critic, editor, essayist, lecturer, novelist, playwright, and poet, Christopher Morley was a most versatile American writer and a true man of letters. The son of a professor of mathematics at Haverford College, Morley was born in Haverford, Pennsylvania, in 1890 and died at his home in Roslyn Heights, Long Island, on March 28, 1957, at the age of sixty-six.

After his graduation from Haverford, young Morley was selected to be a Rhodes Scholar and later studied at New College, Oxford, during 1910–1913. Morley had written in many fields and at the time of his death was the author of about fifty books. Although he preferred to think of himself as primarily a poet, he wrote "Kitty Foyle" (published in 1939), a most successful novel, which was later made into a superior motion picture. Occasionally, in recent years, Morley's verse has appeared in the pages of the New York "Times Magazine" and other publications; he was editor-in-chief of the 1937 and the 1949 editions of Bartlett's "Familiar Quotations"; and since he was interested in the drama, he and Cleon Throckmorton founded a theater in Hoboken, New Jersey, where they produced some of the old-fashioned melodramas. For a number of years, Morley was a member of the staff of the "Saturday Review of Literature"; and he was also one of the judges for the "Book of the Month Club." Indeed, there were few fields of literature in which Christopher Morley had not done some experimenting.

A typical example of Morley's whimsical humor, "The Commutation Chophouse" is a story showing imagination and philosophical understanding of fallible human nature. The surprise ending — especially popular in the first quarter of the present century — is carefully planned and cleverly executed. Although

* From *Tales from a Rolltop Desk*, by Christopher Morley: Copyright, 1921, by Doubleday, Page & Co. Reprinted by permission of the publishers Doubleday & Co., Inc.

the story is light and amusing, it, nevertheless, carries a lesson for all of us, since it is an almost universal human failing to wish to obtain an impossible bargain for ourselves.

IT WAS two days before Christmas, and Dove Dulcet had come down town to have lunch with me. As he had arrived rather early, we were taking a little stroll round the bright, windy streets before our meal, enjoying the color and movement of the scene. We stopped by St. Paul's churchyard to note the curious contrast of the old chocolate spire relieved against the huge glittering shaft of the Woolworth Building. At the noon hour St. Paul's stands in the dark shadow of the great cliffs to the south, while the Woolworth pinnacle leaps up like a spearhead into the golden vacancy of day-long sunshine.

"Saint Paul in the shadow, Saint Frank in the sun," said Dove with gentle irony. "It seems to prove that ten cents put in the cash register gets nearer Heaven than ten cents dropped in the collection plate."

When Dove is philosophical, he is always full of quaint matter, but I was hardly heeding what he said. My eye had been caught by a crowd gathered at the corner of Church Street. Over the heads of the throng was a winking spark of light that flashed this way and that as though spun from a turning mirror.

"Let's go and see what's doing," I said. My poet friend is always docile, and he followed me down Fulton Street.

"It looks to me like a silk hat," he said.

And so it was. On the corner of the pavement stood a tall, stout, and very well-nourished man with a ruddy face, wearing shabby but still presentable cutaway coat and gray trousers, and crowned by a steep and glittering stovepipe hat which twinkled like a heliograph in the dazzling winter glare. But, most amazing, when we elbowed a passage through the jocular crowd, we saw that this personable individual was wearing, instead of an overcoat, two large sandwich boards vigorously lettered as follows:

THE COMMUTATION CHOPHOUSE
OPENS TODAY
59 Ann Street
Celebrate the Merry Yuletide!
One Prodigious Meal, $1
BUY A STRIP TICKET
AND SAVE MONEY
TODAY ONLY
100 meals for $10

This corpulent sandwich man was blithely answering the banter of those who were not awed by the radiance of his headgear and the dignity of his mien, and passing out printed cards to those nearest him.

"Do all the hundred meals have to be eaten today?" asked Dulcet. "If so, the task is beyond my powers."

"Like the man in the Bible," I said, "he probably rented his garments. But he couldn't rent that admirable abdomen that proclaims him a well-fed man. It seems to me a very sound ad for the chophouse."

"Unquestionably," said my friend, gravely, "he is the man who put the ad in adipose."

The sandwich man, unabashed by these remarks, handed me one of his cards, which Dulcet and I read together:

K. Jefferson Gastric, the best-fed man south of 42nd Street, takes this importunity of urging you to become a steakholder in the Commutation Chophouse. Why pay for overhead expense? In the Commutation Chophouse all unnecessaries are discarded and you pay only for food, not for finger-bowls and a lovely female cashier. No tips. Today Only, the Opening Day, to celebrate the jovial Yule, the management will sell Strip Tickets entitling you to 100 Glorious Meals, for $10.

At this point a policeman politely urged Mr. Gastric to move on, and he passed genially down Church Street, his resplendent hat glowing above a trail of followers.

"Come on," I said, "it's time to eat, anyway. Let's go over to Ann Street and have a look at this philanthropic venture."

"Well," said Dulcet, "since it's your turn to buy, far be it from me to protest."

The narrow channel of Ann Street is always crowded at the lunch hour, but on that occasion it was doubly congested with patrons of the amusing toyshops. We pushed patiently along, and passing Nassau Street moved into a darker and shabbier region. A sound of music rose upon the air. To our surprise, at the entrance to an unsuspected alley stood a fiddler playing a merry jig. Beside him was another sandwich man, also stout and well-favoured and in Fifth Avenue attire, carrying boards which read:

ENTRANCE TO
THE COMMUTATION CHOPHOUSE

Eat Drink and Be Merry
For Tomorrow We Die

Today Only, for the Jocund Yule,
Strip Tickets for
100 Square Meals, $10

"This is highly diverting," I said. "Apparently we go down this passage. Come on, everyone seems bound the same way. We won't get a seat unless we make haste."

Dulcet was gazing reflectively at the sandwich boards. His blue eyes had a quizzical twinkle.

"For God, for country, and for Yule," he said. "Queer that this should happen on Ann Street. I seem to remember ——"

"Queer that it should happen anywhere," I interrupted him. "It's a clever advertising stunt, anyway — 100 meals for $10. It seems too good to be true."

"The only thing I'm afraid of," he said, "is that it is literally true."

"Walk in, gents, give us a try," cried the sandwich man. "Try anything once, gents."

"Come on, Dove," I said, seeing that others were crowding ahead of us down the alley. "None of your paradoxes!"

The narrow passage turned into a courtyard overlooked by old grimy warehouses with iron-shuttered windows. In one corner was a fine substantial brick building with a rounded front, and a long flight of wooden stairs that seemed to lead up to a marine junk shop, for old sea-boots and ships' lanterns and fenders hung along the wall. In a basement was an iron foundry where we could see the bright glow of a forge. Half-way down the little area was a low door with a huge stone lintel-piece over which was a large canvas sign:

THE COMMUTATION CHOPHOUSE

I must confess to an irrational affection for quaint eating places, and having explored down-town New York's crowded cafés and lunchrooms rather carefully in quest of a congenial tavern, the Commutation Chophouse struck me as highly original and pleasing. We stepped down into a very large and rather dark cellar that apparently had previously been used as a carpenter's shop, for a good many traces of the earlier tenancy were still visible. The furnishings were of the plainest, consisting simply of heavy wooden tables and benches. There was no linen on the tables, but the wood had been scrubbed scrupulously clean and there were piles of tissue napkins. From a door at the back waiters came rushing with trays of food. A glorious clatter of knives and forks filled the air, and it looked at first as though we would find no place to sit. As Dove expressed it, the room was loaded to the muzzle; and a continuous stream of patrons was coming down the alley, allured by the sandwich man and the absurd thin gayety of the fiddle. By the front door stood a dark young man, behind a small counter, selling tickets.

"One meal for a dollar," he cried, repeatedly, as he took in money. "One hundred meals for ten dollars. Get your commutation tickets here."

"We'll try two single meals to begin with," I said, and put down a ten-dollar bill.

The young man rummaged in a drawer full of greasy notes to get the change. "Better get a commutation," he said. "Tremendous saving."

"I should think you'd need a cash register," said Dulcet.

"Handling all that kale, it would be useful in keeping the accounts straight."

The young man looked up sharply.

"Say," he retorted, "what are you, mister? Cash-register salesman? Step along please, don't block the gangway. Next! Seats in the rear! No, commutation tickets not transferable. Good only to the purchaser. Ten dollars, please. Next!"

"They seem to be coining money," said Dove, as we found places at last in a rear corner.

"Well," I said, "this is just the kind of place I like. By Jove, this building must be well over a hundred years old. Look at those beams in the ceiling. All they need is a few sporting prints and an open fireplace. Lit by candles, too, you see. Well, well, this is the real alehouse atmosphere. Why, it's as good as the Cheshire Cheese. This is the kind of place where I can imagine Doctor Johnson and Charles Lamb sitting in a corner."

"You are an incurable sentimentalist," he said. "Besides, Lamb would have had to sit on Johnson's knee, I expect. If I remember rightly, Lamb was a very small urchin when Doctor Johnson died."

"Why be so literal?" I protested. "Haven't you any sentiment for fine antique flavor, and all that sort of thing?"

"If there is one thing where sentiment plays no part with me," he said, "it is food. At meal times I am distinctly a realist. Fine antique flavor is rather upsetting when you find it in your meat. But still," he continued, "I must admit this looks good." He beamed approvingly at the thick chop and baked potatoes and beans and coffee the waiter had put down in front of us.

"Evidently you don't order your food," I said. "They give you the standardized meal of the day. Fall to! These beans baked in cheese strike me as excellent."

I have never seen waiters rush around with such speed as they did in that crowded cellar, where flickering candle-gleams cast a tawny light over the crowded tables of men packed shoulder to shoulder. They flashed in and out through the rear door like men possessed. They careered in with trays of steaming viands, crashed them down on the bare tables, and fled out again, napkins streaming behind them like pennants. Once they had delivered your food it seemed impossible to catch their gaze, for we tried to hail one to ask for ketchup. It was no use. He flew hither and yon with frantic and single-minded energy.

"These waiters speed like dervishes," I said. "Evidently the no-tip rule does not lessen their zeal."

"Perhaps they get a share in the profits of the enterprise," said Dulcet, placidly.

Just behind us was a small barred window looking out on a street. It was at the ground level, and looking through the dusty pane I could see horses' hoofs going by, and the feet of pedestrians. Suddenly there was a great clang and crash outside, and I turned to look.

"What's up?" said Dulcet, who was cheerfully disposing of his chop as well as his neighbor's elbow would permit him.

"They seem to have spilled some beans," I said, peering through the dusky aperture. "There's a truck delivering food or something at the back door. They've tipped over a can, I think."

"Spilled some beans?" he said, with his first sign of real interest. "That sounds symbolic. Let me have a look."

He stood up on the bench and gazed outward. Presently he sat down again and went on calmly with his meal. Some excellent cheese cake was brought us as dessert.

"That alley behind us," he said. "I suppose it communicates with Beekman Street, doesn't it?"

"I guess so. Why?"

"Just wondering. Ben, I apologize for my skepticism. The food here is jolly good. In fact, it's so good that I think I've tasted it before. I am your debtor for a very enlarging experience. And now as the crowd is becoming almost oppressive and I can see that there are others eager to commute, suppose we smoke our cigars outdoors."

"Right you are," I said. "And since the food is eatabl

and I happen to have the money with me, I think I'll invest in one of those strip tickets. Everyone else seems to be doing it, and it looks to me a good way to save money. A hundred lunches — why, that will see me through till spring. I don't think I'll get tired of eating here, it's so amusing."

"No," said Dove, as he picked up his hat, "I don't think you'll get tired of eating here. Perhaps the money will be well spent."

I bought my commutation, and we stood in the shabby old courtyard for a few minutes watching the crowd stream in. A good many, I noticed, though unable to find seats, still took advantage of the opening-day offer and bought the hundred meal tickets for future consumption.

"The only drawback about this place is the crowd," I said. "If this keeps up, half of down-town New York will be eating here."

"Look here," said Dove, "I think I shall be down this way again tomorrow. It's my turn to buy. Will you lunch with me then? We'll celebrate the jovial Yule together."

"Fine," I said. "Meet you at the old red newspaper-box at the corner of Broadway and Vesey tomorrow at 12 o'clock."

We were both there punctually.

"Have you got your appetite with you?" asked Dove. 'It's a bit early for feasting, but it'll give us time for a stroll after lunch."

"Where do we eat?" I said. "Commutation again? It's all velvet to me, anyway, all my lunches are paid for for the next three months."

"There's a little place on Beekman Street I used to know," he said. "Let's try that."

We found a corner table in an odd old eating house at the corner of Beekman and Gold streets, which I had never seen before.

"I'm a great believer in tit for tat, fair play, and all that sort of thing," said Dulcet when the waiter approached. "You gave me an excellent lunch yesterday. I intend to give you the same lunch to-day, if you can stand eating it again. Waiter!

Mutton chop, baked potato, baked beans, coffee, and cheese cake. For two."

When the beans came, baked with cheese in a little brown dish, just as they were served the day before, I must confess that I was startled.

"Why, these beans are done exactly like those we had at the Commutation," I said. "Are these people doing the cooking for the chophouse?"

"Perhaps you'll have to eat chop and beans for a hundred lunches," Dulcet said. "Well, it's a hearty diet. After all, the sandwich boards simply said a hundred meals. They didn't guarantee that they would be different."

I insisted that on our way back toward the office we should stop at the Commutation Chophouse and find out from a customer what the bill of fare had been on the second day. The vision of a hundred repetitions of any meal, however good, is rather ghastly.

"I don't hear the minstrel today," Dove observed as we drew near the alley.

"Oh, well," I said, "that was just to draw business for the opening."

We turned down the passage at No. 59. Quite a crowd of patrons were waiting their turn, I saw. They were standing in the courtyard by the chophouse door, talking busily.

"You see," I said, "it's still crowded."

We reached the entrance. The door was closed. The sign over the doorway now had additional lettering painted on it and read:

THE COMMUTATION CHOPHOUSE
The Other 99 Meals Will Be Served
In Augusta, Maine

"Come on, Ben," said Dulcet. "No use trying to break through the window. There's no one there. I wonder what the fare is to Augusta?"

"You rascal!" I cried. "If you suspected this, why the devil did you encourage me to squander my $10?"

"I simply said it would probably be well spent," he said, with a clear blue humorous gaze. "If it helps to cauterize your magnificent credulity, it will be."

We sat down on a bench in St. Paul's church-yard to smoke a pipe together while I performed some mental obsequies over my vanished Federal Reserve certificate. Dove looked up at the sparkling gilded turret of the Woolworth.

"I daresay Frank Woolworth would have fallen for it, too," Dove said. "The idea of a hundred meals for 10 cents each would have appealed to him. But you know, old man, there are certain fixed and immutable laws that the observant city dweller is accustomed to. My motto is, whenever you find an apparent exception to those laws, look for an enigma in the woodpile. I suspected something wrong when I saw that sandwich man on Church Street. A man as fat as that doesn't generally take a job sandwiching. Also I have doubts about people who insist on calling Christmas 'Yule.' Moreover, a man doesn't generally take a job sandwiching until his shirt is so ragged that he is ashamed to exhibit it in public, when he is glad to cover it up with the boards. Those two fat sand-wichers were members of the firm, I fear, for their linen was O. K. And, secondly, what are the first things a man gets if he really intends to start a restaurant? A cash register and a bunch of ketchup bottles. There wasn't a cash register nor a ketchup bottle in sight in the Commutation Chophouse. No, my dear; what you admired as carefully arranged atmos-phere of antiquity, the plain board tables and candles and so on, was really stark cheapness. They weren't spending any money on overhead; they said so themselves.

"When you called my attention to the spilled beans, I was sure. For they were not merely beans: they were baked beans; a far more significant matter. When I looked out the window I could see at once that there was no kitchen attached to the Commutation Chophouse. The food was all being delivered from that place on Beekman Street, whose name was on the truck. A few ingenious rogues simply rented that old cellar, cheaply enough I guess, put in a few tables, arranged to have grub shipped in from near by, printed their commutation tickets, and sat down to collect as many dollars as they could lure out of the open-handed Christmas throng."

"Well, of all infernal liars," I cried, "they certainly take the prize."

"Not so," said Dulcet as we got up to go. "You should have read the sandwich boards a little more carefully. Their ingenious author, whom you chide as the Ann Street Ananias, really told the exact and circumstantial truth."

We stood at the gateway of the graveyard, and gazed across the roaring traffic of Broadway. Dove smiled and said he must be starting on his Christmas shopping.

"I tried to warn you," he said, "but you wouldn't listen. As I was about to say just before we visited the place, it was queer that it should happen on Ann Street. Don't you remember that a certain famous gentleman had his museum at the corner of Broadway and Ann? And it was he, I think, who remarked that there's one born every minute. Well, Merry Christmas!"

QUESTIONS

1. What do you think Dove Dulcet's name means? Why do you think Mr. Morley chose this name for him?
2. What does Dove Dulcet mean by "Saint Frank in the sun"? Why is Woolworth mentioned?
3. Who were Lamb and Johnson?
4. When some beans have been spilled, Dulcet says, "That sounds symbolic." What does he mean?
5. What famous museum, run by "a certain famous gentleman," was at the corner of Broadway and Ann Street? What is the meaning of the expression, "There is one born every minute?"
6. What is the climax of this story? What comes after the climax?
7. Give the plot as briefly as possible.
8. Which is most important in the story, the plot, the setting, or the characters?
9. *Word Study.* — What do the following words mean as they are used in the story: *philosophical, jovial, quizzical, substantial, irrational, sentimentalist, aperture, credulity, enigma, antiquity, infernal?*

Problem: SURPRISE ENDING
(See page 22.)

1. Were you prepared for the ending of this story? What facts can you find in the narrative that indicate what the end will be? Why is it easier to select them after the story has been read? Which ones did you notice as you first read the story?

2. What is a surprise ending? What difficulties in planning do you think the author of a surprise-ending story might encounter?

North of Fifty-three *

Rex Beach (1877–1949)

About a year before his death on December 7, 1949, at his home in Sebring, Florida, Rex Beach had sold the film-production rights to his unfinished novel, "Woman in Ambush," for $100,000, the largest amount ever offered for an incomplete, unpublished manuscript. The author's work has always been extremely popular with producers and movie-goers; indeed, fourteen of Rex Beach's novels have been made into films (some of them more than once) and — in addition — the writer completed for the screen sixteen original scenarios. During his busy lifetime, Beach made one large fortune from his writing and a second one from farming and cattle raising in Sebring, Florida.

Born September 1, 1877, in Atwood, Michigan, Rex Beach, some years later, worked his way through Rollins Preparatory and Rollins College in Winter Park, Florida. The author also studied at two different law schools but never followed the legal profession.

In 1897, fired with a spirit of adventure, Beach, a young man of twenty, joined the Alaskan Gold Rush in search of excitement and fortune. Although the youthful adventurer never made a lucky strike as a gold miner, he did discover and mine a literary lode, for life in this new rough civilization furnished good story material and an abundance of local color.

Some years after his Alaskan trip, the author's book, "Pardners," was published. This was the first of a series of popular exciting adventure stories and novels which the author wrote. Among the best-known titles are "The Spoilers," "The Barrier," and "The Silver Horde." At first Beach's books dealt largely with life in the frozen North, but later, after the novelist had traveled about the world, his literary horizon widened, and he

*wrote about Panama, New Orleans, New York City, and various
other places.*

*"North of Fifty-three," one of the author's early stories, is
typical of Rex Beach's first work. We find in it a story of rapid
action, a convincing, vivid picture of life in an Alaskan mining
town about the turn of the century and several lifelike characters.
We have in the story a constantly shifting emphasis: at one time
Big George seems the most important force in the story; at another,
it is the Captain. At first the reader is inclined to dislike Big
George and consider him only a swaggering bully, but before the
conclusion of the story, he realizes that this character has also an
admirable side and can perform an act of unselfish heroism.*

BIG GEORGE was drinking, and the activities of
the little Arctic mining camp were paralyzed. Events invariably ceased their progress and marked time when George
became excessive, and now nothing of public consequence
stirred except the quicksilver, which was retiring fearfully
into its bulb at the song of the wind which came racing over
the lonesome, bitter, northward waste of tundra.

He held the center of the floor at the Northern Club, and
proclaimed his modest virtues in a voice as pleasant as the
cough of a bull-walrus.

"Yes, me! Little Georgie! I did it. I've licked 'em all from
Herschel Island to Dutch Harbor, big uns and little uns.
When they didn't suit I made 'em over. I'm the boss carpenter of the Arctic and I own this camp; don't I, Slim?
Hey? Answer me!" he roared at the emaciated bearer of the
title, whose attention seemed wandering from the inventory
of George's startling traits toward a card game.

"Sure ye do," nervously smiled Slim, frightened out of a
heart-solo as he returned to his surroundings.

"Well, then, listen to what I'm saying. I'm the big chief
of the village, and when I'm stimulated and happy them
fellers I don't like hides out and lets me and Nature operate
things. Ain't that right?" He glared inquiringly at his friends.

Red, the proprietor, explained over the bar in a whisper

to Captain, the new man from Dawson: "That's Big George, the whaler. He's a squaw-man and sort of a bully — see? When he's sober he's on the level strickly, an' we all likes him fine, but when he gets to fightin' the pain-killer, he ain't altogether a gentleman. Will he fight? Oh! Will he fight? Say! he's there with chimes, he is! Why, Doc Miller's made a grubstake rebuildin' fellers that's had a lingerin' doubt cached away about that, an' now when he gets the booze up his nose them patched-up guys oozes away an' hibernates till the gas dies out in him. Afterwards he's sore on himself an' apologizes to everybody. Don't get into no trouble with him, cause he's two checks past the limit. They don't make 'em as bad as him any more. He busted the mould."

George turned, and spying the newcomer, approached, eyeing him with critical disfavor.

Captain saw a bear-like figure, clad cap-a-pie in native fashion. Reindeer pants, with the hair inside, clothed legs like rock pillars, while out of the loose squirrel parka a corded neck rose, brown and strong, above which darkly gleamed a rugged face seamed and scarred by the hate of Arctic winters. He had kicked off his deer-skin socks, and stood bare-footed on the cold and draughty floor, while the poison he had imbibed showed only in his heated face. Silently he extended a cracked and hardened hand, which closed like the armored claw of a crustacean and tightened on the crunching fingers of the other. Captain's expression remained unchanged and gradually slackening his grip, the sailor roughly inquired:

"Where'd you come from?"

"Just got in from Dawson yesterday," politely responded the stranger.

"Well, what're you goin' to do now you're here?" he demanded.

"Stake some claims and go to prospecting, I guess. You see, I wanted to get in early before the rush next spring."

"Oh! I s'pose you're going to jump some of our ground, hey? Well, you ain't! We don't want no claim jumpers here," disagreeably continued the seaman; "we won't stand for

This is my camp — see! I own it, and these is my little children." Then, as the other refused to debate with him, he resumed, groping for a new ground of attack.

"Say! I'll bet you're one of them eddicated dudes, too, ain't you? You talk like a feller that had been to college," and, as the other assented, he scornfully called to his friends, saying, "Look here, fellers! Pipe the jellyfish! I never see one of these here animals that was worth a cuss; they plays football an' smokes cigareets at school; then when they're weaned they come off up here an' jump our claims 'cause we can't write a location notice proper. They ain't no good. I guess I'll stop it."

Captain moved toward the door, but the whaler threw his bulky frame against it and scowlingly blocked the way.

"No, you don't. You ain't goin' to run away till I've had the next dance, Mister Eddication! Humph! I ain't begun to tell ye yet what a useless little barnacle you are."

Red interfered, saying: "Look 'ere, George, this guy ain't no playmate of yourn. We'll all have a jolt of this disturbance promoter, an' call it off." Then, as the others approached, he winked at Captain, and jerked his head slightly toward the door.

The latter, heeding the signal, started out, but George leaped after him and, seizing an arm, whirled him back, roaring:

"Well, of all the cussed impidence I ever see! You too high-toned to drink with us, are you? You don't get out of here now till you take a lickin' like a man."

He reached over his head and, grasping the hood of his fur shirt, with one movement he stripped it from him, exposing a massive naked body whose muscles swelled and knotted beneath a skin as clear as a maiden's, while a map of angry scars strayed across the heavy chest.

As the shirt sailed through the air, Red lightly vaulted to the bar and, diving at George's naked middle, tackled beautifully, crying to Captain: "Get out quick; we'll hold him."

Others rushed forward and grasped the bulky sailor, but

Captain's voice replied: "I sort of like this place, and I guess I'll stay a while. Turn him loose."

"Why, man, he'll kill ye," excitedly cried Slim. "Get out!"

The captive hurled his peacemakers from him and, shaking off the clinging arms, drove furiously at the insolent stranger.

In the cramped limits of the corner where he stood, Captain was unable to avoid the big man, who swept him with a crash against the plank door at his back, grasping hungrily at his throat. As his shoulders struck, however, he dropped to his knees and, before the raging George could seize him, he avoided a blow which would have strained the rivets of a strength-tester and ducked under the other's arms, leaping to the cleared center of the floor.

Seldom had the big man's rush been avoided and, whirling, he swung a boom-like arm at the agile stranger. Before it landed, Captain stepped in to meet his adversary and, with the weight of his body behind the blow, drove a clenched and bony first crashing into the other's face. The big head with its blazing shock of hair snapped backward and the whaler dropped to his knees at the other's feet.

The drunken flush of victory swept over Captain as he stood above the swaying figure; then, suddenly, he felt the great bare arms close about his waist with a painful grip. He struck at the bleeding face below him and wrenched at the circling bands which wheezed the breath from his lungs, but the whaler squeezed him writhing to his breast, and, rising, unsteadily wheeled across the floor and in a shiver of broken glass fell crashing against the bar and to the floor.

As the struggling men writhed upon the planks, the door opened at the hurried entrance of an excited group, which paused at the sight of the ruin, then, rushing forward, tore the men apart.

The panting Berserker strained at the arms about his glistening body, while Captain, with sobbing sighs, relieved his aching lungs and watched his enemy, who frothed at the interference.

"It was George's fault," explained Slim to the questions

of the arrivals. "This feller tried to make a getaway, but George had to have his amusement."

A newcomer addressed the squaw-man in a voice as cold as the wind. "Cut this out, George! This is a friend of mine. You're making this camp a reg'lar hell for strangers, and now I'm going to tap your little snap. Cool off — see?"

Jones's reputation as a bad gun-man went hand in hand with his name as a good gambler, and his scanty remarks invariably evoked attentive answers, so George explained: "I don't like him, Jones, and I was jus' makin' him over to look like a man. I'll do it yet, too," he flashed wrathfully at his quiet antagonist.

"'Pears to me like he's took a hand in the remodelling himself," replied the gambler, "but if you're lookin' for something to do, here's your chance. Windy Jim just drove in and says Barton and Kid Sullivan are adrift on the ice."

"What's that?" questioned eager voices, and, forgetting the recent trouble at the news, the crowd pressed forward anxiously.

"They was crossin' the bay and got carried out by the off-shore gale," explained Jones. "Windy was follerin' 'em when the ice ahead parted and begun movin' out. He tried to yell to 'em, but they was too far away to hear in the storm. He managed to get back to the land and follered the shore ice around. He's over at Hunter's cabin now, most dead, face and hands froze pretty bad."

A torrent of questions followed and many suggestions as to the fate of the men.

"They'll freeze before they can get ashore," said one.

"The ice-pack'll break up in this wind," added another, "and if they don't drown, they'll freeze before the floe comes in close enough for them to land."

From the first announcement of his friends' peril, Captain had been thinking rapidly. His body, sore from his long trip and aching from the hug of his recent encounter, cried woefully for rest, but his voice rose calm and clear: "We've got to get them off," he said. "Who will go with me? Three is enough."

The clamoring voices ceased, and the men wheeled at the sound, gazing incredulously at the speaker. "What!" — "In this storm?" — "You're crazy," many voices said.

He gazed appealingly at the faces before him. Brave and adventurous men he knew them to be, jesting with death, and tempered to perils in this land where hardship rises with the dawn, but they shook their ragged heads hopelessly.

"We *must* save them!" resumed Captain hotly. "Barton and I played as children together, and if there's not a man among you who's got the nerve to follow me I'll go alone, by Heavens!"

In the silence of the room, he pulled the cap about his ears and, tying it snugly under his chin, drew on his huge fur mittens; then with a scornful laugh he turned toward the door.

He paused as his eye caught the swollen face of Big George. Blood had stiffened in the heavy creases of his face like rusted stringers in a ledge, while his mashed and discolored lips protruded thickly. His hair gleamed red, and the sweat had dried upon his naked shoulders, streaked with dirt and flecked with spots of blood, yet the battered features shone with the unconquered, fearless light of a rough, strong man.

Captain strode to him with outstretched hand. "You're a man," he said. "You've got the nerve, George, and you'll go with me, won't you?"

"What! Me?" questioned the sailor vaguely. His wondering glance left Captain, and drifted round the circle of shamed and silent faces — then he straightened stiffly and cried "Will I go with you? Certainly! I'll go to —— with you."

Ready hands harnessed the dogs, dragged from protected nooks where they sought cover from the storm which moaned and whistled round the low houses. Endless ragged folds of sleet whirled out of the North, then writhed and twisted past vanishing into the gray veil which shrouded the landscape in a twilight gloom.

The fierce wind sank the cold into the aching flesh like a knife and stiffened the face to a whitening mask, while a fusillade of frozen ice-particles beat against the eyeballs with blinding fury.

As Captain emerged from his cabin, furred and hooded, he found a long train of crouching, whining animals harnessed and waiting while muffled figures stocked the sled with robes and food and stimulants.

Big George approached through the whirling white, a great squat figure with fluttering squirrel tails blowing from his parka, and at his heels there trailed a figure, skin-clad and dainty.

"It's my wife," he explained briefly to Captain. "She won't let me go alone."

They gravely bade farewell to all, and the little crowd cheered lustily against the whine of the blizzard as, with cracking whip and hoarse shouts, they were wrapped in the cloudy winding sheet of snow.

Arctic storms have an even sameness: the intense cold, the heartless wind which augments tenfold the chill of the temperature, the air thick and dark with stinging flakes rushing by in an endless cloud. A drifting, freezing, shifting eternity of snow, driven by a ravening gale which sweeps the desolate, bald wastes of the Northland.

The little party toiled through the smother till they reached the "egloos" under the breast of the tall coast bluffs, where coughing Eskimos drilled patiently at ivory tusks and gambled the furs from their backs at stud-horse poker.

To George's inquiries they answered that their largest canoe was the three-holed bidarka on the cache outside. Owing to the small circular openings in its deck, this was capable of holding but three passengers, and Captain said: 'We'll have to make two trips, George."

"Two trips, eh?" answered the other. "We'll be doin' well if we last through one, I'm thinking."

Lashing the unwieldy burden upon the sled, they fought their way along the coast again till George declared they were opposite the point where their friends went adrift. They slid their light craft through the ragged wall of ice hummocks guarding the shore pack, and dimly saw, in the gray beyond them, a stretch of angry waters mottled by drifting cakes and floes.

George spoke earnestly to his wife, instructing her to keep the team in constant motion up and down the coast a rifle-shot in either direction, and to listen for a signal of the return. Then he picked her up as he would a babe, and she kissed his storm-beaten face.

"She's been a good squaw to me," he said, as they pushed their dancing craft out into the breath of the gale, "and I've always done the square thing by her; I s'pose she'll go back to her people now, though."

The wind hurried them out from land, while it drove the sea water in freezing spray over their backs and changed their fur garments into scaly armor as they worked through the ice cakes, peering with strained eyes for a sign of their friends.

The sailor, with deft strokes, steered them between the grinding bergs, raising his voice in long signals like the weird cry of a siren.

Twisting back and forth through the floes, they held to their quest, now floating with the wind, now paddling des-perately in a race with some drifting mass which dimly towered above them and splintered hungrily against its neighbor close in their wake.

Captain emptied his six-shooter till his numbed fingers grew rigid as the trigger, and always at his back swelled the deep shouts of the sailor who, with practised eye and mighty strokes, forced their way through the closing lanes between the jaws of the ice pack.

At last, beaten and tossed, they rested disheartened and hopeless. Then, as they drifted, a sound struggled to them against the wind — a faint cry, illusive and fleeting as a dream voice — and, still doubting, they heard it again.

"Thank God! We'll save 'em yet," cried Captain, and they drove the canoe boiling toward the sound.

Barton and Sullivan had fought the cold and wind stoutly hour after hour, till they found their great floe was breaking up in the heaving waters.

Then the horror of it had struck the Kid, till he raved and cursed up and down their little island, as it dwindled gradually to a small acre.

He had finally yielded to the weight of the cold which crushed resistance out of him, and settled, despairing and listless, upon the ice. Barton dragged him to his feet and forced him round their rocking prison, begging him to brace up, to fight it out like a man, till the other insisted on resting, and dropped to his seat again.

The older man struck deliberately at the whitening face of his freezing companion, who recognized the well-meant insult and refused to be roused into activity. Then to their ears had come the faint cries of George, and, in answer to their screams, through the gloom they beheld a long, covered skin canoe and the anxious faces of their friends.

Captain rose from his cramped seat, and, ripping his crackling garments from the boat where they had frozen, he wriggled out of the hole in the deck and grasped the weeping Barton.

"Come, come, old boy! It's all right now," he said.

"Oh, Charlie, Charlie!" cried the other. "I might have known you'd try to save us. You're just in time, though, for the Kid's about all in."

Sullivan apathetically nodded and sat down again.

"Hurry up there; this ain't no G. A. R. Encampment, and you ain't got no time to spare," said George, who had dragged the canoe out and, with a paddle, broke the sheets of ice which covered it. "It'll be too dark to see anything in half an hour."

The night, hastened by the storm, was closing rapidly, and they realized another need of haste, for, even as they spoke, a crack had crawled through the ice-floe where they stood, and, widening as it went, left but a heaving cake supporting them.

George spoke quietly to Captain, while Barton strove to animate the Kid. "You and Barton must take him ashore and hurry him down to the village. He's most gone now."

"But you?" questioned the other. "We'll have to come back for you as soon as we put him ashore."

"Never mind me," roughly interrupted George. "It's too late to get back here. When you get ashore it'll be dark. Besides, Sullivan's freezing, and you'll have to rush him through quick. I'll stay here."

"No! No! George!" cried the other, as the meaning of it bore in upon him. "I got you into this thing, and it's my place to stay here. You must go!"

But the big man had hurried to Sullivan, and, seizing him in his great hands, shook the drowsy one like a rat, cursing and beating a goodly share of warmth back into him. Then he dragged the listless burden to the canoe and forced him to a seat in the middle opening.

"Come, come," he cried to the others; "you can't spend all night here. If you want to save the Kid, you've got to hurry. You take the front seat there, Barton," and, as he did so, George turned to the protesting Captain: "Shut up, curse you, and get in!"

"I won't do it," rebelled the other. "I can't let you lay down your life in this way when I made you come."

George thrust a cold face within an inch of the other's and grimly said: "If they hadn't stopped me, I'd beat you into dog-meat this morning, and if you don't quit this snivelling I'll do it yet. Now get in there and paddle to beat —— or you'll never make it back. Quick!"

"I'll come back for you then, George, if I live to the shore," Captain cried, while the other slid the burdened canoe into the icy waters.

As they drove the boat into the storm, Captain realized the difficulty of working their way against the gale. On him fell the added burden of holding their course into the wind and avoiding the churning ice cakes. The spray whipped into his face like shot, and froze as it clung to his features. He strained at his paddle till the sweat soaked out of him and the cold air filled his aching lungs.

Unceasingly the merciless frost cut his face like a keen blade, till he felt the numb paralysis which told him his features were hardening under the touch of the cold.

An arm's length ahead the shoulders of the Kid protruded from the deck hole where he had sunk again into the death sleep, while Barton, in the forward seat, leaned wearily on his ice-clogged paddle, moaning as he strove to shelter his face from the sting of the blizzard.

An endless time they battled with the storm, slowly gaining, foot by foot, till in the darkness ahead they saw the wall of shore ice and swung into its partial shelter.

Dragging the now unconscious Sullivan from the boat, Captain rolled and threshed him, while Barton, too weak and exhausted to assist, feebly strove to warm his stiffened limbs.

In answer to their signals, the team appeared, maddened by the lash of the squaw. Then they wrapped Sullivan in warm robes, and forced scorching brandy down his throat, till he coughed weakly and begged them to let him rest.

"You must hurry him to the Indian village," directed Captain. "He'll only lose some fingers and toes now, maybe; but you've got to hurry!"

"Aren't you coming, too?" queried Barton. "We'll hire some Eskimos to go after George. I'll pay 'em anything."

"No, I'm going back to him now; he'd freeze before we could send help, and, besides, they wouldn't come out in the storm and the dark."

"But you can't work that big canoe alone. If you get out here and don't find him you'll never get back. Charlie! let me go, too," he said; then apologized. "I'm afraid I won't last, though; I'm too weak."

The squaw, who had questioned not at the absence of her lord, now touched Captain's arm. "Come," she said; "I go with you." Then addressing Barton, "You quick go Indian house; white man die, mebbe. Quick! I go Big George."

"Ah, Charlie, I'm afraid you'll never make it," cried Barton, and wringing his friend's hand he staggered into the darkness behind the sled wherein lay the fur-bundled Sullivan.

Captain felt a horror of the starving waters rise up in him and a panic shook him fiercely, till he saw the silent squaw waiting for him at the ice edge. He shivered as the wind searched through his dampened parka and hardened the wet clothing next to his body, but he took his place and dug the paddle fiercely into the water, till the waves licked the hair of his gauntlets.

The memory of that scudding trip through the darkness was always cloudy and visioned. Periods of keen alertness alternated with moments when his weariness bore upon him till he stiffly bent to his work, wondering what it all meant.

It was the woman's sharpened ear which caught the first answering cry, and her hands which steered the intricate course to the heaving berg where the sailor crouched, for, at their approach, Captain had yielded to the drowse of weariness and, in his relief at the finding, the blade floated from his listless hands.

He dreamed quaint dreams, broken by the chilling lash of spray from the strokes of the others, as they drove the craft back against the wind, and he only partly awoke from his lethargy when George wrenched him from his seat and forced him down the rough trail toward warmth and safety.

Soon, however, the stagnant blood tingled through his veins, and under the shelter of the bluffs they reached the village, where they found the anxious men waiting.

Skilful natives had worked the frost from Sullivan's members, and the stimulants in the sled had put new life into Barton as well. So, as the three crawled wearily through the dog-filled tunnel of the igloo, they were met by two wet-eyed and thankful men, who silently wrung their hands or uttered broken words.

When they had been despoiled of their frozen furs, and the welcome heat of whisky and fire had met in their blood Captain approached the whaler, who rested beside his mate

"George, you're the bravest man I ever knew, and your woman is worthy of you," he said. He continued slowly "I'm sorry about the fight this morning, too."

The big man rose and, crushing the extended palm in his grasp, said: "We'll just let that go double, partner. You're as game as I ever see." Then he added: "It *was* too bad then fellers interfered jest when they did — but we can finish i up whenever you say," and as the other, smiling, shook hi head, he continued: "Well, I'm glad of it, 'cause you'd sure beat me the next time."

QUESTIONS

1. Why, in your opinion, does the story open with the scene in the saloon? Does this scene tell you anything about the principal characters? What does it tell you about the men of the mining camps?
2. Which was the braver man, Big George or Captain? Explain your opinion.
3. Why did most of the men in the saloon refuse to go on the rescue trip? What effect does their refusal have on the reader?
4. Which of the acts of Big George's Eskimo wife showed most bravery? Explain.
5. What do you honestly think of the story?
6. *Word Study.* — What do the following words mean as they are used in the story: *antagonist, stimulate, adversary, apathetically, cache?*

Problem. SETTING
(See page 23.)

1. Could this story have taken place anywhere except "north of fifty-three?" What is the important conflict in the story?
2. How does the author make the setting clear to us? How much actual description is there in the story? How is local color indicated in the dialogue? What clear examples of local color do you find in the first part of the story?
3. Is this a story about a special time and place? Which is more important to the story — time or place? Explain.

A Village Singer *

Mary E. Wilkins Freeman (1852 †–1930)

One of Mrs. Freeman's friends once described her as "A little, frail-looking creature, with a quantity of dull-brown hair, and dark-blue eyes with a direct look and a clear frank expression — eyes that readily grow bright with fun." Like Nathaniel Hawthorne, Mrs. Freeman was descended from a long line of New England ancestry — good, sturdy stock with Puritanical leanings. She received her education at Mount Holyoke Seminary, now Mount Holyoke College. During part of her life she lived in Vermont, but later, after the death of her parents, returned to her home town, Randolph, Massachusetts. She died in Metuchen, New Jersey, March 13, 1930.

Mrs. Freeman is best known for her pictures of life in New England — not the rapid life of the twentieth century, but the more deliberate life of a generation or two ago. Her characters are chiefly New England men and women of the small town or farm. She herself says that she likes "people who drop their 'g's' and use the double negative as well as people who don't."

Her first literary work was writing short stories and poems for children. Later she contributed stories of New England life to "Harper's Magazine," stories that were successful from the very start. Few writers are able to draw a better picture of life or the isolated New England farms or in the little New England villages. Her work abounds in local color and clever character drawing. She has written a number of volumes of short stories and some novels.

"A Village Singer" is a typical Mary E. Wilkins Freeman story. The plot of the story is slight and is subordinated to the author's skilful character development. Employing unmistakable types of New England village life, the author by her subtle ar

† According to the editor of *Authors Today and Yesterday*, the parish records prove that Mrs. Freeman was born in 1852 instead of 1862 — the date usually given.

commands the interest and sympathy of her readers as she reveals heroic and pathetic qualities in an apparently commonplace person. She has handled the ordinary incidents of everyday life in such a simple and convincingly artistic manner that she has created a story of real merit where a less gifted author would have seen nothing to write about.

THE trees were in full leaf, a heavy south wind was blowing, and there was a loud murmur among the new leaves. The people noticed it, for it was the first time that year that the trees had so murmured in the wind. The spring had come with a rush during the last few days.

The murmur of the trees sounded loud in the village church, where the people sat waiting for the service to begin. The windows were open; it was a very warm Sunday for May.

The church was already filled with this soft sylvan music — the tender harmony of the leaves and the south wind, and the sweet, desultory whistles of birds — when the choir arose and began to sing.

In the center of the row of women singers stood Alma Way. All the people stared at her, and turned their ears critically. She was the new leading soprano. Candace Whitcomb, the old one, who had sung in the choir for forty years, had lately been given her dismissal. The audience considered that her voice had grown too cracked and uncertain on the upper notes. There had been much complaint, and after long deliberation the church officers had made known their decision as mildly as possible to the old singer. She had sung for the last time the Sunday before, and Alma Way had been engaged to take her place. With the exception of the organist, the leading soprano was the only paid musician in the large choir. The salary was very modest, still the church people considered it large for a young woman. Alma was from the adjoining village of East Derby; she had quite a local reputation as a singer.

Now she fixed her large solemn blue eyes; her long, delicate face, which had been pretty, turned paler; the blue flowers on her bonnet trembled; her little thin gloved hands, clutching the singing-book, shook perceptibly; but she sang out bravely. That most formidable mountain-height of the world, self-distrust and timidity, arose before her, but her nerves were braced for its ascent. In the midst of the hymn she had a solo; her voice rang out piercingly sweet; the people nodded admiringly at each other; but suddenly there was a stir; all the faces turned toward the windows on the south side of the church. Above the din of the wind and the birds, above Alma Way's sweetly straining tones, arose another female voice, singing another hymn to another tune.

"It's her," the women whispered to each other; they were half aghast, half smiling.

Candace Whitcomb's cottage stood close to the south side of the church. She was playing on her parlor organ, and singing, to drown out the voice of her rival.

Alma caught her breath; she almost stopped; the hymn-book waved like a fan; then she went on. But the long, husky drone of the parlor organ and the shrill clamor of the other voice seemed louder than anything else.

When the hymn was finished, Alma sat down. She felt faint; the woman next her slipped a peppermint into her hand. "It ain't worth minding," she whispered, vigorously. Alma tried to smile; down in the audience a young man was watching her with a kind of fierce pity.

In the last hymn Alma had another solo. Again the parlor organ droned above the carefully delicate accompaniment of the church organ, and again Candace Whitcomb's voice clamored forth in another tune.

After the benediction, the other singers pressed around Alma. She did not say much in return for their expressions of indignation and sympathy. She wiped her eyes furtively once or twice, and tried to smile. William Emmons, the choir leader, elderly, stout, and smooth-faced, stood over her, and raised his voice. He was the old musical dignitary of the village, the leader of the choral club and the singing-schools. "A most outrageous proceeding," he said. People had coupled his name with Candace Whitcomb's. The old bachelor tenor and old maiden soprano had been wont to walk together to her home next door after the Saturday night rehearsals, and they had sung duets to the parlor organ. People had watched sharply her old face, on which the blushes of youth sat pitifully, when William Emmons entered the singing-seats. They wondered if he would ever ask her to marry him.

And now he said further to Alma Way that Candace Whitcomb's voice had failed utterly of late, that she sang shockingly, and ought to have had sense enough to know it.

When Alma went down into the audience-room, in the midst of the chattering singers, who seemed to have descended, like birds, from song flights to chirps, the minister approached her. He had been waiting to speak to her. He was a steady-faced, fleshy old man, who had preached from that one pulpit over forty years. He told Alma, in his slow way, how much he regretted the annoyance to which she had been subjected, and intimated that he would endeavor to prevent a recurrence of it. "Miss Whitcomb — must be — reasoned with," said he; he had a slight hesitation of speech, not an impediment. It was as if his thoughts did not slide readily into his words, although both were present. He walked down the aisle with Alma, and bade her good-morning when he saw Wilson Ford waiting for her in the doorway. Everybody knew that Wilson Ford and Alma were lovers; they had been for the last ten years.

Alma colored softly, and made a little imperceptible motion with her head; her silk dress and the lace on her mantle fluttered, but she did not speak. Neither did Wilson, although they had not met before that day. They did not look at each other's faces — they seemed to see each other without that — and they walked along side by side.

They reached the gate before Candace Whitcomb's little house. Wilson looked past the front yard, full of pink and white spikes on flowering bushes, at the lace-curtained windows; a thin white profile, stiffly inclined, apparently over a book, was visible at one of them. Wilson gave his head a shake. He was a stout man, with features so strong that they overcame his flesh. "I'm going up home with you, Alma," said he; "and then — I'm just coming back, to give Aunt Candace one blowing up."

"Oh, don't, Wilson."

"Yes, I shall. If you want to stand this kind of a thing you may; I sha'n't."

"There's no need of your talking to her. Mr. Pollard's going to."

"Did he say he was?"

"Yes. I think he's going in before the afternoon meeting, from what he said."

"Well, there's one thing about it, if she does that thing again this afternoon, I'll go in there and break that old organ up into kindling-wood." Wilson set his mouth hard, and shook his head again.

Alma gave little side glances up at him, her tone was deprecatory, but her face was full of soft smiles. "I suppose she does feel dreadfully about it," said she. "I can't help feeling kind of guilty, taking her place."

"I don't see how you're to blame. It's outrageous, her acting so."

"The choir gave her a photograph album last week, didn't they?"

"Yes. They went there last Thursday night, and gave her an album and a surprise party. She ought to behave herself."

"Well, she's sung there so long, I suppose it must be dreadful hard for her to give it up."

Other people going home from church were very near Wilson and Alma. She spoke softly that they might not hear he did not lower his voice in the least. Presently Alma stopped before a gate.

"What are you stopping here for?" asked Wilson.

"Minnie Lansing wanted me to come and stay with her this noon."

"You're going home with me."

"I'm afraid I'll put your mother out."

"Put Mother out! I told her you were coming, this morning. She's got all ready for you. Come along; don't stand here."

He did not tell Anna of the pugnacious spirit with which his mother had received the announcement of her coming, and how she had stayed at home to prepare the dinner, and make a parade of her hard work and her injury.

Wilson's mother was the reason why he did not marry Alma. He would not take his wife home to live with her, and was unable to support separate establishments. Alma was willing enough to be married and put up with Wilson's mother, but she did not complain of his decision. Her delicate blonde features grew sharper and her blue eyes more hollow. She had had a certain fine prettiness, but now she was losing it, and beginning to look old, and there was a prim, angular, old maiden carriage about her narrow shoulders.

Wilson never noticed it, and never thought of Alma as not possessed of eternal youth, or capable of losing or regretting it.

"Come along, Alma," said he; and she followed meekly after him down the street.

Soon after they passed Candace Whitcomb's house, the minister went up the front walk and rang the bell. The pale profile at the window had never stirred as he opened the gate and came up the walk. However, the door was promptly opened in response to his ring. "Good-morning, Miss Whitcomb," said the minister.

"*Good*-morning." Candace gave a sweeping toss of her head as she spoke. There was a fierce upward curl to her thin nostrils and her lips, as if she scented an adversary. Her black eyes had two tiny cold sparks of fury in them like an enraged bird's. She did not ask the minister to enter, but he stepped lumberingly into the entry and she retreated rather than led the way into her little parlor. He settled into the great rocking-chair and wiped his face. Candace sat down again in her old place by the window. She was a tall woman, but very slender and full of pliable motions, like a blade of grass.

"It's a — very pleasant day," said the minister.

Candace made no reply. She sat still, with her head drooping. The wind stirred the looped lace-curtains; a tall rose-tree outside the window waved; soft shadows floated through the room. Candace's parlor organ stood in front of an open window that faced the church; on the corner was a pitcher with a bunch of white lilacs. The whole room was scented with them. Presently the minister looked over at them and sniffed pleasantly.

"You have — some beautiful — lilacs there."

Candace did not speak. Every line of her slender figure looked flexible, but it was a flexibility more resistant than rigor.

The minister looked at her. He filled up the great rocking-chair; his arms in his shiny black coat-sleeves rested squarely and comfortably upon the hair-cloth arms of the chair.

"Well, Miss Whitcomb, I suppose I — may as well come to — the point. There was — a little — matter I wished to speak to you about. I don't suppose you were — at least I can't suppose you were — aware of it, but — this morning, during the singing by the choir, you played and — sang a little too — loud. That is, with — the windows open. It — disturbed us — a little. I hope you won't feel hurt — my dear Miss Candace, but I knew you would rather I would speak of it, for I knew — you would be more disturbed than anybody else at the idea of such a thing."

Candace did not raise her eyes; she looked as if his words might sway her through the window. "I ain't disturbed at it," said she. "I did it on purpose; I meant to."

The minister looked at her.

"You needn't look at me. I know jest what I'm about. I sung the way I did on purpose, an' I'm goin' to do it again, an' I'd like to see you stop me. I guess I've got a right to set down to my own organ, an' sing a psalm tune on a Sabbath day, 'f I want to; an' there ain't no amount of talkin' an' palaverin' a-goin' to stop me. See there!" Candace swung aside her skirts a little. "Look at that!"

The minister looked. Candace's feet were resting on a large red-plush photograph album.

"Makes a nice footstool, don't it?" said she.

The minister looked at the album, then at her; there was a slowly gathering alarm in his face; he began to think she was losing her reason.

Candace had her eyes full upon him now, and her head up. She laughed, and her laugh was almost a snarl. "Yes; I thought it would make a beautiful footstool," said she. "I've been wantin' one for some time." Her tone was full of vicious irony.

"Why Miss —" began the minister; but she interrupted him:

"I know what you're a-goin' to say, Mr. Pollard, an' now I'm goin' to have my say; I'm a-goin' to speak. I want to know what you think of folks that pretend to be Christians treatin' anybody the way they've treated me? Here I've sung in those singin'-seats forty year. I ain't never missed a Sunday, except when I've been sick, an' I've gone an' sung a good many times when I'd better been in bed, an' now I'm turned out without a word of warnin'. My voice is jest as good as ever 'twas; there can't anybody say it ain't. It wa'n't ever quite so high-pitched as that Way girl's, mebbe; but she flats the whole durin' time. My voice is as good an' high to-day as it was twenty year ago; an' if it wa'n't, I'd like to know where the Christianity comes in. I'd like to know if it wouldn't be more to the credit of folks in a church to keep an old singer an' an old minister, if they didn't sing an' hold forth quite so smart as they used to, ruther than turn 'em off an' hurt their feelin's. I guess it would be full as much to the glory of God. S'pose the singin' an' the preachin' wa'n't quite so good, what difference would it make? Salvation don't hang on anybody's hittin' a high note, that I ever heard of. Folks are gettin' as high-steppin' an' fussy in a meetin'-house as they are in a tavern, nowadays. S'pose they should turn you off, Mr. Pollard, come an' give you a photograph album, an' tell you to clear out, how'd you like it? I ain't findin' any fault with your preachin'; it was always good enough to suit me; but it don't stand to reason folks'll be as took up with your sermons as when you was a young man. You can't expect it.

S'pose they should turn you out in your old age, an' call in some young bob squirt, how'd you feel? There's William Emmons, too; he's three years older'n I am, if he does lead the choir an' run all the singin' in town. If my voice has gi'en out, it stan's to reason his has. It ain't, though. William Emmons sings jest as well as he ever did. Why don't they turn him out the way they have me, an' give him a photograph album? I dun know but it would be a good idea to send everybody, as soon as they get a little old an' gone by, an' young folks begin to push, onto some desert island, an' give 'em each a photograph album. Then they can sit down an' look at pictures the rest of their days. Mebbe government'll take it up.

"There they come here last week Thursday, all the choir, jest about eight o'clock in the evenin', an' pretended they'd come to give me a nice little surprise. Surprise! h'm! Brought cake an' oranges, an' was jest as nice as they could be, an' I was real tickled. I never had a surprise party before in my life. Jenny Carr she played, an' they wanted me to sing alone, an' I never suspected a thing. I've been mad ever since to think what a fool I was, an' how they must have laughed in their sleeves.

"When they'd gone I found this photograph album on the table, all done up as nice as you please, an' directed to Miss Candace Whitcomb from her many friends, an' I opened it, an' there was the letter inside givin' me notice to quit.

"If they'd gone about it any decent way, told me right out honest that they'd got tired of me, an' wanted Alma Way to sing instead of me, I wouldn't minded so much; I should have been hurt 'nough, for I'd felt as if some that had pretended to be my friends wa'n't; but it wouldn't have been as bad as this. They said in the letter that they'd always set great value on my services, an' it wa'n't from any lack of appreciation that they turned me off, but they thought the duty was gettin' a little too arduous for me. H'm! I hadn't complained. If they'd turned me right out fair an' square, showed me the door, an' said, 'Here, you get out,' but to go an' spill molasses, as it were, all over the threshold, tryin' to make me think it's all nice an' sweet ——

"I'd sent that photograph album back quick's I could pack it, but I didn't know who started it, so I've used it for a footstool. It's all it's good for, 'cordin' to my way of thinkin'. And I ain't been particular to get the dust off my shoes before I used it neither."

Mr. Pollard, the minister, sat staring. He did not look at Candace; his eyes were fastened upon a point straight ahead. He had a look of helpless solidity, like a block of granite. This country minister, with his steady, even temperament, treading with heavy precision his one track for over forty years, having nothing new in his life except the new sameness of the seasons, and desiring nothing new, was incapable of understanding a woman like this, who had lived as quietly as he, and all the time held within herself the elements of revolution. He could not account for such violence, such extremes, except in a loss of reason. He had a conviction that Candace was getting beyond herself. He himself was not a typical New Englander; the national elements of character were not pronounced in him. He was aghast and bewildered at this outbreak, which was tropical, and more than tropical, for a New England nature has a floodgate, and the power which it releases is an accumulation. Candace Whitcomb had been a quiet woman, so delicately resolute that the quality had been scarcely noticed in her, and her ambition had been unsuspected. Now the resolution and the ambition appeared raging over her whole self.

She began to talk again. "I've made up my mind that I'm goin' to sing Sundays the way I did this mornin', an' I don't care what folks say," said she. "I've made up my mind that I'm goin' to take matters into my own hands. I'm goin' to let folks see that I ain't trod down quite flat, that there's a little rise left in me. I ain't goin' to give up beat yet a while; an' I'd like to see anybody stop me. If I ain't got a right to play a psalm tune on my organ an' sing, I'd like to know. If you don't like it, you can move the meetin'-house."

Candace had had an inborn reverence for all clergymen. She had always treated Mr. Pollard with the utmost deference. Indeed, her manner toward all men had been marked by a certain delicate stiffness and dignity. Now she was talking to the old minister with the homely freedom with which she might have addressed a female gossip over the back fence. He could not say much in return. He did not feel competent to make headway against any such tide of passion; all he could do was to let it beat against him. He made a few expostulations, which increased Candace's vehemence; he expressed his regret over the whole affair, and suggested that they should kneel and ask the guidance of the Lord in the matter, that she might be led to see it all in a different light.

Candace refused flatly. "I don't see any use prayin' about it," said she. "I don't think the Lord's got much to do with it, anyhow."

It was almost time for the afternoon service when the minister left. He had missed his comfortable noon-tide rest through this encounter with his revolutionary parishioner. After the minister had gone, Candace sat by the window and waited. The bell rang, and she watched the people file past. When her nephew Wilson Ford with Alma appeared, she grunted to herself. "She's thin as a rail," said she; "guess there won't be much left of her by the time Wilson gets her. Little soft-spoken nippin' thing, she wouldn't make him no kind of a wife, anyway. Guess it's jest as well."

When the bell had stopped tolling, and all the people entered the church, Candace went over to her organ and seated herself. She arranged a singing-book before her, and sat still, waiting. Her thin, colorless neck and temples were full of beating pulses; her black eyes were bright and eager she leaned stiffly over toward the music-rack, to hear better When the church organ sounded out, she straightened herself her long skinny fingers pressed her own organ-keys with nervous energy. She worked the pedals with all her strength all her slender body was in motion. When the first notes o Alma's solo began, Candace sang. She had really possessed fine voice, and it was wonderful how little she had lost it. Straining her throat with jealous fury, her notes were still for the main part true. Her voice filled the whole room; she sang with wonderful fire and expression. That, at least, mild little Alma Way could never emulate. She was full of steadfastness and unquestioning constancy, but there were in her no smoldering fires of ambition and resolution. Music was not to her what it had been to her older rival. To this obscure woman, kept relentlessly by circumstances in a narrow track, singing in the village choir had been as much as Italy was to Napoleon — and now on her island of exile she was still showing fight.

After the church service was done, Candace left the organ and went over to her old chair by the window. Her knees felt weak, and shook under her. She sat down, and leaned back her head. There were red spots on her cheeks. Pretty soon she heard a quick slam of her gate, and an impetuous tread on the gravel-walk. She looked up, and there was her nephew Wilson Ford hurrying up to the door. She cringed a little, then she settled herself more firmly in her chair.

Wilson came into the room with a rush. He left the door open, and the wind slammed it to after him.

"Aunt Candace, where are you?" he called out, in a loud voice.

She made no reply. He looked around fiercely, and his eyes seemed to pounce upon her.

"Look here, Aunt Candace," said he, "are you crazy?" Candace said nothing. "Aunt Candace!" She did not seem to see him. "If you don't answer me," said Wilson, "I'll just go over there and pitch that old organ out of the window!"

"Wilson Ford!" said Candace, in a voice that was almost a scream.

"Well, what say! What have you got to say for yourself, acting the way you have? I tell you what 'tis, Aunt Candace, I won't stand it."

"I'd like to see you help yourself."

"I will help myself. I'll pitch that old organ out of the

window, and then I'll board up the window on that side of your house. Then we'll see."

"It ain't your house, and it won't never be."

"Who said it was my house? You're my aunt, and I've got a little lookout for the credit of the family. Aunt Candace, what are you doing this way for?"

"It don't make no odds what I'm doin' so for. I ain't bound to give my reasons to a young fellar like you, if you do act so mighty toppin'. But I'll tell you one thing, Wilson Ford, after the way you've spoke today, you sha'n't never have one cent of my money, an' you can't never marry that Way girl if you don't have it. You can't never take her home to live with your mother, an' this house would have been mighty nice an' convenient for you some day. Now you won't get it. I'm goin' to make another will. I'd made one, if you did but know it. Now you won't get a cent of my money, you nor your mother, neither. An' I ain't goin' to live a dreadful while longer, neither. Now I wish you'd go home; I want to lay down. I'm 'bout sick."

Wilson could not get another word from his aunt. His indignation had not in the least cooled. Her threat of disinheriting him did not cow him at all; he had too much rough independence, and indeed his Aunt Candace's house had always been too much of an air-castle for him to contemplate seriously. Wilson, with his burly frame and his headlong common-sense, could have little to do with air-castles, had he been hard enough to build them over graves. Still, he had not admitted that he never could marry Alma. All his hopes were based upon a rise in his own fortunes, not by some sudden convulsion, but by his own long and steady labor. Some time, he thought, he should have saved enough for the two homes.

He went out of his aunt's house still storming. She rose after the door had shut behind him, and got out into the kitchen. She thought that she would start a fire and make a cup of tea. She had not eaten anything all day. She put some kindling-wood into the stove and touched a match to it then she went back to the sitting-room, and settled down again into the chair by the window. The fire in the kitchen stove roared, and the light wood was soon burned out. She thought no more about it. She had not put on the tea-kettle. Her head ached, and once in a while she shivered. She sat at the window, while the afternoon waned and the dusk came on. At seven o'clock the meeting bell rang again, and the people flocked by. This time she did not stir. She had shut her parlor organ. She did not need to outsing her rival this evening; there was only congregational singing at the Sunday-night prayer-meeting.

She sat still until it was nearly time for meeting to be done; her head ached harder and harder, and she shivered more. Finally she arose. "Guess I'll go to bed," she muttered. She went about the house, bent over and shaking, to lock the doors. She stood a minute in the back door, looking over the fields to the woods. There was a red light over there. "The woods are on fire," said Candace. She watched with a dull interest the flames roll up, withering and destroying the tender green spring foliage. The air was full of smoke, although the fire was half a mile away.

Candace locked the door and went in. The trees with their delicate garlands of new leaves, with the new nests of song birds, might fall, she was in the roar of an intenser fire; the growths of all her springs and the delicate wontedness of her whole life were going down in it. Candace went to bed in her little room off the parlor, but she could not sleep. She lay awake all night. In the morning she crawled to the door and hailed a little boy who was passing. She bade him go for the doctor as quickly as he could, then to Mrs. Ford's, and ask her to come over. She held on to the door while she was talking. The boy stood staring wonderingly at her. The spring wind fanned her face. She had drawn on a dress skirt and put her shawl over her shoulders, and her gray hair was blowing over her red cheeks.

She shut the door and went to her bed. She never arose from it again. The doctor and Mrs. Ford came and looked after her, and she lived a week. Nobody but herself thought until the very last that she would die; the doctor called her illness merely a light run of fever; she had her senses fully.

But Candace gave up at the first. "It's my last sickness," she said to Mrs. Ford that morning when she first entered; and Mrs. Ford had laughed at the notion; but the sick woman held to it. She did not seem to suffer much physical pain; she only grew weaker and weaker, but she was distressed mentally. She did not talk much, but her eyes followed everybody with an agonized expression.

On Wednesday William Emmons came to inquire for her. Candace heard him out in the parlor. She tried to raise herself on one elbow that she might listen better to his voice.

"William Emmons come in to ask how you was," Mrs. Ford said, after he was gone.

"I — heard him," replied Candace. Presently she spoke again. "Nancy," said she, "where's that photograph album?"

"On the table," replied her sister, hesitatingly.

"Mebbe — you'd better — brush it up a little."

"Well."

Sunday morning Candace wished that the minister should be asked to come in at the noon intermission. She had refused to see him before. He came and prayed with her, and she asked his forgiveness for the way she had spoken the Sunday before. "I — hadn't ought to — spoke so," said she. "I was dreadful wrought up."

"Perhaps it was your sickness coming on," said the minister soothingly.

Candace shook her head. "No — it wa'n't. I hope the Lord will — forgive me."

After the minister had gone, Candace still appeared unhappy. Her pitiful eyes followed her sister everywhere with the mechanical persistency of a portrait.

"What is it you want, Candace?" Mrs. Ford said at last. She had nursed her sister faithfully, but once in a while her impatience showed itself.

"Nancy!"

"What say?"

"I wish — you'd go out when — meetin's done, an' — head off Alma an' Wilson, an' — ask 'em to come in. I feel as if — I'd like to — hear her sing."

Mrs. Ford stared. "Well," said she.

The meeting was now in session. The windows were all open, for it was another warm Sunday. Candace lay listening to the music when it began, and a look of peace came over her face. Her sister had smoothed her hair back, and put on a clean cap. The white curtain in the bedroom window waved in the wind like a white sail. Candace almost felt as if she were better, but the thought of death seemed easy.

Mrs. Ford at the parlor window watched for the meeting to be out. When the people appeared, she ran down the walk and waited for Alma and Wilson. When they came she told them what Candace wanted, and they all went in together.

"Here's Alma an' Wilson, Candace," said Mrs. Ford, leading them to the bedroom door.

Candace smiled. "Come in," she said, feebly. And Alma and Wilson entered and stood beside the bed. Candace continued to look at them, the smile straining her lips.

"Wilson!"

"What is it, Aunt Candace?"

"I ain't altered that — will. You an' Alma can — come here an' — live — when I'm gone. Your mother won't mind livin' alone. Alma can have — all — my things."

"Don't, Aunt Candace." Tears were running over Wilson's cheeks, and Alma's delicate face was all of a quiver.

"I thought — maybe — Alma'd be willin' to — sing for me," said Candace.

"What do you want me to sing?" Alma asked, in a trembling voice.

"'Jesus, lover of my soul.'"

Alma, standing there beside Wilson, began to sing. At first she could hardly control her voice; then she sang sweetly and clearly.

Candace lay and listened. Her face had a holy and radiant expression. When Alma stopped singing it did not disappear, but she looked up and spoke, and it was like a secondary glimpse of the old shape of a forest tree through the smoke and flame of the transfiguring fire the instant before it falls. "You flatted a little on — soul," said Candace.

QUESTIONS

1. Was Alma Way at all like Candace Whitcomb? Explain.
2. Did the minister's visit have any effect on Candace's decision? Do you think Wilson Ford's visit had any effect? Give reasons for your answers.
3. Do you think Candace felt sorry for Alma Way?
4. What part does the engagement of Alma Way and Wilson Ford play in the story?
5. What reasons did Candace give for being angry over her dismissal from the choir? What was the real reason?
6. What use does the author make of the forest fire?
7. Explain the last paragraph of the story.
8. *Word Study.* — What do the following words mean as they are used in the story: *desultory, furtively, impediment, deprecatory, pugnacious, temperament, expostulation, impetuous?*

Problem: STORY OF CHARACTER
(See page 24.)

1. Which is more important to this story, Candace Whitcomb's struggle with the other members of the church, or her struggle with herself? What elements in her character caused the inner conflict?
2. Study the story to discover the means by which the author presents her leading character to us. Read the passages describing Candace's character. Read Candace's speeches to the other characters. Read the passages describing Candace's acts. Read what the other characters say about Candace. Which means of presenting character seems to you most important in this story? Would it be possible to do without any one of them?
3. How does the use of local color aid in the presentation of the village singer?

The Grudge *

Albert Payson Terhune (1872–1942)

Albert Payson Terhune, a member of a family of authors, once wrote, "I was born in Newark, New Jersey, in the parsonage of my father's church. While I was still a child, the whole family went to Europe to live for several years, and it was there — at Paris and Geneva — that my education began. We came back to America, and I was graduated from Columbia in 1893. After I finished college, I went back to Europe for a while and thence to the Near East, where I wandered through Egypt and Syria. . . . Back in America, I took up newspaper work. I hated it. I wanted to be a writer, not a reporter or an editor. It was slow, grinding work until I began to write about dogs and the outdoors."

Terhune's first book, "Syria from the Saddle," gave an interest-account of the young traveler's experiences in the Near East. The author's second, "Dr. Dale," was written in collaboration with his mother, who wrote under the pen name of Marion Harland.

While he was raising many fine collies at his home, Sunnybank, near Pompton Lakes, New Jersey, Albert Payson Terhune began writing stories about them. "Lad: a Dog" was published in 1919 and sold 50,000 copies in ten years. It was followed by others — for example, "Buff: a Collie" and "Further Adventures of Lad." It was his success in the field of animal stories which permitted Terhune to retire from newspaper work and devote himself to the two things he loved to do most — raise collies and write stories about them. The entire Terhune family — father, mother, and daughter — were all interested in and fond of animals — especially collies.

Terhune wrote two autobiographies — "Now That I'm Fifty," in 1925, and "To the Best of My Memory" in 1929. "Loot," *the author's last book, was published in 1940. After more than thirty-four years of successful writing, Terhune died of a heart ailment at Sunnybank, at the age of sixty-nine.*

In an article, "Why You Can't Write Dog Stories," Terhune explained that few authors really understand dogs well enough to write credible stories about them. As Terhune raised, knew, understood, and loved every dog at Sunnybank, it was his extensive knowledge of canine psychology which helped to make his many animal stories successful. To write an interesting, convincing dog story, the author must make his canine characters real, distinct, and believable to the reader. He must lead the latter to have the same interest in the animal heroes and heroines that he has in human ones. At the same time, he must be careful to see that his dog remains a dog and does not become a human being. In the following selection, "The Grudge," Albert Payson Terhune has accomplished this difficult task successfully.

FRAYNE'S FARMS is the alliterative name for the hundred-acre tract of rich bottom land; in the shadow of the Ramapo Mountains — a range that splits north Jersey's farm country for some twenty odd miles.

Back in these mountains are queer folk, whose exploits sometimes serve as a page story for some Sunday newspaper. Within forty miles of New York City as the crow flies, the handful of mountaineers are well-nigh as primitive as any South Sea Islanders. They are as a race apart; and with their own barbarous codes and customs.

Down from the mountains, in the starvingly barren winter time, every few years, a band of huge black mongrel dogs used to swoop upon the Valley, harrying it from end to end in search of food; and leaving a trail of ravaged hen roosts and sheepfolds in their wake.

These plunderers were the half-wild black dogs of the mountaineers — dogs blended originally from a tangle of diverse breeds; hound predominating; and with a splash of wolf-blood in their rangy carcases.

When famine and cold gripped the folk of the mountains,

the dogs were deprived of even such scanty crusts and bones as were their summer portion. And, under the goad of hunger, the black brutes banded for a raid on the richer pickings of the Valley.

At such times, every able-bodied farmer, from Trask Frayne to the members of the Italian garden-truck colony, up Suffern-way, would arm himself and join the hunt. Rounding up the horde of mongrels, they would shoot fast and unerringly. Such few members of the pack as managed to break through the cordon and make a dash for the mountains were followed hotly up into the fastnesses of the gray rocks and were exterminated by trained huntsmen.

The mountaineers were too shrewd to make any effort to protect their sheep-slaying and chicken-stealing pets from the hunters. Much as they affected to despise the stolid toilers of the Valley, yet they had learned from more than one bitter and long bygone experience that the Valley men were not safe to trifle with when once righteous indignation drove them to the warpath.

For years after such a battle the Valley was wholly free from the marauding black-dog pack. Not only did the dogs seem to shun, by experience, the peril of invading the lowlands, but their numbers were so depleted that there was more than enough food for all of the few survivors in the meager garbage of the mountain shacks. Not until numbers and forgetfulness again joined hands with famine did the pack renew its Valley forays.

When this story begins, a mere two years had passed since the latest of the mongrel hunts. Forty farmers and hired men, marshalled and led by young Trask Frayne, had rounded up not less than seventy-five of the great black raiders at the bank of the frozen little Ramapo River, which winds along at the base of the mountain wall, dividing the Valley from the savage hinterland.

The pack's depredations had beaten all records that season. And the farmers were grimly vengeful. Mercilessly, they had poured volley after volley into the milling swarm of freebooters. Led by a giant dog, ebony-black and with the fore-quarters of a timber wolf, the handful of remaining pillagers had burst through the cordon and crossed the river to the safety of the bleak hills.

It was Trask Frayne who guided the posse of trackers in pursuit. For the best part of two days the farmers kept up the hunt. An occasional far-off report of a shotgun would be wafted to the Valley below, in token of some quarry trailed to within buckshot range.

The gaunt black giant leading the pack seemed to be invulnerable. No less than five times during that two-day pursuit some farmer caught momentary sight of him; only to miss aim by reason of the beast's uncanny craftiness and speed.

Trask Frayne himself was able to take a hurried shot at the ebony creature as the fugitive slunk shadow-like between two hillock boulders.

At the report of Trask's gun, the huge mongrel had whirled about, snarling and foaming at the mouth and had snapped savagely at his own shoulder, where a single buckshot had just seared a jagged groove. But, before Frayne could fire a second shot, the dog had vanished.

Thus the hunt ended. Nearly all the black dogs of the mountaineers had met the death penalty. It was the most thorough and successful of the historic list of such battles. The raiders were practically exterminated. Many a year must pass before the pack could hope again to muster numbers for an invasion. And the Valley breathed easier.

Yet, Trask Frayne was not content. He knew dog-nature as it is given to few humans to know it. And he could not forget the wily black giant that had led the band of mongrels. The Black was a super-dog for cunning and strength and elusiveness. That had been proven by certain ultra-devastating features of the raid as well as by his own escape from the hunters.

And the Black still lived — still lived, and with no worse reminder of his flight than a bullet-cut on one mighty shoulder. Such a dog was a menace so long as he should continue alive.

Wherefore, Trask Frayne wanted to kick himself for his own ill luck in not killing him. And he was obsessed by a foreboding that the Valley had not seen the last of the Black. He could not explain this premonition.

He could not explain it, even to himself. For Valley history showed that each battle serves as a wholesome lesson to the black dogs for years thereafter. Never, between forays, was one of them seen on the hither side of the Ramapo. Yet the idea would not get out of Frayne's head.

Trask had hated the necessary job of destroying the mongrels. For he loved dogs. Nothing short of stark need would have lured him into shooting one of them. His own two thoroughbred collies, Tam-o'-Shanter and Wisp, were honored members of the Frayne household.

Dogs of the same breed differ as much in character as do humans of the same race. For example, no two humans could have been more widely divergent in nature than were these two collies of Trask's.

Tam-o'-Shanter was deep-chested, mighty of coat, tawny as befitted the son of his illustrious sire, old Sunnybank Lad. Iron-firm of purpose and staunchly loyal to his master, Tam was as steady of soul as a rock. Whether guarding the farm buildings or rounding up a bunch of scattered sheep that had broken bounds, he was calmly reliable.

He adored Trask Frayne with a worship that was none the less all-absorbing because it was so undemonstrative. And he cared for nothing and nobody else on earth — except Wisp.

Wisp had been the runt of a thoroughbred litter. He was slender and fragile and wholly lovable; a dainty little tricolor, scarce forty pounds in weight. Not enough for heavy work, yet Wisp was a gallant guard and a gaily affectionate house dog — the cherished pet and playfellow of the three Frayne babies. Also, he was Tam's dearest friend.

The larger collie, from puppyhood, had established a protection over Wisp; ever conceding to him the warmest corner of the winter hearth, the shadiest spot in the dooryard in summer, the best morsels of their joint daily meal. He would descend from his calm loftiness to romp with the frolicsome Wisp; though the sight of stately Tam, trying to romp, was somehow suggestive of Marshal Joffre playing pat-a-cake.

In short, he loved Wisp, as he loved not even Trask Frayne. More than once, in the village, when a stray cur misunderstood Wisp's gay friendliness and showed his teeth at the frail little dog, Tam so far departed from his wonted noble dignity as to hurl himself upon the aggressor and thrash the luckless canine into howling submission.

He was Wisp's guardian as well as his dearest comrade. Once in a very great while such inseparable friendships spring up between two collies.

One morning in June, Trask set forth for Suffern with a flock of sixty sheep. The day was hot, and the journey promised to be tiresome. So, when the two collies had worked the sixty out from the rest of the Frayne bunch of sheep and had started them, bleating and milling, toward the highroad, Trask whistled Wisp back to him.

"Home, boy!" he ordered, patting the friendly uplifted head and playfully rumpling the collie's silken ears. "Back home, and take care of things there to-day. It's a long, hot trip for a pup that hasn't any more stamina than you have, Wispy. Tam and I can handle them all right. Chase back home!"

The soft brown eyes of the collie filled with infinitely pathetic pleadings. Wisp understood the meaning of his master's words as well as might any of the Frayne children. From birth he had been talked to, and his quick brain had responded as does every clever collie's.

Wisp knew he had been bidden to stay at home from this delightful outing. And every inch of his body as well as his eloquent eyes cried aloud in appeal to be taken along. Yet when, once more, Frayne patted his head and pointed towards the dooryard, the good little chap turned obediently back.

As he passed Tam, the two dogs touched noses as if exchanging speech of some sort — as perhaps they were. Then, disconsolately, Wisp trotted to the house and curled up on the doormat in a small and furry and miserably unhappy heap. There he was still lying, his sorrowful eyes fixed on his master and on his busily herding chum, as the huddle of sheep were guided out of the gateway into the highroad beyond.

Glancing back, Frayne smiled encouragingly at the pathetic little waiting figure at the door. Tam, too, paused, as he maneuvered the last silly sheep into the highroad; and stood beside Frayne, for a second, peering back at his chum. Under their momentary glance, Wisp made shift to wag his plumy tail once by way of affectionate farewell.

Long afterward, Trask Frayne could summon up memory of the daintily graceful little dog, lying so obediently on the doormat and wagging such a brave good-bye to the master who had just deprived him of a jolly day's outing. Possibly the picture remained in Tam-o'-Shanter's memory, too.

It is to be hoped so. For never again were Frayne or Tam to see their lovable little collie chum.

Dusk was sifting down the Valley from beyond the mountain wall that afternoon when Trask Frayne turned once more into the gateway leading to his farm. At his side trotted Tam. It had been a hard day, both for dog and man. At best, it is no light task to marshal a flock of sixty bolting sheep along miles of winding road. But when that road is infested with terrifying motor-cars and when it goes past two or three blast-emitting stone-quarries and a railway, the labor is spectacular in spots and arduous at all times.

But, at last, thanks to Tam, the sheep had reached Suffern without a single mishap and had been driven skilfully into the herd-pens. The seven-mile homeward tramp had been, by contrast, a mere pleasure-stroll. Yet both the collie and his master were glad of the prospect of rest and of supper.

Frayne, reviewing the labor of the day, was pleased with his own foresight in making Wisp stay at home. He knew such an ordeal, in such weather, would have tired the delicate collie half to death.

Coming up the dusky lane from the house to meet the returning wanderers was a slender, white-clad woman. As he saw her, Frayne waved his hat and hurried forward at new speed. Thus, always, after one of his few absences from home, his pretty young wife came up the lane to welcome him. And, as ever, the sight of her made him forget his fatigue.

Yet, now, after that first glance, worry took the place of eagerness in Frayne's mind. For his wife was advancing slowly and spiritlessly; and not in the very least with her wonted springy walk.

"The heat's been too much for her!" he muttered worriedly to Tam. "It's been a broiling day. She ought to have ——"

But Tam was no longer beside him. The big collie had started ahead, toward the oncoming woman.

Usually, when Mildred Frayne came thus to greet her returning husband, Wisp was with her. The little dog would bound ahead of his mistress, as Frayne appeared, and come galloping merrily up to him and Tam. Tam, too, always cantered forward to touch noses with his chum.

But, by this evening's dim light, Frayne could not see Wisp. Nor did Tam rush forward as usual. Instead, he was pacing slowly toward Mildred, with head and tail adroop.

As Tam had turned in at the gate beside his master, the collie had come to a convulsive halt. His nostrils had gone upward in a series of eagerly suspicious sniffs. Then his shaggy body had quivered all over, as if with a spasm of physical pain. At that moment, Mildred's white-clad figure had caught his wandering eye. And he had moved forward, downcast and trembling, to meet her.

It was Tam — long before Trask — who discovered that Mildred was weeping. And this phenomenon, for the instant, turned his attention from his vain search for Wisp and from the confusingly menacing scents which had just assailed his nostrils.

Departing from his lifelong calm, the big dog whined softly as he came up with Mildred; and he thrust his cold muzzle sympathizingly into her loose-hanging hand. Within him stirred all his splendid race's pitiful yearning to comfort a human in grief. So poignant was this craving that it almost made him forget the increasingly keen scents which had put him on his guard when he came in through the gateway.

"Hello!" called Trask, cheerily, as he neared his wife. "Tired, dear? You shouldn't have bothered to walk all this way out to meet me. After a rotten day like this, you ought to be resting. . . . Where's Wisp? Is he 'disciplining' me for making him stay home? I ——"

Then he, too, saw Mildred was crying. And before he could speak again, she had thrown her arms around his neck and was sobbing out an incoherent story, broken by an occasional involuntary shiver. Holding her close to him and asking eagerly futile questions, Trask Frayne, bit by bit, drew forth the reason for her grief.

Harry and Janet, the two older children, had gone down to the river that noon to fish off the dock for perch. Mildred, at an upper window where she was sewing, had watched them from time to time. For the river was high and rapid from recent rains.

But Wisp was with them; and she had experience in the little collie's sleepless care over the youngsters. More than once indoors Wisp had thrust his own slight body between a Frayne child and the fire. Again and again, at the dock, he had interposed his puny bulk and had shoved with all his force, when one or another of the babies ventured too close to the edge.

To-day, as she looked up from her sewing, she had seen the trio leave the dock and start homeward. Janet had been in the lead, swinging the string of perch and sunfish and shiners they had caught. They had skirted a riverside thicket on their way to the home-path.

Out from the bushes had sprung a gigantic lean dog, jet-black except for a zig-zag patch of white on one shoulder. The wind had been strong in the other direction. So no scent of the dog had reached Wisp, who was dawdling along a bit to the rear of the children.

The Black had made a lightning grab at the carelessly swung string of fish and had snatched them away from Janet.

As he turned to bolt back into the thicket with his stolen feast, Harry had caught up a stick and had charged in pursuit of the string of laboriously caught fish. The child had brought his stick down with a resounding thwack on the head of the escaping beast.

The blow must have stung. For instantly the Black dropped the fish and leaped upon the tiny chap. All this in a single second or less.

But, before the mongrel's teeth could reach their mark, Wisp had flashed past the two startled children and had launched his weak body straight at the Black's throat.

Down went the two dogs in a tearing, snarling heap.

Mildred, realizing how hopelessly unequal was the contest, had run to the aid of her beloved Wisp. Fleeing downstairs, she had snatched Trask's gun from its peg above the mantel, had seized at random a handful of shells, and run out of the house and towards the river, loading the gun as she went.

By the time she came in sight, the Black had already recovered the advantage he had lost by Wisp's unexpected spring. By dint of strength and of weight, he had torn himself free of Wisp's weak grip, had flung the lighter dog to earth and had pinned him there. Right gallantly did little Wisp battle in the viselike grasp of the giant. Fiercely he strove to bite at the rending jaws and to rip free from the crushing weight above him.

But, as ever, mere courage could not atone for dearth of brute strength and ferocity. Undeterred by his foe's puny efforts or by the fusillade of blows from Harry's stick and from Janet's pudgy fists, the Black had slung Wisp to one side and had lunged once more at him.

This time he found the mark he sought — the back of the neck, just below the base of the brain. He threw all his vast jaw-power into one terrific bite. And little Wisp's frantic struggles ceased. The valiant collie lay inert and moveless, his neck broken.

Maddened by conquest, the Black tossed the lifeless body in air. It came to ground on the edge of the river. There, from the momentum of the toss, it had rebounded into the water. The swift current had caught it and borne it downstream.

Then, for the first time, the Black seemed to realize that both frantically screaming children were showering futile blows on him. With a snarl he turned on Harry. But, as he did so, Mildred's flying feet brought her within range. Halting, she raised the gun and fired.

She was a good shot. And excitement had not robbed her aim of steadiness. But excitement had made her catch up a handful of cartridges loaded lightly with Number Eight shot instead of anything more deadly.

The small pellets buzzed, hornetlike, about the Black's head and shoulders; several of them stinging hotly. But at that distance, the birdshot could do no lasting damage. Nor did any of it chance to reach one of his eyes.

With a yell of pain he wheeled to face the woman. And she let him have the second barrel. Memories of former clashes with gunners seemed to wake in the brute's crafty brain. Snarling, snapping, shaking his tormented head, he turned and plunged into the narrow river, gaining the farther bank and diving into the waterside bushes before Mildred could think to reload.

The balance of the day had been spent in a vain search of the bank, downstream, for Wisp's lost body; and in trying to comfort the heartbroken children. Not until she had gotten the babies to bed and had soothed them to sleep did Mildred have scope to think of her own grief in the loss of the gentle dog who had been so dear to her.

"He — he gave his life for them!" she finished her sobbing recital. "He knew — he must have known — that he had no chance against that horrible monster. And Wisp had never fought, you know, from the day he was born. He knew that brute would kill him. And he never hesitated at all. He gave his life for the children. And — and we can't — can't even say a prayer over his grave!"

But Trask Frayne, just then, was not thinking of prayers. Deep down in his throat he was cursing — softly, but with much venom. And the nails of his hard-clenched fists bit deep into his palms.

"Black, with a white scar on the shoulder?" he said at last, his own harsh voice not unlike a dog's growl. "Hound ears, and the build of a timber-wolf? Almost as big as a Dane; and bone-thin? H'm! That's my buckshot-scar on his shoulder — that zig-zag mark. Tomorrow morning, I'm going hunting. Up in the mountains. Want to come along, Tam?"

But, as before, Tam was not there when his master turned to speak to him. The collie had waited only long enough to note that the task of comforting the weeping Mildred had been taken over by more expert powers than his. Then he had trotted off towards the house; not only to solve the problem of these sinister scents which hung so heavy on the moist night air, but to find his strangely absent chum, Wisp.

Circling the house, he caught Wisp's trail. It was some hours old; but by no means too cold to be followed by a collie whose scenting powers had once tracked a lost sheep for five miles through a blizzard. With Wisp's trail was mingled that of two of the children. And it led to the river-path.

True, there were other trails of Wisp's that the sensitive nostrils caught. But all of them were older than this which led to the water. Therefore, as any tracking dog would have known, Wisp had gone riverward since he had been near the house. And down the path, nose to ground, followed Tam-o'-Shanter.

He did not move with his wonted stolidity. For, over and above the mere trail scent, his nostrils were assailed by other and more distressingly foreboding smells — the smells he had caught as he had entered the gate — the smells which grew ranker at every loping step he took.

In half a minute he was at the bank. And before that time, he had abandoned the nose-to-earth tracking. For now all around him was that terrible scent.

Back and forth dashed and circled and doubled Tam. And every evolution told him more of the gruesome story.

Here among the bushes had lain a strange animal, an unwashed and pungent and huge animal, apparently sleeping after a gorge of chicken or lamb. Here, along the path, had come the children, with Wisp behind them. Here the strange dog had leapt forth; and here — alongside that string of forgotten and sunblown fish on the ground — Wisp and the stranger had clashed.

The dullest of scents could have told the story from that point — the trampled earth, the spatters of dried blood, the indentation in the grass, where Wisp's writhing body had striven so heroically to free itself from the crushing weight above it and to renew the hopeless battle.

Wisp was dead. He was slain by that huge and rank-scented creature. His body had touched the river-brink, fully five feet from the scene of the fight. After that it had disappeared. For running water will not hold a scent.

Yes, Wisp was dead. He had been murdered. He had been murdered — this adored chum of his — by the great beast whose scent was already graven so indelibly on Tam's heart-sick memory.

There, at the river-edge a few minutes later, Trask Frayne found Tam-o'-Shanter padding restlessly about from spot to spot of the tragedy, whimpering under his breath. But the whimper carried no hint of pathos. Rather was it the expression of a wrath that lay too deep for mere growling.

At his master's touch, the great collie started nervously and shrunk away from the caress he had always craved. And his furtively swift motion, in eluding the loved hand, savored far more of the wolf than of the trained house dog. The collie, in look and in action, had reverted to the wild.

Tam trotted, for the tenth time, to the spot at the river-shore, where the Black had bounded into the water. Impatiently — always with that queer little throaty whimper — he cast up and down along the bank, in quest of some place where Wisp's slayer might perhaps have doubled back to land.

Presently, Trask called to him. For the first time in his blameless life, Tam hesitated before obeying. He was standing, hock-deep, in the swirling water, sniffing the air and peering through the dusk along the wooded banks on the far side of the stream.

Again, more imperatively, Frayne called him. With visible distaste, the collie turned and made his way back towards his master. Frayne had finished his own fruitless investigations and was starting homeward.

Halfway to the house he paused and looked back. Tam had ceased to follow him and was staring once more at the patches of trampled and dyed earth. A third and sharper call from Trask brought the collie to heel.

"I don't blame you, old boy," said Frayne, as they made their way towards the lighted kitchen. "But you can't find him that way. Tomorrow you and I are going to take a little trip through the mountains. I'd rather have your help on a hunt like that than any hound's. You won't forget his scent in a hurry. And you know, as well as I, what he's done."

On the way to the house, Frayne paused at the sheep-fold and made a careful detour of it. But the inspection satisfied him that the fence (built long ago with special regard to the mountain pack's forays) was still too stout to permit of any dog's breaking through it. And he passed on to the house, again having to summon the newly-furtive collie from an attempt to go back to the river.

"He won't pay us another visit tonight, Tam," he told the sullen dog, as they went indoors. "He's tricky. And if he's really on the rampage, here in the Valley, he'll strike next in some place miles away from here. Wait till tomorrow."

But once more Tam did not follow his overlord's bidding. For, at dawn of the morrow, when Trask came out of the house, shotgun in hand, the dog was nowhere to be found. Never before had Tam forsaken his duties as guardian of the farm to wander afield without Frayne.

The jingle of the telephone brought Trask back into the house. On the other end of the wire was an irate farmer.

"I'm sending word all along the line," came his message "Last night a dog bust into my hencoop and killed every last one of my prize Hamburgs and fifty-three other chickens, besides. He worked as quiet as a fox. 'Twasn't till I heard a chicken squawk that I came out. That must have been the last of the lot; and the dog had got careless. I had just a glimpse of him as he sneaked off in the dark. Great big cuss he was. As big as a house. Looked something like a wolf by that bum light, and something like a collie, too. Last evening I got news that Gryce, up Suffern-way, lost a lamb, night before, from some prowling dog. D'you s'pose the dogs from the mountains is loose again?"

"One of them is," returned Frayne. "I'm going after him, now."

He hung up the receiver, and, gun under arm, made his way to the scow lying at the side of the dock. Crossing the river, he explored the bank for a half mile in both directions. Failing to find sign or trail of the Black, he struck into the mountains.

It was late that night when Trask slouched wearily into his own house and laid aside his gun.

"Any trace of him?" asked Mildred, eagerly.

"Not a trace," answered Frayne. "I quartered the range, farther back than we ever hunted before. And I asked a lot of questions at that God-forsaken mountaineer settlement, up there. That's all the good it did. I might hunt for a year and not get any track of the beast. Those mountaineers are all liars, of course. Not one of 'em would admit they'd ever seen or heard of the dog. If I'd had Tam with me, I might have caught the trail. Tomorrow, I'll see he goes along. He ——"

"Tam?" repeated Mildred, in surprise. "Why, wasn't he with you? He hasn't been home all day. He ——"

"Hasn't been home? Do you mean to say he didn't come back?"

"No," said his wife, worriedly. "When I got up this morning and found you both gone, I thought of course you'd taken him along, as you said you were going to. Didn't ——"

"He wasn't anywhere around when I started," replied

Frayne. "He's — he's never been away for a whole day, or even for a whole hour, before. I wonder ——"

"Oh, do you suppose that horrible brute has killed Tam, too?" quavered Mildred, in new terror.

"Not he," Trask reassured her. "Not he, or any mortal dog. But," he hesitated, then went on, shame-facedly, "but I'll tell you what I *do* think. I believe Tam has gone hunting, on his own account. I believe he's trailing that mongrel. If he is, he has a man's size job cut out for him. For the Black is as tricky as a weasel. Tam thought more of Wisp than he thought of anything else. And he was like another animal when he found what had happened down yonder. Take my word for it, he is after the dog that murdered his chum. Whether he'll ever get him is another matter. But, if he really is after him, he'll never give up the hunt as long as he has a breath of life left in him. Either he'll overhaul the cur or — well, either that or we'll never see him again. There's no sense in my poking around in the mountains without him. All we can do is wait. That and try to find Tam and chain him up till he forgets this crazy revenge-idea."

But even though the Fraynes did not see their cherished collie when they arose next morning, they did not lack for news of him. In the middle of a silent and doleful breakfast a telephone ring summoned Trask from the table.

"That you, Frayne?" queried a truculent voice. "This is Trippler — at Darlington. I got rotten news for you. But it's a whole lot rottener for *me*. Last night my cow-yard was raided by a dog. He killed two of the month-old Jersey calves and pretty near ripped the throat out of one of my yearlings. I heard the racket and I run out with my gun and a flashlight. The cow-yard looked like a battlefield. The dog had skipped. Couldn't see a sign of him anywheres. But about half an hour later he came back. He came back while I was redding up the yard and trying to quiet the scared critters. He came right to the cow-yard gate and stood sniffing there as bold as brass; like he was trying to catch the scent of more of my stock to kill. I heard his feet a-pattering and I turned the flashlight on him. He was your dog, Frayne! That big dark-colored collie dog of yours. I saw him as plain as day. I upped with my gun and let him have it. For I was pretty sore. But I must have missed him, clean. For there wasn't any blood near his footprints, in the mud, when I looked. He just lit out. But I'm calling up to tell you you'll have a big bill to pay on this; and ——"

"Hold on," interrupted Frayne, quietly. "I'll be up there in twenty minutes. Good-bye."

As fast as his car could carry him, Trask made his way up the Valley to Darlington, and to the Trippler farm. There an irately unloving host awaited him.

"Before you go telling me the whole story all over again," Trask broke in on an explosive recital, "take me over to the exact spot where you saw Tam standing and sniffing. The ground all around here is soaked from the shower we had last evening. I want to see the tracks you were speaking of."

Muttering dire threats and whining lamentations for his lost calves, Trippler led the way to the cow-yard; pointing presently to a gap in the privet hedge which shut off the barns from the truck garden. Frayne went over to the gap and proceeded to inspect the muddy earth, inch by inch.

"It was here Tam stood when you turned the light on him?" he asked.

"Right just there," declared Trippler. "And I c'n swear to him. He ——"

"Come over here," invited Trask. "There are his footprints. As you said. And I'd know them anywhere. There's no other dog of his size with such tiny feet. He gets them from his sire, Sunnybank Lad. Those are Tam's footprints, I admit that. I'd know them anywhere — even if they didn't show the gash in the outer pad of the left forefoot, where he gouged himself on barbed wire when he was a pup."

"You admit it was him, then!" orated Trippler. "That's all I need to hear you say! Now, how much ——"

"No, no," gently denied Frayne. "It isn't anywhere near

all you need to hear. Now, let's go back into the cow-yard. As I crossed it, just now, I saw dozens of dog-footprints among the hoofmarks of the calves. Let's take another look at them."

Grumblingly, yet eager to add this corroboratory evidence, Trippler followed him to the wallow of churned mud which marked the scene of slaughter. At the first clearly defined set of footprints, Trask halted.

"Take a good look at those," he adjured. "Study them carefully. Here, these, for instance — where the dog planted all fours firmly for a spring. They're the marks of splay feet, a third larger than Tam's; and not one of them has that gash in the pad — the one I pointed out to you, back at the gap. Look for yourself."

"Nonsense!" fumed Trippler, albeit a shade uneasily as he stood up stiffly after a peering study of the prints. "Anyhow," he went on, "all it proves is that there was two of 'em. This big splay-footed cuss and your collie. They was working in couples, like killers often does."

"Were they?" Frayne caught him up. "Were they? Then suppose you look carefully all through this welter of cowyard mud and see if you can find a single footprint of Tam's. And while you're looking, let me tell you something."

As Trippler went over the yard's mud with gimlet eyes, Trask related the story of Wisp's killing and his own theory as to Tam.

"He's trailing that black dog," he finished. "He struck his scent somewhere, and followed him. He got here a half-hour too late. And then when you fired at him he ran off to pick up the trail again. But I doubt if he got it. For the Black would probably be cunning enough to take to the river, after a raid like this. He'd have sense enough to know that somebody would track him. That brute has true wolf-cunning."

"Maybe — maybe you're right," hesitated Trippler, after a minute search of the yard had failed to reveal a footprint corresponding with Tam's. "And the county's got to pay for 'any damage done to stock by an unknown dog.' That's the law. I'm kind of glad, too. You see, I like old Tam. Besides,

I c'n c'llect more damages from the county than I c'd c'llect from a lawsoot with a neighbor. What'll we do now? Fix up a posse like we did the other times?"

"No," replied Trask. "It would do no good. The Black is too clever. And in summer there are too many ways to throw off the scent. Tam will get him — if any one can. Let's leave it to him."

But other farmers were not so well content to leave the punishment of the mysterious raider to Tam. As the days went on, there were more and more tidings of the killer. Up and down the Valley he worked; never twice in succession in the same vicinity.

Twice, an hour or so after his visits, men saw Tam prowling along the mongrel's cooling tracks. They reported to Frayne that the collie had grown lean and gaunt and that his beautiful coat was one mass of briar and burr; and that he had slunk away, wolf-fashion, when they called to him.

Frayne, himself, caught no slightest sight of his beloved dog; though, occasionally, in the mornings, he found empty the dish of food he had set out on the previous night. Trask was working out the problem for himself, nowadays, deaf to all requests that he head another band of hunters into the mountains. He was getting no sleep to speak of. But he was thrilling with the suspense of what sportsmen know as "the still hunt."

Every evening, when his chores and his supper were finished, Frayne went to the sheepfold and led thence a fat wether that had a real genius for loud bleating. This vocal sheep he would tether to a stake near the river-bank. Then he himself would study the trend of the faint evening breeze and would take up a position in the bushes, somewhere to leeward of the sheep. There, gun across knees, he would sit, until early daylight.

Sometimes he dozed. Oftener he crouched, tense and wakeful, in his covert, straining his eyes through the gloom for the hoped-for sight of a slinking black shadow creeping towards the decoy. Not alone to avenge the death of Wisp and to rid the Valley of a scourge did he spend his nights in this way.

He knew Tam; as only a born dogman can know his dog. He missed the collie, keenly. And he had solid faith that on the death of the Black the miserable quest would end and Tam would return to his old home and to his old habits.

So, night after night, Frayne would keep his vigil. Morning after morning, he would plod home, there to hear a telephoned tale of the Black's depredations at some other point of the Valley. At first his nightly watch was kept in dense darkness. But soon the waxing moon lightened the river-bank and made the first hours of the sentry duty easier.

Frayne began to lose faith in his own scheme. He had an odd feeling that the Black somehow knew of his presence in the thicket and that Frayne's Farms was left unvisited for that reason. Trask's immunity from the Black's depredations was the theme of much neighborhood talk, as time went on. Once more was revived Trippler's theory that Tam and the Black were hunting in couples and that the collie (like so many dogs which have "gone bad") was sparing his late master's property.

On all these unpleasant themes Trask Frayne was brooding one night late in the month as he sat in uncomfortable stillness amid the bushes and stared glumly out at the occasionally-bleating wether. He had had a hard day. And the weeks of semi-sleeplessness were beginning to tell cruelly on him. His senses had taken to tricking him of late. For instance, at one moment, this night, he was crouching there, waiting patiently for the full moon to rise above the eastern hills, to brighten his vigil. The next moment — though he was certain he had not closed his eyes — the moon had risen and was riding high in the clear heavens.

Frayne started a little, and blinked. As he did so, his disturbed mind told him he had not awakened naturally, but that he had been disturbed by some sound. He shifted his drowsy gaze towards the tethered sheep. And at once all slumber was wiped from his brain.

The wether was lying sprawled on the ground, in a posture that nature neither intends nor permits. Its upflung legs were still jerking convulsively, like galvanized stilts. And above it was bending a huge dark shape.

The moon beat down mercilessly on the tableau of the slain sheep, and of the Black, with his fangs buried deep in the twisting throat.

Now that the longed-for moment had at last come, Trask found himself seized by an unaccountable numbness of mind and of body. By a mighty effort he regained control of his faculties. Slowly, and in utter silence, he lifted the cocked gun from his knees and put its butt to the hollow of his shoulder.

The Black looked up in quick suspicion from his meal. Even in the excitement of the instant, Frayne found scope to wonder at the brute's ability to hear so noiseless a motion. And his sleep-numbed finger sought the trigger.

Then, in a flash, he knew why the Black's great head had lurched so suddenly up from the interrupted meal. From out a clump of alder, twenty feet to shoreward of the river-bank, whirled a tawny shape. With the speed of a flung spear it sped, straight for the feasting mongrel. And, in the mere breath of time it took to dash through the intervening patch of moonlight, Frayne recognized the newcomer.

The Black sprang up from beside the dead sheep, and faced the foe he could no longer elude. Barely had he gained his feet when Tam was upon him.

Yet the mongrel was not taken unaware. His crafty brain was alert and the master of his sinewy body. As Tam leaped, the black dog reared to meet him. Then, in practically the same gesture, the Black shifted his direction and dived beneath the charging collie, lunging for the latter's unprotected stomach. It was a maneuver worthy of a wolf and one against which the average dog must have been helpless.

But the Black's opponent was a collie. And, in the back of his brain, though never in his chivalric heart, a collie is forever reverting to his own wolf ancestors. Thus, as the Black changed the course of his lunge, Tam, in midair, changed his. By a violent twist of every whalebone muscle, Tam whirled himself sidewise. And the Black's ravening jaws closed on nothing.

In another instant — even before he had touched ground — Tam had slashed with his curving eye-teeth. This is another trick known to practically no animal save the wolf and the wolf's direct descendant, the collie. The razor-like teeth cut the Black's left ear and cheek as cleanly as might a blade.

But, in the same motion, the Black's flying head had veered, and his jaws had found a hold above Tam's jugular. Again, with the normal dog, such a hold might well have ended the fight. But the Providence which ordained that a collie should guard sheep on icy Highland moors also gave him an unbelievably thick coat to fend off the weather. And this coat serves as an almost invulnerable armor, especially at the side of the throat. The Black's teeth closed upon a quantity of tangled fur, but on only the merest patch of skin and on none of the under flesh at all.

Tam ripped himself free, leaving a double handful of ruff between the Black's grinding jaws. As the mongrel spat out the encumbering gag of fur, Tam's curved fang laid bare the scarred shoulder once grazed by Trask Frayne's buckshot. And in a rolling, fighting heap, the two enemies rolled over and over together on the dew-drenched grass.

Frayne's gun was levelled. But the man did not dare fire. By that deceptive light, he had no assurance of hitting one dog without also killing the other. And, chafing at his own impotence, he stood stock-still, watching the battle.

Both dogs were on their feet again, rearing and rending in mute fury. No sound issued from the back-curled lips of either. This was no mere dog fight, as noisy as it was pugnacious. It was a struggle to the death. And the dogs realized it.

Thrice more, the Black struck for the jugular. Twice, thanks to Tam's lightning quickness, he scored a clean miss. The third time he annexed only another handful of hair.

With his slashes he was luckier. One of Tam's forelegs was bleeding freely. So was a cut on his stomach, where the Black had sought to disembowel him. And one side of his muzzle was laid open. But the collie had given over such mere fencing tactics as slashing. He was tearing into his powerful and wily foe with all the concentrated fury of his month's vain pursuit of vengeance.

The Black dived for the collie's forelegs, seeking to crack their bones in his mighty jaws and thus render his foe helpless. Nimbly, Tam's tiny white forefeet whisked away from the peril of each dive. In redoubled fury he drove for the throat. And the two clashed, shoulder to shoulder.

Then, amid the welter, came the final phase of the fight. The Black, as the two reared, lunged again for the collie's hurt throat. Tam jerked his head and neck aside to avoid the grip. And, as once before, the Black changed the direction of his lunge. With the swiftness of a striking snake, he made the change. And, before the other could thwart or as much as divine his purpose, he had secured the coveted hold, far up on Tam's left foreleg.

No mere snap or slash, this, but a death grip. The Black's teeth sank deep into the captured leg, grinding with a force which presently must snap the bones of the upper leg and leave the collie crippled against a practically uninjured and terrible antagonist. The rest would be slaughter.

Tam knew his own mortal peril. He knew it even before Trask Frayne came rushing out from his watching place, brandishing the gun, club-fashion. The collie did not try to wrench free and thereby hurry the process of breaking his leg or of tearing out the shoulder muscles. He thought as quickly as the mongrel had lunged.

Rearing his head aloft, he drove down at the Black. The latter was clinging with all his might to the collie's foreleg. And, in the rapture of having gained at last a disabling grip, he ignored the fact that he had left an opening in his own defence — an opening seldom sought in a fight, except by a wolf or a wolf's descendant.

It was for this opening that Tam-o'-Shanter struck. In a trice his white teeth had buried themselves in the exposed nape of the Black's neck.

Here, at the brain's base, lies the spinal cord, dangerously within reach of long and hard-driven fangs. And here Tam had fastened himself.

An instant later — but an instant too late — the Black knew his peril. Releasing his grip on the collie's leg, before the bond had begun to yield, he threw his great body madly from side to side, fighting crazily to shake off the death-hold. With all his mighty strength, he thrashed about.

Twice he lifted the seventy-pound collie clean off the ground. Once he fell, with Tam under him. But the collie held on. Tam did more than hold on. Exerting every remaining atom of his waning power, he let his body be flung here and there, in the Black's struggles; and he concentrated his force upon cleaving deeper and deeper into the neck-nape.

This was the grip whereby the Black, a month agone, had crushed the life out of friendly little Wisp. And, by chance or by fate, Tam had been enabled to gain the same hold. Spasmodically, he set his fangs in a viselike tightening of his grip.

At one instant, the Black was whirling and writhing in the fulness of his wiry might. At the next, with a sickening snapping sound, his giant body went limp, and his forequarters hung, a lifeless weight, from his conqueror's jaws.

Tam relaxed his hold. The big body slumped to earth and lay there. The collie, panting and swaying, stood over his dead enemy. The bitterly long quest was ended. Heavenward went his bleeding muzzle. And he waked the solemn stillnesses of the summer night with an eerie wolf howl, the awesome primal yell of Victory.

For a few seconds Trask Frayne, unnoticed, stared at his dog. And, as he looked, it seemed to him he could see the collie change gradually back from a wild thing of the forests to the staunch and adoring watchdog of other days. Then the man spoke.

"Tam!" he said, quietly. "*Tam!* Old friend!"

The exhausted victor lurched dizzily about at sound of the voice. Catching sight of Trask, he trembled all over.

He took a dazed step toward Frayne. Then, with something

queerly like a human sob, the collie sprang forward and gambolled weakly about the man: licking Trask's feet and hands; springing up in a groggy effort to kiss his face; patting his master's chest with eager forepaws; crying aloud in an ecstasy of joy at the reunion.

Then, all at once, he seemed to remember he was a staid and dignified middle-aged dog and not a hoodlum puppy. Ceasing his unheard-of demonstrations, he stood close beside Frayne, looking up into Trask's eyes in silent worship.

"You've done a grand night's work, Tam," said Frayne, seeking to steady his own voice. "And your hurts need bathing. Come home."

His plumed tail proudly wagging, his splendid head aloft, Tam-o'-Shanter turned and led the way to the house he loved.

QUESTIONS

1. What does the title of the story mean? Try to find other titles for it. Are any of the new titles better than the author's?

2. Why was Trask Frayne not satisfied after the hunt of the mongrel dogs? What effect does his dissatisfaction have on the reader?

3. How soon did you realize that the black dog was to play an important part in the story?

4. What was Tam's grievance against the Black? What other grievance might the author have used to make a reasonable plot?

5. Do you think the author could have told the story better by directly following Tam in his wanderings? Why did he choose to tell the story as Trask Frayne learned it? Is there any information in the story that he could not have given if he had followed Tam?

6. How did Tam behave when he went to the scene of Wisp's death? How did he behave after his fight with the Black?

7. Do you think the author attributes to dogs more intelligence than they have? Explain. If you can, tell of some incident in which a dog showed extraordinary intelligence.

8. Do you like or dislike animal stories? Why?

9. *Word Study.* — What do the following words mean as they are used in the story: *alliterative, primitive, marauding, imperatively, fruitless, invulnerable, illusiveness, fusillade, inert?*

Problem: CHARACTER IN THE STORY
(See page 24.)

1. What is the conflict in the early part of the story? What is the conflict at the end? Which is more important to the plot?

2. What do you know about the character of the black dog? Contrast his character with that of Tam-o'-Shanter.

3. Name the chief character in "The Grudge." What is the chief means of presenting him to the reader? What other means are used? What ordinary means of presenting character is not used here? Why not?

How Santa Claus Came to Simpson's Bar *

Francis Bret Harte (1839–1902)

Francis Bret Harte, best known for his stories of California in the gold-rush days, was born in Albany, New York, in 1839. Young Harte was attracted to California in 1854 by the tales of fabulous discoveries by the gold-miners. He tried his hand at mining, but failed to discover gold in any appreciable quantities. After an attempt at teaching school, Harte became compositor on "The Golden Era," and it was then that he wrote his first few sketches on life in California. He next joined the staff of "The Californian," but later, in 1868, left to become editor of "The Overland Monthly."

Meanwhile, Bret Harte's reputation had been growing as his stories of the quaint characters and colorful scenes of gold-rush days were read by more and more thousands of Americans. Harte became one of the most popular writers of the day. He went to New York in 1871 and signed a contract to furnish stories for "The Atlantic Monthly." In 1878, he was appointed United States consul at Crefeld, Germany, and two years later was transferred to Glasgow. As he was popular in England as well as in America, he made his home in London after 1885. He died in Aldershot, England, on May 6, 1902.

It is unfortunately true that Bret Harte's early work was his best. He wrote a few novels, a few poems, and many short stories, but only the early stories are remembered. In them, he caught the spirit of a time and showed it to us in its proper setting. Most of his stories are exaggerated; almost all of them are sentimental; but there is no denying that there is something about them that holds our interest.

"How Santa Claus Came to Simpson's Bar" contains many of the characteristics of Harte's best work. It has a real story and real characters, a little over-drawn, and it presents clearly, humorously, and at times sentimentally the mining village in a

* From *Mrs. Skagg's Husbands*, by Bret Harte. Used by permission of and by arrangement with Houghton Mifflin Company.

dull time. When we consider that local color was very new indeed when this story was written, we must admit that Harte has earned his place in the history of the short story.

IT HAD been raining in the valley of the Sacramento. The North Fork had overflowed its banks and Rattlesnake Creek was impassable. The few boulders that had marked the summer ford at Simpson's Crossing were obliterated by a vast sheet of water stretching to the foothills. The up stage was stopped at Grangers; the last mail had been abandoned in the *tules*, the rider swimming for his life. "An area," remarked the *Sierra Avalanche*, with pensive local pride, "as large as the State of Massachusetts is now under water."

Nor was the weather any better in the foothills. The mud lay deep on the mountain road; wagons that neither physical force nor moral objuration could move from the evil ways into which they had fallen, encumbered the track, and the way to Simpson's Bar was indicated by broken-down teams and hard swearing. And farther on, cut off and inaccessible, rained upon and bedraggled, smitten by high winds and threatened by high water, Simpson's Bar, on the eve of Christmas day, 1862, clung like a swallow's nest to the rocky entablature and splintered capitals of Table Mountain, and shook in the blast.

As night shut down on the settlement, a few lights gleamed through the mist from the windows of cabins on either side of the highway now crossed and gullied by lawless streams and swept by marauding winds. Happily most of the population were gathered at Thompson's store, clustered around a red-hot stove, at which they silently spat in some accepted sense of social communion that perhaps rendered conversation unnecessary. Indeed, most methods of diversion had long since been exhausted on Simpson's Bar; high water had suspended the regular occupations on gulch and on river, and a consequent lack of money and whiskey had taken the zest from most illegitimate recreation. Even Mr. Hamlin was fain to leave the Bar with fifty dollars in his pocket — the only amount actually realized of the large sums won by him in successful exercise of his arduous profession. "Ef I was asked," he remarked somewhat later — "ef I was asked to pi'nt out a purty little village where a retired sport as didn't care for money could exercise hisself, frequent and lively, I'd say Simpson's Bar; but for a young man with a large family depending on his exertions, it don't pay." As Mr. Hamlin's family consisted mainly of female adults, this remark is quoted rather to show the breadth of his humor than the exact extent of his responsibilities.

Howbeit, the unconscious objects of this satire sat that evening in the listless apathy begotten of idleness and lack of excitement. Even the sudden splashing of hoofs before the door did not arouse them. Dick Bullen alone paused in the act of scraping out his pipe, and lifted his head, but no other one of the group indicated any interest in, or recognition of, the man who entered.

It was a figure familiar enough to the company, and known in Simpson's Bar as "The Old Man." A man of perhaps fifty years, grizzled and scant of hair, but still fresh and youthful of complexion. A face full of ready but not very powerful sympathy, with a chameleon-like aptitude for taking on the shade and color of contiguous moods and feelings. He had evidently just left some hilarious companions, and did not at first notice the gravity of the group, but clapped the shoulder of the nearest man jocularly, and threw himself into a vacant chair.

"Jest heard the best thing out, boys! Ye know Smiley, over yar — Jim Smiley — funniest man in the Bar? Well, Jim was jest telling the richest yarn about ——"

"Smiley's a —— fool," interrupted a gloomy voice.

"A particular —— skunk," added another in sepulchral accents.

A silence followed these positive statements. The Old Man glanced quickly around the group. Then his face slowly changed. "That's so," he said reflectively, after a pause, "certingly a sort of skunk and suthin of a fool. In course." He was silent for a moment as in painful contemplation of the unsavoriness and folly of the unpopular Smiley. "Dismal weather, ain't it?" he added, now fully embarked on the current of prevailing sentiment. "Mighty rough papers on the boys, and no show for money this season. And tomorrow's Christmas."

There was a movement among the men at this announcement, but whether of satisfaction or disgust was not plain. "Yes," continued the Old Man in the lugubrious tone he had, within the last few moments, unconsciously adopted — "Yes, Christmas, and tonight's Christmas Eve. Ye see, boys, I kinder thought — that is, I sorter had an idee, jest passin' like, you know — that maybe ye'd all like to come over to my house tonight and have a sort of tear round. But I suppose, now, you wouldn't? Don't feel like it, maybe?" he added with anxious sympathy, peering into the faces of his companions.

"Well, I don't know," responded Tom Flynn with some cheerfulness. "P'r'aps we may. But how about your wife, Old Man? What does *she* say to it?"

The Old Man hesitated. His conjugal experience had not been a happy one, and the fact was known to Simpson's Bar. His first wife, a delicate, pretty little woman, had suffered keenly and secretly from the jealous suspicions of her husband, until one day he invited the whole Bar to his house to expose her infidelity. On arriving, the party found the shy, *petite* creature quietly engaged in her household duties, and retired abashed and discomfited. But the sensitive woman did not easily recover from the shock of this extraordinary outrage. It was with difficulty she regained her equanimity sufficiently to release her lover from the closet in which he was concealed and escape with him. She left a boy of three years to comfort her bereaved husband. The Old Man's present wife had been his cook. She was large, loyal, and aggressive.

Before he could reply, Joe Dimmick suggested with great directness that it was the "Old Man's house," and that, invoking the Divine Power, if the case were his own, he would invite whom he pleased, even if in so doing he imperilled his salvation. The Powers of Evil, he further remarked, should contend against him vainly. All this delivered with a terseness and vigor lost in this necessary translation.

"In course. Certainly. Thet's it," said the Old Man with a sympathetic frown. "Thar's no trouble about *thet*. It's my own house, built every stick on it myself. Don't you be afeard o' her, boys. She *may* cut up a trifle rough — ez wimmin do — but she'll come round." Secretly the Old Man trusted to the exaltation of liquor and the power of courageous example to sustain him in such an emergency.

As yet, Dick Bullen, the oracle and leader of Simpson's Bar, had not spoken. He now took his pipe from his lips. "Old Man, how's that yer Johnny gettin' on? Seems to me he didn't look so peart last time I seed him on the bluff heavin' rocks at Chinamen. Didn't seem to take much interest in it. Thar was a gang of 'em by yar yesterday — drownded out up the river — and I kinder thought o' Johnny, and how he'd miss 'em! Maybe now, we'd be in the way ef he wus sick?"

The father, evidently touched not only by this pathetic picture of Johnny's deprivation, but by the considerate delicacy of the speaker, hastened to assure him that Johnny was better and that a "little fun might 'liven him up." Whereupon Dick arose, shook himself, and saying, "I'm ready. Lead the way, Old Man; here goes," himself led the way with a leap, a characteristic howl, and darted out into the night. As he passed through the outer room he caught up a blazing brand from the hearth. The action was repeated by the rest of the party, closely following and elbowing each other, and before the astonished proprietor of Thompson's grocery was aware of the intention of his guests, the room was deserted.

The night was pitchy dark. In the first gust of wind their temporary torches were extinguished, and only the red brands dancing and flitting in the gloom like drunken will-o'-the-wisps indicated their whereabouts. Their way led up Pine-Tree Cañon, at the head of which a broad, low, bark-thatched cabin burrowed in the mountain side. It was the home of the Old Man, and the entrance to the tunnel in which he worked when he worked at all. Here the crowd paused for a moment, out of delicate deference to their host, who came up panting in the rear.

"P'r'aps ye'd better hold on a second out yer whilst I go in and see thet things is all right," said the Old Man, with an indifference he was far from feeling. The suggestion was graciously accepted, the door opened and closed on the host, and the crowd, leaning their backs against the wall and cowering under the eaves, waited and listened.

For a few moments there was no sound but the dripping of water from the eaves and the stir and rustle of wrestling boughs above them. Then the men became uneasy, and whispered suggestion and suspicion passed from the one to the other. "Reckon she's caved in his head the first lick!" "Decoyed him inter the tunnel and barred him up, likely." "Got him down and sittin' on him." "Prob'ly bilin' suthin to heave on us: stand clear the door, boys!" For just then the latch clicked, the door slowly opened, and a voice said, "Come in out o' the wet."

The voice was neither that of the Old Man nor of his wife. It was the voice of a small boy, its weak treble broken by that preternatural hoarseness which only vagabondage and the habit of premature self-assertion can give. It was the face of a small boy that looked up at theirs — a face that might have been pretty and even refined but that it was darkened by evil knowledge from within and dirt and hard experience from without. He had a blanket around his shoulders and had evidently just risen from his bed. "Come in," he repeated, "and don't make no noise. The Old Man's in there talking to mar," he continued, pointing to an adjacent room which seemed to be a kitchen, from which the Old Man's voice came in deprecating accents. "Let me be," he added, querulously, to Dick Bullen, who had caught him up, blanket and all, and was affecting to toss him into the fire, "let go o' me, you —— old fool, d' ye hear?"

Thus adjured, Dick Bullen lowered Johnny to the ground with a smothered laugh, while the men, entering quietly, ranged themselves around a long table of rough boards which occupied the center of the room. Johnny then gravely proceeded to a cupboard and brought out several articles which he deposited on the table. "Thar's whiskey. And crackers. And red herons. And cheese." He took a bite of the latter on his way to the table. "And sugar." He scooped up a mouthful *en route* with a small and very dirty hand. "And terbacker. Thar's dried appils, too, on the shelf, but I don't admire 'em. Appils is swellin'. Thar," he concluded, "now wade in, and don't be afeared. *I* don't mind the old woman. She don't b'long to *me*. S'long."

He had stepped to the threshold of a small room, scarcely larger than a closet, partitioned off from the main apartment, and holding in its dim recess a small bed. He stood there a moment looking at the company, his bare feet peeping from the blanket, and nodded.

"Hello, Johnny! You ain't goin' to turn in agin, are ye?" said Dick.

"Yes, I are," responded Johnny, decidedly.

"Why, what's up, old fellow?"

"I'm sick."

"How sick?"

"I've got a fevier and childblains. And roomatiz," returned Johnny, and vanished within. After a moment's pause, he added in the dark, apparently from under the bedclothes — "And biles!"

There was an embarrassing silence. The men looked at each other, and at the fire. Even with the appetizing banquet before them, it seemed as if they might again fall into the despondency of Thompson's grocery, when the voice of the Old Man, incautiously lifted, came deprecatingly from the kitchen.

"Certainly! Thet's so. In course they is. A gang o' lazy

drunken loafers, and that ar Dick Bullen's the ornariest of all. Didn't hev no more *sabe* than to come round yar with sickness in the house and no provision. Thet's what I said: 'Bullen,' sez I, 'it's crazy drunk you are, or a fool,' sez I, 'to think o' such a thing.' 'Staples,' I sez, 'be you a man, Staples, and 'spect to raise h— under my roof and invalids lyin' round?' But they would come — they would. Thet's wot you must 'spect o' such trash as lays round the Bar."

A burst of laughter from the men followed this unfortunate exposure. Whether it was overheard in the kitchen, or whether the Old Man's irate companion had just then exhausted all other modes of expressing her contemptuous indignation, I cannot say, but a back door was suddenly slammed with great violence. A moment later and the Old Man reappeared, happily unconscious of the cause of the late hilarious outburst, and smiled blandly.

"The old woman thought she'd jest run over to Mrs. McFadden's for a sociable call," he explained, with jaunty indifference, as he took a seat at the board.

Oddly enough it needed this untoward incident to relieve the embarrassment that was beginning to be felt by the party, and their natural audacity returned with their host. I do not propose to record the convivialities of that evening. The inquisitive reader will accept the statement that the conversation was characterized by the same intellectual exaltation, the same cautious reverence, the same fastidious delicacy, the same rhetorical precision, and the same logical and coherent discourse somewhat later in the evening, which distinguish similar gatherings of the masculine sex in more civilized localities and under more favorable auspices. No glasses were broken in the absence of any; no liquor was uselessly spilt on the floor or table in the scarcity of that article.

It was nearly midnight when the festivities were interrupted. "Hush," said Dick Bullen, holding up his hand. It was the querulous voice of Johnny from his adjacent closet: "O dad!"

The Old Man arose hurriedly and disappeared in the closet.

Presently he reappeared. "His rheumatiz is coming on agin bad," he explained, "and he wants rubbin'." He lifted the demijohn of whiskey from the table and shook it. It was empty. Dick Bullen put down his tin cup with an embarrassed laugh. So did the others. The Old Man examined their contents and said hopefully, "I reckon that's enough; he don't need much. You hold on, all o' you for a spell, and I'll be back"; and vanished in the closet with an old flannel shirt and the whiskey. The door closed but imperfectly and the following dialogue was distinctly audible:

"Now, sonny, whar does she ache worst?"

"Sometimes over yar and sometimes under yer; but it's most powerful from yer to yer. Rub yer, dad."

A silence seemed to indicate a brisk rubbing. Then Johnny:

"Hevin' a good time out yer, dad?"

"Yes, sonny."

"To-morrer's Chrismiss — ain't it?"

"Yes, sonny. How does she feel now?"

"Better. Rub a little furder down. Wot's Chrismiss, anyway? Wot's it all about?"

"Oh, it's a day."

This exhaustive definition was apparently satisfactory for there was a silent interval of rubbing. Presently Johnny again:

"Mar sez that everywhere else but yer everybody gives things to everybody Chrismiss, and then she jist waded inter you. She sez thar's a man they call Sandy Claws, nor a white man, you know, but a kind o' Chinemin, comes down the chimbley night afore Chrismiss and gives things to chillern — boys like me. Puts 'em in their butes! Thet's what she tried to play upon me. Easy now, pop, whar are you rubbin' to — thet's a mile from the place. She jest made that up, didn't she, jest to aggrewate me and you? Don't rub thar. . . . Why, dad!"

In the great quiet that seemed to have fallen upon the house the sigh of the near pines and the drip of leaves without were very distinct. Johnny's voice, too, was lowered as he went on, "Don't you take on now, fur I'm gettin' all right fast. Wot's the boys doin' out thar?"

The Old Man partly opened the door and peered through. His guests were sitting there sociably enough, and there were a few silver coins and a lean buckskin purse on the table. "Bettin' on suthin — some little game or 'nother. They're all right," he replied to Johnny, and recommenced his rubbing.

"I'd like to take a hand and win some money," said Johnny, reflectively, after a pause.

The Old Man glibly repeated what was evidently a familiar formula, that if Johnny would wait until he struck it rich in the tunnel he'd have lots of money, etc., etc.

"Yes," said Johnny, "but you don't. And whether you strike it or I win it, it's about the same. It's all luck. But it's mighty cur'o's about Chrismiss — ain't it? Why do they call it Chrismiss?"

Perhaps from some instinctive deference to the overhearing of his guests, or from some vague sense of incongruity, the Old Man's reply was so low as to be inaudible beyond the room.

"Yes," said Johnny, with some slight abatement of interest, "I've heerd o' *him* before. Thar, that'll do, dad. I don't ache near so bad as I did. Now wrap me tight in this yer blanket. So. Now," he added in a muffled whisper, "sit down yer by me till I go asleep." To assure himself of obedience, he disengaged one hand from the blanket and, grasping his father's sleeve, again composed himself to rest.

For some moments the Old Man waited patiently. Then the unwonted stillness of the house excited his curiosity, and without moving from the bed, he cautiously opened the door with his disengaged hand, and looked into the main room. To his infinite surprise it was dark and deserted. But even then a smouldering log on the hearth broke, and by the up-springing blaze he saw the figure of Dick Bullen sitting by the dying embers.

"Hello!"

Dick started, rose, and came somewhat unsteadily toward him.

"Whar's the boys?" said the Old Man.

"Gone up the cañon on a little *pasear*. They're comin' back for me in a minit. I'm waitin' round for 'em. What are you starin' at, Old Man?" he added with a forced laugh; "do you think I'm drunk?"

The Old Man might have been pardoned the supposition, for Dick's eyes were humid and his face flushed. He loitered and lounged back to the chimney, yawned, shook himself, buttoned up his coat, and laughed. "Liquor ain't so plenty as that, Old Man. Now, don't you git up," he continued, as the Old Man made a movement to release his sleeve from Johnny's hand. "Don't you mind manners. Sit jest whar you be; I'm goin' in a jiffy. Thar, that's them now."

There was a low tap at the door. Dick Bullen opened it quickly, nodded "Good-night" to his host, and disappeared. The Old Man would have followed him but for the hand that still unconsciously grasped his sleeve. He could have easily disengaged it: it was small, weak, and emaciated. But perhaps because it *was* small, weak, and emaciated, he changed his mind, and, drawing his chair closer to the bed, rested his head upon it. In this defenceless attitude the potency of his earlier potations surprised him. The room flickered and faded before his eyes, reappeared, faded again, went out, and left him — asleep.

Meantime Dick Bullen, closing the door, confronted his companions. "Are you ready?" said Staples. "Ready," said Dick; "what's the time?" "Past twelve," was the reply; "can you make it? — it's nigh on fifty miles, the round trip hither and yon." "I reckon," returned Dick, shortly. "Whar's the mare?" "Bill and Jack's holdin' her at the crossin'." "Let 'em hold on a minit longer," said Dick.

He turned and reëntered the house softly. By the light of the guttering candle and dying fire he saw that the door of the little room was open. He stepped toward it on tiptoe and looked in. The Old Man had fallen back in his chair, snoring, his helpless feet thrust out in a line with his collapsed shoulders, and his hat pulled over his eyes. Beside him, on a narrow wooden bedstead, lay Johnny, muffled tightly in a blanket that hid all save a strip of forehead and a few curls damp with perspiration. Dick Bullen made a step forward, hesitated, and glanced over his shoulder into the deserted room. Everything was quiet. With a sudden resolution he parted his huge mustaches with both hands and stooped over the sleeping boy. But even as he did so a mischievous blast, lying in wait, swooped down the chimney, rekindled the hearth, and lit up the room with a shameless glow from which Dick fled in bashful terror.

His companions were already waiting for him at the crossing. Two of them were struggling in the darkness with some strange misshapen bulk, which as Dick came nearer took the semblance of a great yellow horse.

It was the mare. She was not a pretty picture. From her Roman nose to her rising haunches, from her arched spine hidden by the stiff *machillas* of a Mexican saddle, to her thick, straight, bony legs, there was not a line of equine grace. In her half-blind but wholly vicious white eyes, in her protruding under lip, in her monstrous color, there was nothing but ugliness and vice.

"Now then," said Staples, "stand cl'ar of her heels, boys, and up with you. Don't miss your first holt of her mane, and mind ye get your off stirrup *quick*. Ready!"

There was a leap, a scrambling struggle, a bound, a wild retreat of the crowd, a circle of flying hoofs, two springless leaps that jarred the earth, a rapid play and jingle of spurs, a plunge, and then the voice of Dick somewhere in the darkness, "All right!"

"Don't take the lower road back onless you're hard pushed for time! Don't hold her in down hill! We'll be at the ford at five. G'lang! Hoopa! Mula! GO!"

A splash, a spark struck from the ledge in the road, a clatter in the rocky cut beyond, and Dick was gone.

.   .   .

Sing, O Muse, the ride of Richard Bullen! Sing, O Muse of chivalrous men! the sacred quest, the doughty deeds, the battery of low churls, the fearsome ride and grewsome perils of the Flower of Simpson's Bar! Alack! she is dainty, this Muse! She will have none of this bucking brute and swaggering, ragged rider, and I must fain follow him in prose, afoot!

It was one o'clock, and yet he had only gained Rattlesnake hill. For in that time Jovita had rehearsed to him all her imperfections and practised all her vices. Thrice had she stumbled. Twice had she thrown up her Roman nose in a straight line with the reins, and, resisting bit and spur, struck out madly across country. Twice had she reared, and, rearing, fallen backward; and twice had the agile Dick, unharmed, regained his seat before she found her vicious legs again. And a mile beyond them, at the foot of a long hill, was Rattlesnake Creek. Dick knew that here was the crucial test of his ability to perform his enterprise, set his teeth grimly, put his knees well into her flanks, and changed his defensive tactics to brisk aggression. Bullied and maddened, Jovita began the descent of the hill. Here the artful Richard pretended to hold her in with ostentatious objurgation and well-feigned cries of alarm. It is unnecessary to add that Jovita instantly ran away. Nor need I state the time made in the descent; it is written in the chronicles of Simpson's Bar. Enough that in another moment, as it seemed to Dick, she was splashing on the overflowed banks of Rattlesnake Creek. As Dick expected, the momentum she had acquired carried her beyond the point of balking, and, holding her well together for a mighty leap, they dashed into the middle of the swiftly flowing current. A few moments of kicking, wading, and swimming, and Dick drew a long breath on the opposite bank.

The road from Rattlesnake Creek to Red Mountain was tolerably level. Either the plunge in Rattlesnake Creek had dampened her baleful fire, or the art which led to it had shown her the superior wickedness of her rider, for Jovita no longer wasted her surplus energy in wanton conceits. Once she bucked, but it was from force of habit; once she shied, but it was from a new freshly painted meeting-house at the crossing of the country road. Hollows, ditches, gravelly deposits, patches of freshly springing grasses, flew from beneath her rattling hoofs. She began to smell unpleasantly, once or twice she coughed slightly, but there was no abatement of her strength or speed. By two o'clock she had passed Red Mountain and begun the descent to the plain. Ten minutes later the driver of the fast Pioneer coach was overtaken and passed by a "man on a Pinto hoss," — an event sufficiently notable for remark. At half-past two Dick rose in his stirrups with a great shout. Stars were glittering through the rifted clouds, and beyond him, out of the plain, rose two spires, a flagstaff, and a straggling line of black objects. Dick jingled his spurs and swung his *reata*, Jovita bounded forward, and in another moment they swept into Tuttleville and drew up before the wooden piazza of "The Hotel of All Nations."

What transpired that night at Tuttleville is not strictly a part of this record. Briefly I may state, however, that after Jovita had been handed over to a sleepy ostler, whom she at once kicked into unpleasant consciousness, Dick sallied out with the bar keeper for a tour of the sleeping town. Lights still gleamed from a few saloons and gambling-houses; but, avoiding these, they stopped before several closed shops, and by persistent tapping and judicious outcry roused the proprietors from their beds, and made them unbar the doors of their magazines and expose their wares. Sometimes they were met by curses, but oftener by interest and some concern in their needs, and the interview was invariably concluded by a drink. It was three o'clock before this pleasantry was given over, and with a small waterproof bag of india-rubber strapped on his shoulders Dick returned to the hotel. But here he was waylaid by Beauty — Beauty opulent in charms, affluent in dress, persuasive in speech, and Spanish in accent! In vain she repeated the invitation in "Excelsior," happily scorned by all Alpine-climbing youth, and rejected by this child of the Sierras — a rejection softened in this instance by a laugh and his last gold coin. And then he sprang to the saddle and dashed down the lonely street and out into the lonelier plain, where presently the lights, the black line of houses, the spires, and the flagstaff sank into the earth behind him again and were lost in the distance.

The storm had cleared away, the air was brisk and cold, the outlines of adjacent landmarks were distinct, but it was half-past four before Dick reached the meeting-house and the crossing of the country road. To avoid the rising grade he had taken a longer and more circuitous road, in whose viscid mud Jovita sank fetlock deep at every bound. It was a poor preparation for a steady ascent of five miles more; but Jovita, gathering her legs under her, took it with her usual blind, unreasoning fury, and a half-hour later reached the long level that led to Rattlesnake Creek. Another half-hour would bring him to the creek. He threw the reins lightly upon the neck of the mare, chirruped to her, and began to sing.

Suddenly Jovita shied with a bound that would have un-seated a less practised rider. Hanging to her rein was a figure that had leaped from the bank, and at the same time from the road before her arose a shadowy horse and rider. "Throw up your hands!" commanded this second apparition with an oath.

Dick felt the mare tremble, quiver, and apparently sink under him. He knew what it meant and was prepared.

"Stand aside, Jack Simpson, I know you, you — thief. Let me pass or ——"

He did not finish the sentence. Jovita rose straight in the air with a terrific bound, throwing the figure from her bit with a single shake of her vicious head, and charged with deadly malevolence down on the impediment before her. An oath, a pistol-shot, horse and highwayman rolled over in the road, and the next moment Jovita was a hundred yards away. But the good right arm of her rider, shattered by a bullet, dropped helplessly at his side.

Without slacking his speed, he shifted the reins to his left hand. But a few moments later he was obliged to halt and tighten the saddle-girths that had slipped in the onset. This in his crippled condition took some time. He had no fear of pursuit, but looking up he saw that the eastern stars were already paling, and that the distant peaks had lost their ghostly whiteness, and now stood out blackly against a lighter sky. Day was upon him. Then completely absorbed in a single idea, he forgot the pain of his wound, and mounting again dashed on toward Rattlesnake Creek. But now Jovita's breath came broken by gasps, Dick reeled in his saddle, and brighter and brighter grew the sky.

Ride, Richard; run, Jovita; linger, O day!

For the last few rods there was a roaring in his ears. Was it exhaustion from loss of blood, or what? He was dazed and giddy as he swept down the hill, and did not recognize his surroundings. Had he taken the wrong road, or was this Rattlesnake Creek?

It was. But the brawling creek he had swum a few hours before had risen, more than doubled its volume, and now rolled a swift and resistless river between him and Rattlesnake Hill. For the first time that night Richard's heart sank within him. The river, the mountain, the quickening east, swam before his eyes. He shut them to recover his self-control. In that brief interval, by some fantastic mental process, the little room at Simpson's Bar and the figures of the sleeping father and son rose upon him. He opened his eyes wildly, cast off his coat, pistol, boots, and saddle, bound his precious pack tightly to his shoulders, grasped the bare flanks of Jovita with his bared knees, and with a shout dashed into the yellow water. A cry rose from the opposite bank as the head of a man and horse struggled for a few moments against the battling current, and then were swept away amidst uprooted trees and whirling driftwood.

.   .   .

The Old Man started and woke. The fire on the hearth was dead, the candle in the outer room flickering in its socket, and somebody was rapping at the door. He opened it, but fell back with a cry before the dripping, half-naked figure that reeled against the door-post.

"Dick?"

"Hush! Is he awake yet?"

"No — but, Dick? ——"

"Dry up, you old fool! Get me some whiskey *quick!*" The Old Man flew and returned with — an empty bottle! Dick would have sworn, but his strength was not equal to the occasion. He staggered, caught at the handle of the door, and motioned to the Old Man.

"Thar's suthin' in my pack yer for Johnny. Take it off. I can't."

The Old Man unstrapped the pack and laid it before the exhausted man.

"Open it, quick!"

He did so with trembling fingers. It contained only a few poor toys — cheap and barbaric enough, goodness knows, but bright with paint and tinsel. One of them was broken; another, I fear, was irretrievably ruined by water; and on the third — ah me! — there was a cruel spot.

"It don't look like much, that's a fact," said Dick, ruefully. . . . "But it's the best we could do. . . . Take 'em, Old Man, and put 'em in his stocking, and tell him — tell him, you know — hold me, Old Man ——" The Old Man caught at his sinking figure. "Tell him," said Dick, with a weak little laugh, — "tell him Sandy Claus has come."

And even so, bedraggled, ragged, unshaven, and unshorn, with one arm hanging helplessly at his side, Santa Claus came to Simpson's Bar and fell fainting on the first threshold. The Christmas dawn came slowly after, touching the remoter peaks with the rosy warmth of ineffable love. And it looked so tenderly on Simpson's Bar that the whole mountain, as if caught in a generous action, blushed to the skies.

QUESTIONS

1. Why does the author discuss the weather at the beginning of the story? What effect has the weather on the plot? What effect does it have on the atmosphere of the story?

2. Is this primarily a story about certain characters, a certain locality, or certain actions?

3. Who was Dick Bullen? What kind of man was he? Would you like to have known him?

4. How does the author appeal to the reader's sympathies? Where?

5. Does he make Johnny a good little boy? Does he make him unpleasant to the reader?

6. Tell of Dick Bullen's encounter with the highwayman. How did he escape?

7. *Word Study.* — What do the following words mean as they are used in the story: *obliterated, objurgation, entablature, illegitimate, jocularly, lugubrious, equanimity, aggressive, preternatural, irretrievably?*

Problem: THE DEVELOPMENT OF THE STORY (REVIEW)

1. What is the plot of "How Santa Claus Came to Simpson's Bar"? Tell it as briefly as possible.

2. Where does the introduction to this story end? What is the climax? What is your opinion of Bret Harte's conclusion?

3. Does the story proceed too rapidly or too slowly? How much of the material in the story is really necessary to it? What do you think is the reason for the inclusion of the extra material? Do you think the reason a sound one?

4. What characters are clearly presented? How are they presented? Do you think some of them are exaggerated? Which ones? Which character do you consider most natural?

5. How is the setting important to this story? Find examples of local color. About when would you fix the time of the story? How do you know?

The Only Child *

Booth Tarkington (1869–1946)

About three years before Tarkington's death on May 19, 1946, at his home in Indianapolis, the Pasadena Community Playhouse had presented a Tarkington Cycle consisting of six of the author's best plays. The year before (1942), the Roosevelt Memorial Association had awarded to Tarkington the Roosevelt Distinguished Service Medal for his "service to American Literature in depicting the life of the Middle West."

Born in Indianapolis on July 29, 1869, young Tarkington was educated at Phillips Exeter Academy, Purdue University, and Princeton. At first, Booth Tarkington was interested in art and planned to become an artist, but eventually he decided to be an author instead and wrote steadily for more than forty-five years — beginning with his first novel, "The Gentleman from Indiana," in 1899 and ending with "Image of Josephine," published in 1945, a year before his death. Tarkington was the author of two Pulitzer prize-winning novels — "The Magnificent Ambersons" and "Alice Adams." Among his twenty dramas are "The Man from Home," "Mr. Antonio," "The Intimate Strangers," and "Clarence."

Tarkington also wrote about the youth of his day and depicted them sympathetically and accurately in "Penrod," "Penrod and Sam," "Seventeen," and "Little Orvie." Indeed, all of Booth Tarkington's stories about boys and girls show very clearly that the author liked his characters and fully understood their problems. If they occasionally misbehaved as Ludlum did in "The Only Child," then Tarkington knew why and was willing and anxious to share his knowledge with the reader. Students who desire to read more of the author's work will probably enjoy the numerous stories about the adventures and escapades of both Penrod Schofield and Little Orvie.

---

* From *The Fascinating Stranger*, by Booth Tarkington: Copyright, 1923, by Doubleday, Page & Co. Reprinted by permission of the publishers, Doubleday, Doran & Co., Inc.

THE little boy was afraid to go into the dark room on the other side of the hall, and the little boy's father was disgusted with him. "Aren't you ashamed of yourself, Ludlum Thomas?" the father called from his seat by the library lamp. "Eight years old and scared! Scared to step into a room and turn the light on! Why, when I was your age I used to go out to the barn after dark in the winter-time, and up into the loft, all by myself, and pitch hay down to the horse through the chute. You walk straight into that dining-room, turn on the light, and get what you want; and don't let's have any more fuss about it. You hear me?"

Ludlum disregarded this speech. "Mamma," he called, plaintively, "I want you to come and turn the light on for me. *Please*, mamma!"

Mrs. Thomas, across the library table from her husband, looked troubled, and would have replied, but the head of the house checked her.

"Now let me," he said. Then he called again: "You going in there and do what I say, or not?"

"Please come on, mamma," Ludlum begged. "Mamma, I lef' my bow-an'-arry in the dining-room, an' I want to get it out o' there so's I can take it up to bed with me. Mamma, won't you please come turn the light on for me?"

"No, she will not!" Mr. Thomas shouted. "What on earth are you afraid of?"

"Mamma ——"

"Stop calling your mother! She's not coming. You were sitting in the dining-room yourself, not more than an hour ago, at dinner, and you weren't afraid then, were you?"

Ludlum appeared between the brown curtains of the library doorway — the sketch of a rather pale child-prince in black velvet. "No, but ——" he said.

"But what?"

"It was all light in there then. Mamma an' you were in there, too."

"Now look here!" Mr. Thomas paused, rested his book upon his knee, and spoke slowly. "You know there's nothing in that dining-room except the table and the chairs and the sideboard, don't you?"

Ludlum's eyes were not upon his father but upon the graceful figure at the other side of the table. "Mamma," he said, "won't you *please* come get my bow-an'-arry for me?"

"Did you hear what I said?"

"Yes, sir," the boy replied, with eyes still pleading upon his mother.

"Well, then, what is there to be afraid of?"

"I'm not afraid," said Ludlum. "It's dark in there."

"It won't be dark if you turn on the light, will it?"

"Mamma ——"

"Now, that's enough!" the father interrupted testily. "It's after eight. You go on up to bed."

Ludlum's tone began to indicate a mental strain. "I don't *want* to go to bed without my bow-an'-arry!"

"What do you want your bow and arrow when you're in bed for?"

"I got to have it!"

"See here!" said Mr. Thomas. "You march up to bed and quit talking about your bow and arrow. You can take them with you if you go in there right quick and get them; but whether you do that or not you'll march to bed inside of one minute from now!"

"I *got* to have my bow-an'-arry. I got to, to go upstairs *with!*"

"You don't want your bow and arrow in bed with you, do you?"

"Mamma!" Thus Ludlum persisted in his urgent appeal to that court in whose clemency he trusted. "Mamma, will you *please* come get my bow-an' ——"

"No, she won't."

"Then will you come upstairs with me, mamma?"

"No, she won't! You'll go by yourself, like a man."

"Mamma ——"

Mrs. Thomas intervened cheerily. "Don't be afraid, dearie," she said. "Your papa thinks you ought to begin to learn how

to be manly; but the lights are lit all the way, and I told Annie
to turn on the one in your room. You just go ahead like a good
boy, and when you're all undressed and ready to jump in bed,
then you just whistle for me ———"

"I don't want to whistle," said Ludlum irritably. "I want
my bow-an'-arry!"

"Look here!" cried his father. "You start for ———"

"I got to have my bow-an' ———"

"You mean to disobey me?"

"I *got* to have my ———"

Mr. Thomas rose; his look became ominous. "We'll see
about that!" he said; and he approached his son, whose
apprehensions were expressed in a loud cry.

"*Mamma!*"

"Don't hurt his feel——" Mrs. Thomas began.

"Something's got to be done," her husband said grimly,
and his hand fell upon Ludlum's shoulder. "You march!"

Ludlum muttered vaguely.

"You march!"

"I got to have my bow-an'-arry! I *can't* go to bed 'less
mamma comes with me! She's *got* to come with me!"

Suddenly he made a scene. Having started it, he went in
for all he was worth and made it a big one. He shrieked,
writhed away from his father's hand, darted to his mother,
and clung to her with spasmodic violence throughout the
protracted efforts of the sterner parent to detach him.

When these efforts were finally successful, Ludlum plunged
upon the floor, and fastened himself to the leg of a heavy
table. Here, for a considerable time, he proved the superiority
of an earnest boy's wind and agility over those of a man: as
soon as one part of him was separated from the leg of the
table another part of him became attached to it; and all the
while was he vehemently eloquent, though unrhetorical.

The pain he thus so powerfully expressed was undeniable;
and nowadays few adults are capable of resisting such determined agony. The end of it was, that when Ludlum retired
he was accompanied by both parents, his father carrying him,

and Mrs. Thomas following close behind with the bow-an'-arry.

They were thoughtful when they returned to the library.

"I *would* like to know what got him into such a state," said the father, groaning, as he picked up his book from the floor. "He used to march upstairs like a little man, and he wasn't afraid of the dark, or of anything else; but he's beginning to be afraid of his own shadow. What's the matter with him?"

Mrs. Thomas shook her head. "I think it's his constitution," she said. "I don't believe he's as strong as we thought he was."

"'Strong'!" her husband repeated incredulously. "Have I been dreaming, or *were* you looking on when I was trying to pry him loose from that table-leg?"

"I mean nervously," she said. "I don't think his nerves are what they ought to be at all."

"His nerve isn't!" he returned. "That's what I'm talking about! Why was he afraid to step into our dining-room — not thirty feet from where we were sitting?"

"Because it was dark in there. Poor child, he *did* want his bow and arrow!"

"Well, he got 'em! What did he want 'em for?"

"To protect himself on the way to bed."

"To keep off burglars on our lighted stairway?"

"I suppose so," said Mrs. Thomas. "Burglars or something."

"Well, where'd he get such ideas *from?*"

"I don't know. Nearly all children do get them."

"I know one thing," Mr. Thomas asserted, "*I* certainly never was afraid like that, and none of my brothers was, either. Do you suppose the children Ludlum plays with tell him things that make him afraid of the dark?"

"I don't think so, because he plays with the same children now that he played with before he got so much this way. Of course he's always been a *little* timid."

"Well, I'd like to know what's at the root of it. Something's got into his head. That's certain, isn't it?"

"I don't know," Mrs. Thomas said musingly. "I believe fear of the dark is a sort of instinct, don't you?"

"Then why does he keep having it more and more? Instinct? No, sir! I don't know where he gets his silly scaredness from, nor what makes it, but I know that it won't do to humor him in it. We've got to be firmer with him after this than we were to-night. I'm not going to have a son of mine grow up to be afraid!"

"Yes; I suppose we ought to be a *little* firmer with him," she said dreamily.

However, for several days and nights there was no occasion to exercise this new policy of firmness with Ludlum, one reason being that he was careful not to leave his trusty bow and arrow in an unlighted room after dark. Three successive evenings, weapon in hand, he "marched" sturdily to bed; but on the fourth he was reluctant, even though equipped as usual.

"Is Annie upstairs?" he inquired querulously, when informed that his hour had struck.

"I'm not sure, dearie," said his mother. "I think so. It's her evening out, but I don't think she's gone."

Standing in the library doorway, Ludlum sent upward a series of piercing cries: "Annie! Ann*ee!* Ann-*ee!* Oh, *Ann-nee-ee!*"

"Stop it!" Mr. Thomas commanded fiercely. "You want to break your mother's ear-drums?"

"Ann-nee-*eeee!*"

"Stop that noise!"

"Ann ——"

"Stop it!" Mr. Thomas made the gesture of rising, and Ludlum, interrupting himself abruptly, was silent until he perceived that his father's threat to rise was only a gesture, whereupon he decided that his vocalizations might safely be renewed.

"Ann-*nee-ee!*"

"What *is* the matter with him?"

"Ludlum, dear," said Mrs. Thomas, "what is it you want Annie for?"

"I want to know if she's upstairs."

"But what for?"

Ludlum's expression became one of determination. "Well, I want to know," he replied. "I got to know if Annie's upstairs."

"By George!" Mr. Thomas exclaimed suddenly, "I believe *now* he's afraid to go upstairs unless he knows the housemaid's up there!"

"Martha's probably upstairs if Annie isn't," Mrs. Thomas hurriedly intervened. "You needn't worry about whether Annie's up there, Luddie, if Martha is. Martha wouldn't let anything hurt you any more than Annie would, dear."

"Great heavens!" her husband cried. "There's nothing up there that's going to hurt him whether a hundred cooks and housemaids are upstairs or downstairs, or in the house or out of it! *That's* no way to talk to him, Jennie! Ludlum, you march straight ——"

"Ann-*nee-ee!*"

"But, dearie," said Mrs. Thomas, "I told you that Martha wouldn't let anything hurt ——"

"She isn't there," Ludlum declared. "I can hear her chinkin' tin and dishes around in the kitchen." And, again exerting all his vocal powers of penetration, "*Oh, Ann-ee-ee!*" he bawled.

"By George!" Mr. Thomas exclaimed. "This is awful! It's just awful!"

"Don't call any more, darling," the mother gently urged. "It disturbs your papa."

"But, Jennie, that isn't the reason he oughtn't to call. It does disturb me, but the real reason he oughtn't to do it is because he oughtn't to be afraid to ——"

"*Ann-ee-EE!*"

Mr. Thomas uttered a loud cry of his own, and, dismissing gestures, rose from his chair prepared to act. But his son briskly disappeared from the doorway; he had been reassured from the top of the stairs, Annie had responded, and Ludlum sped upward cheerfully. The episode was closed — except in meditation.

There was another one during the night, however. At least, Mr. Thomas thought so, for at the breakfast table he inquired: "Was any one out of bed about half-past two? Something half woke me, and I thought it sounded like somebody knocking on a door, and then whispering."

Mrs. Thomas laughed. "It was only Luddie," she explained. "He had bad dreams, and came to my door, so I took him in with me for the rest of the night. He's all right, now, aren't you, Luddie? Mamma didn't let the bad dream hurt her little boy, did she?"

"It wasn't dreams," said Ludlum. "I was awake. I thought there was somep'm in my room. I bet there *was* somep'm in there, las' night!"

"Oh, murder!" his father lamented. "Boy nine years old got to go and wake up his *mamma* in the middle of the night, because he's scared to sleep in his own bed with a hall-light shining through the transom! What on earth were you afraid of?"

Ludlum's eyes clung to the consoling face of his mother. "I never said I *was* afraid. I woke up, 'an I thought I saw somep'm in there."

"What kind of a 'something'?"

Ludlum looked resentful. "Well, I guess I know what I'm talkin' about," he said importantly. "I bet there *was* somep'm, too!"

"I declare I'm ashamed," Mr. Thomas groaned. "Here's the boy's godfather coming to visit us, and how's he going to help find out we're raising a coward?"

"John!" his wife exclaimed. "The idea of speaking like that just because Luddie can't help being a little imaginative!"

"Well, it's true," he said. "I'm ashamed for Lucius to find it out."

Mrs. Thomas laughed, and then, finding the large eyes of Ludlum fixed upon her hopefully, she shook her head. "Don't you worry, darling," she reassured him. "You needn't be afraid of what Uncle Lucius will think of his dear little Luddie."

"I'm not," Ludlum returned complacently. "He gave me a dollar las' time he was here."

"Well, he won't this time," his father declared crossly. "Not after the way you've been behaving lately. I'll see to that!"

Ludlum's lower lip moved pathetically and his eyes became softly brilliant — manifestations that increased the remarkable beauty he inherited from his mother.

"John!" cried Mrs. Thomas indignantly.

Ludlum wept at once, and between his gulpings implored his mother to prevent his father from influencing Uncle Lucius against the giving of dollars. "Don't *let* him, mamma!" he quavered. "An' 'fif Uncle Lucius wuw-wants to give me a dollar, he's got a right to, hasn't he, mamma? *Hasn't* he got a right to, mamma?"

"There, dearie! Of course!" she comforted him. "Papa won't tell Uncle Lucius. Papa is sorry, and only wants you to be happy and not cry any more."

Papa's manner indicated somewhat less sympathy than she implied; nevertheless, he presently left the house in a condition vaguely remorseful, which still prevailed, to the extent of a slight preoccupation, when he met Uncle Lucius at the train at noon.

Uncle Lucius — Lucius Brutus Allen, attorney-at-law of Marlow, Illinois, population more than three thousand, if you believed him — this Uncle Lucius was a reassuring sight, even to the eyes of a remorseful father who had been persecuting the beautiful child of a lovely mother.

Mr. Allen was no legal uncle to Ludlum: he was really Mrs. Thomas's second cousin, and, ever since she was eighteen and he twenty-four, had been her favored squire. In fact, during her young womanhood, Mrs. Thomas and others had taken it as a matter of course that Lucius was in love with her; certainly that appeared to be his condition.

However, with the advent of Mr. John Thomas, Lucius Brutus Allen gave ground without resistance, and even assisted matters in a way which might have suggested to an outsider that he was something of a matchmaker as well as something of a lover. With a bravery that touched both the bride and bridegroom, he had stood up to the function of Best Man without a quaver — and, of course, since the day of Ludlum's arrival in the visible world, had been "Uncle Lucius."

He was thirty-five; of a stoutish, stocky figure; large-headed and thin-haired; pinkish and cheerful and warm. His warmth was due partly to the weather, and led to a continuous expectance on the part of Ludlum, for it was the habit of Uncle Lucius to keep his handkerchief in a pocket of his trousers. From the hour of his arrival, every time that Uncle Lucius put his hand in his pocket and drew forth a handkerchief to dry his dewy brow, Ludlum suffered a disappointment.

In fact, the air was so sticky that these disappointments were almost continuous, with the natural result that Ludlum became peevish; for nobody can be distinctly disappointed a dozen or so times an hour, during the greater part of an afternoon, and remain buoyantly amiable.

Finally he could bear it no longer. He had followed his parents and Uncle Lucius out to the comfortable porch, which gave them ampler air and the pretty sight of Mrs. Thomas's garden, but no greater coolness; and here Uncle Lucius, instead of bringing forth from his pocket a dollar, produced, out of that storage, a fresh handkerchief.

"Goodness me, but you got to wipe your ole face a lot!" said Ludlum in a voice of pure spitefulness. "I guess why you're so hot mus' be you stuff yourself at meals, an' got all fat the way you are!"

Wherewith, he emitted a shrill and bitter laugh of self-applause for wit, while his parents turned to gaze upon him — Mrs. Thomas with surprise, and Mr. Thomas with dismay. To both of them his rudeness crackled out of a clear sky; they saw it as an effect detached from cause; therefore inexplicable.

"Ludlum!" said the father sharply.

"Dearie!" said the mother.

But the visitor looked closely at the vexed face. "What is it yu've decided you don't like about me, Luddie?" he asked.

"You're too fat!" said Ludlum.

Both parents uttered exclamations of remonstrance, but Mr. Allen intervened. "I'm not so very fat," he said. "I've just realized what the trouble between us is, Luddie. I overlooked something entirely, but I'll fix it all right when we're alone together. Now that I've explained about it, you won't mind how often I take my handkerchief out of my pocket, will you?"

"What in the world!" Mrs. Thomas exclaimed. "What are you talking about?"

"It's all right," said Lucius.

Ludlum laughed; his face was restored to its serene beauty. Obviously, he again loved his Uncle Lucius, and a perfect understanding, mysterious to the parents, now existed between godfather and godson. In celebration, Ludlum shouted and ran to caper in the garden.

"By George!" said John Thomas. "You seem to understand him! I don't. I don't know what the dickens is in his mind, half the time."

Mrs. Thomas laughed condescendingly. "No wonder!" she said. "You're down-town all the daytime and never see him except at breakfast and in the evenings."

"There's one thing puzzles me about it," said John. "If you understand him so well, why don't you ever tell *me* how to? What made him so smart-alecky to Lucius just now?"

Again she laughed with condescension. "Why, Luddie didn't mean to be fresh at all. He just spoke without thinking."

But upon hearing this interpretation, Mr. Allen cast a rueful glance at his lovely cousin. "Quite so!" he said. "Children can't tell their reasons, but they've always got 'em!"

"Oh, no, they haven't," she laughed. And then she jumped, for there came a heavy booming of thunder from that part of the sky which the roof of the porch concealed from them. The sunshine over the pink-speckled garden vanished; all the blossoms lost color and grew wan, fluttering in an ominous breeze; at once a high wind whipped around the house and the row of straight poplars beyond the garden showed silver sides.

"*Luddie!*" shrieked Mrs. Thomas; and he shrieked in answer; came running, just ahead of the rain. She seized his hand, and fled with him into the house.

"You remember how afraid they are of lightning," said John apologetically. "Lightning and thunder. I never could understand it, but I suppose it's genuine and painful."

"It's both," the visitor remarked. "You wouldn't think I'm that way, too, would you?"

"You are?"

"Makes me nervous as a cat."

"Did you inherit it?"

"I don't think so," said Lucius; and he waved his host's silent offer of a cigar. "No, thanks. Never want to smoke in a thunderstorm. I — *Whoo!*" he interrupted himself, as a flare of light and a catastrophe of sound came simultaneously. "Let's go in," he said mildly.

"Not I. I love to watch it."

"Well ——" Lucius paused, but at a renewal of the catastrophe, "Excuse *me!*" he said, and tarried no longer.

He found Mrs. Thomas and Ludlum in the center of the darkened drawing-room. She was sitting in a gilt chair with her feet off the floor, and upon a rung of the chair; and four heavy, flat-bottomed drinking-glasses were upon the floor, each of them containing the foot of a leg of the gilt chair. Ludlum was upon her lap.

"Don't you believe in insulation, Lucius?" she asked anxiously. "As long as we sit like this, we can't be struck, can we?"

He put on his glasses and gave her a solemn stare before replying. "I don't know about that," he said. "Of course John is safer out on the porch than we are in here."

"Oh, no, no!" she cried. "A porch is the most dangerous place there *is!*"

"I don't know whether or not he's safe from the lightning,"

Lucius explained. "I mean he's safe from being troubled about it the way we are."

"I don't call that being safe," his lady-cousin began. "I don't see what——"

But she broke off to find place for a subdued shriek, as an admiral's salute of great guns jarred the house. Other salutes followed, interjected, in spite of drawn shades and curtains, with spurts of light into the room, and at each spurt Mrs. Thomas shivered and said "Oh!" in a low voice, whereupon Ludlum jumped and said "Ouch!" likewise in a low voice. Then, at the ensuing crash, Mrs. Thomas emitted a little scream, and Ludlum emitted a large one.

"Ouch! *Ow!*" he vociferated. "Mamma, I want it to stop! Mamma, I can't stand it! I can't *stand* it!"

"It's odd," said Lucius, during an interregnum. "The thunder frightens us more than the lightning, doesn't it?"

"They're both so horrible," she murmured. "I'm glad they affect you this way, too, Lucius. It's comforting. Do you think it's almost over?"

"I'll see," he said; and he went to a window, whither Ludlum, having jumped down, followed him.

"Don't open the curtains much," Mrs. Thomas begged, not leaving her chair. "Windows are always dangerous. And come away from the window, Luddie. The lightning might——"

She shrieked at a flash and boom, and Luddie came away from the window. Voiceless — he was so startled — he scrambled toward his mother, his arms outstretched, his feet slipping on the polished floor; then, leaping upon her lap, he clung to her wildly; gulped, choked, and found his voice. He howled.

"That was about the last, I think," observed Lucius, from the window. "It's beginning to clear already. Nothing but a shower to make things cooler for us. Let's go play with old John again. Come on, Luddie."

But Ludlum clung to his mother, remonstrating. "No!" he cried. "Mamma, you got to stay in the house. I don't want to go out there. It might begin again!"

She laughed soothingly. "But Uncle Lucius says it's all over now, darling. Let's go and ———"

"I *d'wan'* to! I won't go out of the house. You tell me a story."

"Well," she began, "once upon a time there was a good fairy and there was a bad fairy ———"

"Where'd they live?"

"Oh, in a town — under some flowers in a garden in the town."

"Like our garden?"

"I suppose so," she assented. "And the good fairy ———"

"Listen, mamma," said Ludlum. "If they lived in the garden like those fairies you were tellin' me about yesterday, they could come in the windows of the house where the pretty little boy lived, couldn't they?"

"I suppose so."

At this Ludlum's expression became apprehensive and his voice peevish. "Well, then," he complained, "if there was a window open at night, or just maybe through a crack under the door, the bad fairy could slip up behind the pretty little boy, or into the pretty little boy's bedroom, an' ———"

"No, no!" his mother laughed, stroking his head. "You see, the good fairy would always be watching, too, and the good fairy wouldn't let the bad fairy hurt the pretty little boy."

The apprehensive expression was not altogether soothed from the pretty little boy's face. However, he said: "Go on. Tell what happened. Did the pretty little boy ———"

"Lucius!" Mrs. Thomas exclaimed, "don't stay here to be bored by Luddie and me. I've got to tell him this story ———"

"Yes," Ludlum eagerly agreed. "An' then afterward she has to read me a chapter in our book."

"So you go and make John tell *you* a story, Lucius. I have to be polite to Luddie because he's had such a fright, poor blessed child!"

Lucius was obedient: he rejoined John upon the porch, and the two men chatted for a time.

"What book is Jennie reading to the boy?" Mr. Allen inquired, after a subsequent interval of silence.

"I don't know just now. Classic fiction of some sort, probably. She's great on preparing his mind to be literary; reads an hour to him every day, and sometimes longer — translations — mythology — everything. All about gods and goddesses appearing out of the air to heroes, and Medusa heads and what not. Then standard works: Cooper, Bulwer, Scott, Hugo — some of the great romances."

"I see," said Lucius. "She always did go at things thoroughly. I remember," he went on, with a musing chuckle, "I remember how I got hold of Bulwer's *Zanoni* and *Strange Story* when I was about ten years old. By George! I've been afraid to go home in the dark ever since!"

"You have?" John smiled; then sent a serious and inquiring glance at the visitor, who remained placid. "Of course Jennie doesn't read *Zanoni* to Ludlum."

"No, she wouldn't," said Lucius. "Not till he's older. She'd read him much less disturbing things at his age, of course."

His host made no additional comment upon the subject, but appeared to sit in some perplexity.

Mr. Allen observed him calmly; then, after a time, went into the house — to get a cigar of his own, he said.

In the hall he paused, listening. From the library came Mrs. Thomas's voice, reading with fine dramatic fire:

"'What! thou frontless dastard, thou — thou who didst wait for opened gate and lowered bridge, when Conrad Horst forced his way over moat and wall, must *thou* be a malapert? Knit him up to the stanchions of the hall-window! He shall beat time with his feet while we drink a cup to his safe passage to the devil!'

"'The doom was scarce sooner pronounced than accomplished; and in a moment the wretch wrested out his last agonies, suspended from the iron bars. His body still hung there when our young hero entered the hall, and, intercepting the pale moonbeam, threw on the castle-floor an uncertain shadow, which dubiously yet fearfully intimated the nature of the substance which produced it.

"'When the syndic ——'"

Ludlum interrupted. "Mamma, what's a stanchion?" His voice was low and a little husky.

"It's a kind of an iron bar, or something, I think," Mrs. Thomas answered. "I'm not sure."

"Well, does it mean — mamma, what does it mean when it says 'he wrested out his last annogies'?"

"'Agonies,' dear. It doesn't mean anything that little boys ought to think about. This is a very unpleasant part of the book, and we'll hurry on to where it's all about knights and ladies, and pennons fluttering in the sunshine and ——"

"No; I don't want you to hurry. I like to hear this part, too. It's nice. Go on, mamma."

She continued, and between the curtains at the door, Lucius caught a glimpse of them. Sunlight touched them through a window; she sat in a highbacked chair; the dark-curled boy, upon a stool, huddling to her knee; and, as they sat thus, reading *Quentin Durward*, they were like a mother and son in stained glass — or like a Countess, in an old romance, reading to the Young Heir. And Lucius Brutus Allen had the curious impression that, however dimly, both of them were conscious of some such picturesque resemblance.

Unseen, he withdrew from the renewed sound of the reading, and again went out to sit with John upon the porch, but Mrs. Thomas and Ludlum did not rejoin them until the announcement of dinner. When the meal was over, Lucius and his hostess played cribbage in the library; something they did at all their reunions — a commemoration of an evening habit of old days. But tonight their game was interrupted, a whispering in the hall becoming more and more audible as it increased in virility; while protests on the part of a party of the second part punctuated and accented the whispering:

"I *d'wan'* to!" . . . "I won't!"

"I *will* ast mamma!" . . . "Leggo!"

The whispering became a bass staccato, though subdued, under the breath; protests became monosyllabic, but increased in passion; short-clipped squealings and infantile grunts were heard — and then suddenly, yet almost deliberately, a wide-mouthed roar of human agony dismayed the echoing walls.

The cavern whence issued the horrid sound was the most conspicuous thing in the little world of that house, as Ludlum dashed into the library. Even in her stress of sympathy, the mother could not forbear to cry: "Don't, Luddie! Don't stretch your mouth like that! You'll spoil the shape of it."

But Ludlum cared nothing for shape. Open to all the winds, he plunged toward his mother; and cribbage-board, counters, and cards went to the floor.

"Darling!" she implored. "What has hurt mamma's little boy so awfully? Tell mamma!"

In her arms, his inclement eyes salting his cheeks, the vocal pitch of his despair rose higher and higher like the voice of a reluctant pump.

"*Papa twissud my wrist!*" he finally became coherent enough to declare.

"What!"

"He did!" All in falsetto Ludlum sobbed his version of things. "He — he suss-said I had to gug-go up to bed all — all alone. He grabbed me! He hurt! He said I couldn't interrup' your ole gug-game! 'N' he said, 'I'll show you!' 'N' then — then — then — he *twissud* my *wrist!*"

At that she gathered him closer to her, and rose, holding him in her arms. Her face was deeply flushed, and her shining eyes avoided her husband, who stood near the doorway.

"Put him down, Jennie," he said mildly. "I ——"

Straightway she strode by him, carrying her child. She did not pause, nor speak aloud, yet Lucius and John both heard the whispered word that crumpled the latter as the curtains waved with the angry breeze of her passing. "Shame!"

Meanwhile, Lucius, on his knees — for he never regarded his trousers seriously — began to collect dispersed cards and pegs. "What say?" he inquired upon some gaspings of his unfortunate friend, John.

"She believed it!" (These stricken words came from a deep

chair in the shadows.) "She thought I actually did twist his wrist!"

"Oh, no," said Lucius. "She didn't believe anything of the kind. Darn that peg!" With face to the floor and in an attitude of Oriental devotion, he appeared to be worshipping the darkness under a divan. "She was merely reacting to the bellow of her offspring. She knew he invented it, as well as you did."

"It's incredible!" said John. "The cold-blooded cunning of it! He was bound to have his way, and make her go up with him; and I'd turned him toward the stair-way by his shoulders, and he tried to hold himself back by catching at one of those big chairs in the hall. I caught his wrist to keep him from holding to the chair — and I held him a second or two, not moving. The little pirate decided on the thing then and there, in his mind. He understood perfectly well he could make it all the more horrible because you were here, visiting us. I swear it appals me! What sort of a nature *is* that?"

"Oh," said Lucius, "just natural nature. Same as you and me."

"I'd hate to believe that!"

"You and I got ashamed long ago of the tricks that came in our minds to play," said Lucius, groping under the divan. "We got ashamed so often that they don't come any more."

"Yes, but it ought to be time they stopped coming into that boy's mind. He was eight last month."

"Yes — darn that peg! — there seems to be something in what you say. But of course Luddie thought he was in a fix that was just as bad to him as it would be to me if somebody were trying to make me walk to Pancho Villa's camp all alone. *I'd* make a fuss about that, if the fuss would bring up the whole United States Army to go with me. That's what it amounted to with Luddie."

"I suppose so," groaned the father. "It all comes down to his being a coward."

"It all comes down to the air being full of queer things when he's alone," said Lucius.

"Well, I'd like to know what makes it full of queer things. Where does his foolishness come *from?*"

"And echo answers ——" Lucius added, managing to get his head and shoulders under the divan, and thrusting with arms and legs to get more of himself under.

But a chime of laughter from the doorway answered in place of echo. "What are you doing, Lucius?" Mrs. Thomas inquired. "Swimming lessons? I never saw anything ——" And laughter so overcame her that she could speak no further, but dropped into a chair, her handkerchief to her mouth.

Lucius emerged crabwise, and placed a cribbage-peg upon the table, but made no motion to continue the game. Instead he dusted himself uselessly, lit a cigar, and sat.

"Luddie's all right," said the lady, having recovered her calmness. "I think probably something he ate at dinner upset him a little. Anyhow, he was all right as soon as he got upstairs. Annie's sitting with him and telling him stories."

"I wonder if that lightning struck anything this afternoon," Lucius said absently. "Some of it seemed mighty near."

"It was awful."

"Do you remember," Lucius asked her, "when you first began to be nervous about it?"

"Oh, I've always been that way, ever since I was a little child. I haven't the faintest idea how it got hold of me. Children just get afraid of certain things, it seems to me, and that's all there is to it. You know how Luddie is about lightning, John."

John admitted that he knew how Luddie was about lightning. "I do," was all he said.

Mrs. Thomas's expression became charmingly fond, even a little complacent. "I suppose he inherits it from me," she said.

"My mother has that fear to this day," Lucius remarked. "And I have it, too, but I didn't inherit it from her."

"How do you know?" his cousin asked quickly. "What makes you think you didn't inherit it?"

"Because my father used to tell me that when I was three and four years old he would sit out on the porch during a thunderstorm, and hold me in his lap, and every time the thunder came both of us would laugh, and shout 'Boom!' Children naturally like a big noise. But when I got a little bit older and more imaginative, and began to draw absurd conclusions from things, I found that my mother was frightened during thunderstorms — though she tried her best to conceal it — and, of course, seeing *her* frightened, I thought something pretty bad must be the matter. So the fear got fastened on me, and I can't shake it off though I'm thirty-five years old. Curious thing it is!''

Mrs. Thomas's brilliant eyes were fixed upon her cousin throughout this narrative with an expression at first perplexed, then reproachful, finally hostile. A change, not subtle but simple and vivid, came upon her face, while its habitual mobility departed, leaving it radiantly still, with a fierce smoldering just underneath. How deep and fast her breathing became, was too easily visible.

"Everything's curious, though, for the matter of that," Lucius added. And without looking at his cousin — without needing to look at her, to understand the deadliness of her silence — he smoked unconcernedly. "Yes, sir, it's all curious; and *we're* all curious," he continued, permitting himself the indulgence of a reminiscent chuckle. "You know I believe my father and mother got to be rather at outs about me — one thing and another, goodness knows what! — and it was years before they came together and found a real sympathy between them again. Truth is, I suspect where people aren't careful, their children have about twice as much to do with driving 'em apart as with drawing 'em together — especially in the case of an only child. I really do think that if *I* hadn't been an only child my father and mother might have been ——''

A sibilant breath, not a word and not quite a hiss, caused Lucius to pause for a moment, though not to glance in the direction of the lips whence came the sound. He appeared to forget the sentence he had left incomplete; at all events he neglected to finish it. However, he went on, composedly:

"Some of my aunts tell me I was the worst nuisance they ever knew. In fact, some of 'em go out of their way to tell me that, even yet. They never could figure out what was the matter with me — except that I was spoiled; but I never meet Aunt Mira Hooper on the street at home, to this day, that she doesn't stop to tell me she hasn't learned to like me, because she got such a set against me when I was a child — and I meet her three or four times a week! She claims there was *some* kind of a little tragedy over me, in our house, every day or so, for years and years. She blames *me* for it, but Lord knows it wasn't my fault. For instance, a lot of it was my father's."

"What did he do?" asked John.

Lucius chuckled again. "The worst he did was to tell me stories about Indians and pioneer days. Sounds harmless enough, but father was a good story-teller, and that was the trouble. You see, the foundation of nearly all romance, whether it's Indian stories or fairy-stories — it's all hero and villain. Something evil is always just going to jump out of somewhere at the hero, and the reader or the listener is always the hero. Why, *I* got so I wouldn't go into a darkened room, even in the daytime! As we grow older we forget the horrible visions we had when we were children; and what's worse, we forget there's no need for children to have 'em. Children ought to be raised in the *real* world, not the dream one. Yes, sir, I lay all my Aunt Mira Hooper's grudge against me to my father's telling me stories so well and encouraging me to read the classics and ——"

"Lucius," Mrs. Thomas spoke in a low voice, but in a tone that checked him abruptly.

"Yes, Jennie?"

"Don't you think that's enough?"

"I suppose it is tiresome," he said. "Too much autobiography. I was just rambling on about ——"

"You meant me!" she cried.

"You, Jennie?"

"You did! And you meant Ludlum was a 'nuisance'; not you. And I don't think it's very nice! Do you?"

"Why, I nev ——"

But his cousin's emotions were no longer to be controlled. She rose, trembling. "What a fool I was this afternoon!" she exclaimed bitterly. "I didn't suspect you; yet I never remembered your being nervous in a thunderstorm before. I thought you were sympathetic, and all the time you were thinking these cruel, wicked things 'bout Luddie and me!"

Lucius rose, too. "You know what I think about you, all the time, Jennie," he said genially. "John, if you can remember where you put my umbrella when we came in, it's about time for me to be catching a street-car down to the station."

She opposed him with a passionate gesture. "No!" she cried fiercely. "You can't say such things to me and then slip out like that! You tell me I've taught my child to be a coward and that I've made a spoilt brat of him ——"

"Jennie!" he protested. "I was talking about *me!*"

"Shame on you to pretend!" she said. "You think I'm making John *hate* Luddie ——"

"*Jennie!*" he shouted in genuine astonishment.

"You do! And you come here pretending to be such a considerate, sympathetic friend — and every minute you're criticizing and condemning me in your heart for all my little stories to my child — all because — because" — suddenly she uttered a dry sob — "because I want to raise my boy to be a — a poet!"

"John," said Lucius desperately, "*do* you think you can find that umbrella?"

With almost startling alacrity John rose and vanished from the room, and Lucius would have followed, but the distressed lady detained him. She caught a sagging pocket of his coat, and he found it necessary to remain until she should release him.

"You sha'n't!" she cried. "Not till you've taken back that accusation."

"But what accusa ——"

"Shame on you! Ah, I didn't think you'd ever come here and do such a thing to me. And this morning I was looking forward to a happy day! It's a good thing you're a bachelor!"

With which final insult she hurled his pocket from her —
at least that was the expression of her gesture — and sank
into a chair, weeping heart-brokenly. "You don't understand!" she sobbed. "How could any man understand — or
any woman not a mother. You think these hard things of me,
but — but John doesn't always love Luddie. Don't you get
even a little glimpse of what that means to me? There are
times when John doesn't even *like* Luddie!"

"Take care," said Lucius gently. "Take care that those
times don't come oftener."

She gasped, and would have spoken, but for a moment she
could not, and was able only to gaze at him fiercely through
her tears. Yet there was a hint of fear behind the anger.

"You dare to say such a thing as that to a mother?" she
said, when she could speak.

Lucius's eyes twinkled genially; he touched her upon the
shoulder, and she suffered him. "Mother," he said lightly,
"have pity on your child!" Somehow, he managed to put
more solemnity into this parting prayer of his than if he had
spoken it solemnly; and she was silent.

Then he left the room, and, on his way, stumbled over a
chair, as he usually did at the dramatic moments in his life.

John was standing in the open doorway, Lucius's umbrella
in his hand. "I think I hear a car coming, old fellow," he said.

"Got to get my hat," Mr. Allen muttered. He had been
reminded of something; a small straw hat, with a blue ribbon
round it, was upon the table, and he fumbled with it a moment before seizing his own and rushing for the door at the
increasing warning of a brass gong in the near distance. Thus,
when he had gone, a silver dollar was pocketed within the
inside band of the small straw hat with the blue ribbon. . . ,
John Thomas, returning in sharp trepidation to the lovely,
miserable figure in the library, encountered one of the many
surprises of his life.

"He never could tell the truth to save his life!" she said.
"He doesn't know what truth *means!* Did you hear him sitting
up there and telling us he was 'an only child'? He has a

brother and four sisters living, and I don't know how many dead!"

"You don't mean it!" said John, astounded. "That certainly was pecu ——"

He lost his breath at that moment. She rose and threw her arms round him with the utmost heartiness. "He's such an old smart Aleck!" she cried, still weeping. "That's why I married you instead of him. I love you for not being one! If you want to spank Luddie for telling that story about his wrist I wish you'd go and wake him up and do it!"

"No," said John. "Lucius called to me as he was running for the car that he's going to be married next week. I'll wait and spank one of his children. They'll be the worst spoiled children in the world!"

QUESTIONS

1. Was Ludlum really afraid of the dark?
2. What was the difference between the attitude of his father and that of his mother toward Ludlum? Which of them was right? Explain your answer.
3. Why is it significant that the child wins his own way each time?
4. What is the author's purpose in introducing the incident of the thunder shower?
5. Prove that Uncle Lucius understands Ludlum better than his parents do.
6. What is the climax of the story?
7. When did you first suspect that Lucius's tales about his own life were not strictly true?
8. Does Mrs. Thomas really resent the things Lucius tells her? Why?
9. Do you think Mr. Thomas's remark about Lucius's children ("They'll be the worst spoiled children in the world") is a true prophecy? Explain.
10. *Word Study.* — What do the following words mean as they are used in the story: *clemency, apprehension, protracted, penetration, remorseful, ominous, simultaneously, virility, sibilant, trepidation?*

Problem: THE DEVELOPMENT OF THE STORY (REVIEW)

1. Where is the introduction to this story? How does this treatment of the introduction differ from that of preceding stories?

2. What is the climax of the story? How do you know?

3. Pick out the incidents that lead up to the climax. Do they follow one another logically?

4. Is there as much suspense in this story as there is in the story of "The Grudge"? Is it the same kind of suspense?

5. Who is the most important character in the story? Who comes next in importance? Give reasons for your choices. Are the characters well drawn? Are they exaggerated? Find examples of each of the methods of character presentation used in this story.

6. Re-read passages of dialogue. Is it good? Tell why you think it is or is not. For what purposes is dialogue used in this story?

The Adventure of the Three Garridebs *

Sir Arthur Conan Doyle (1859–1930)

The police of London say that letters still come to Scotland Yard addressed to Sherlock Holmes. The great detective and the faithful Dr. Watson are personal friends of thousands of persons who have never given a second thought to the personality of their author.

This feeling of readers for Sherlock Holmes is the stranger since he appears only in stories of a type that cannot lay any emphasis upon the chief character as a man. The detective-story writer must concentrate his energies on the production of a plot. He must keep a secret from his readers at the same time that he gives them all the clues that would enable them to discover it. He can overawe readers with reports of the detective's fame; he can present certain marked peculiarities of his hero in an incidental fashion; he can even show him briefly in a moment of relaxation; but he must always remember that the plot, the action, the puzzle, comes first.

Sir Arthur Conan Doyle, author of the Sherlock Holmes stories, has clearly succeeded in his task; he preserves his secrets well. He has done something more than that, however, and the something more has made the name of his creature, Sherlock Holmes, a general term for a whole category of short stories.

Conan Doyle was not merely a writer of detective stories. He was a Doctor of Medicine of Edinburgh University and for years was a practising physician. He served in the hospital corps through the Boer War in South Africa, for which service he was knighted in 1902. He wrote historical romances ("Sir Nigel," "The White Company," and "Rodney Stone"), other novels, and books on the Boer War and the World War, as well as the dozens of clever detective stories that have made his special reputation.

---

* From *The Case Book of Sherlock Holmes*, by A. Conan Doyle: Copyright, 1927, by George H. Doran Co. Reprinted by permission of A. P. Watt & Son, agents for the author and of Doubleday, Doran & Co., Inc.

"The Adventure of the Three Garridebs," taken from "The Case Book of Sherlock Holmes," is one of the more recent of Conan Doyle's detective stories. It follows the general method of the detective story in every particular. It will be interesting to the reader to see at what point in the story the mystery can be solved.

IT MAY have been a comedy, or it may have been a tragedy. It cost one man his reason, it cost me a bloodletting, and it cost yet another man the penalties of the law. Yet there was certainly an element of comedy. Well, you shall judge for yourselves.

I remember the date very well, for it was in the same month that Holmes refused a knighthood for services which may perhaps some day be described. I only refer to the matter in passing, for in my position of partner and confidant I am obliged to be particularly careful to avoid any indiscretion. I repeat, however, that this enables me to fix the date, which was the latter end of June, 1902, shortly after the conclusion of the South African War. Holmes had spent several days in bed, as was his habit from time to time, but he emerged that morning with a long foolscap document in his hand and a twinkle of amusement in his austere gray eyes.

"There is a chance for you to make some money, friend Watson," said he. "Have you ever heard the name of Garrideb?"

I admitted that I had not.

"Well, if you can lay your hand upon a Garrideb, there's money in it."

"Why?"

"Ah, that's a long story — rather a whimsical one, too. I don't think in all our explorations of human complexities we have ever come upon anything more singular. The fellow will be here presently for cross-examination, so I won't open the matter up till he comes. But meanwhile, that's the name we want."

The telephone directory lay on the table beside me, and I

turned over the pages in a rather hopeless quest. But to my amazement there was this strange name in its due place. I gave a cry of triumph.

"Here you are, Holmes! Here it is!"

Holmes took the book from my hand.

"'Garrideb, N.,'" he read, "'136 Little Ryder Street, W.' Sorry to disappoint you, my dear Watson, but this is the man himself. That is the address upon his letter. We want another to match him."

Mrs. Hudson had come in with a card upon a tray. I took it up and glanced at it.

"Why, here it is!" I cried in amazement. "This is a different initial. John Garrideb, Counsellor at Law, Moorville, Kansas, U. S. A."

Holmes smiled as he looked at the card. "I am afraid you must make yet another effort, Watson," said he. "This gentleman is also in the plot already though I certainly did not expect to see him this morning. However, he is in a position to tell us a good deal which I want to know."

A moment later he was in the room. Mr. John Garrideb, Counsellor at Law, was a short, powerful man with the round, fresh, clean-shaven face characteristic of so many American men of affairs. The general effect was chubby and rather childlike, so that one received the impression of quite a young man with a broad set smile upon his face. His eyes, however, were arresting. Seldom in any human head have I seen a pair which bespoke a more intense inward life, so bright were they, so alert, so responsive to every change of thought. His accent was American, but was not accompanied by any eccentricity of speech.

"Mr. Holmes?" he asked, glancing from one to the other. "Ah, yes! Your pictures are not unlike you, sir, if I may say so. I believe you have had a letter from my namesake, Mr. Nathan Garrideb, have you not?"

"Pray sit down," said Sherlock Holmes. "We shall, I fancy, have a good deal to discuss." He took up his sheets of foolscap. "You are, of course, the Mr. John Garrideb mentioned in this document. But surely you have been in England some time?"

"Why do you say that, Mr. Holmes?" I seemed to read sudden suspicion in those expressive eyes.

"Your whole outfit is English."

Mr. Garrideb forced a laugh. "I've read of your tricks, Mr. Holmes, but I never thought I would be the subject of them. Where do you read that?"

"The shoulder cut of your coat, the toes of your boots — could anyone doubt it?"

"Well, well, I had no idea I was so obvious a Britisher. But business brought me over here some time ago, and so, as you say, my outfit is nearly all London. However, I guess your time is of value, and we did not meet to talk about the cut of my socks. What about getting down to that paper you hold in your hand?"

Holmes had in some way ruffled our visitor, whose chubby face had assumed a far less amiable expression.

"Patience! Patience, Mr. Garrideb!" said my friend in a soothing voice. "Dr. Watson would tell you that these little digressions of mine sometimes prove in the end to have some bearing on the matter. But why did Mr. Nathan Garrideb not come with you?"

"Why did he ever drag you into it at all?" asked our visitor, with a sudden outflame of anger. "What in thunder had you to do with it? Here was a bit of professional business between two gentlemen, and one of them must needs call in a detective! I saw him this morning, and he told me this fool-trick he had played me, and that's why I am here. But I feel bad about it, all the same."

"There was no reflection upon you, Mr. Garrideb. It was simply zeal upon his part to gain your end — an end which is, I understand, equally vital for both of you. He knew that I had means of getting information, and, therefore, it was very natural that he should apply to me."

Our visitor's angry face gradually cleared.

"Well, that puts it different," said he. "When I went to

see him this morning and he told me he had sent to a detective, I just asked for your address and came right away. I don't want police butting into a private matter. But if you are content just to help us find the man, there can be no harm in that."

"Well, that is just how it stands," said Holmes. "And now, sir, since you are here, we had best have a clear account from your own lips. My friend here knows nothing of the details."

Mr. Garrideb surveyed me with not too friendly a gaze.

"Need he know?" he asked.

"We usually work together."

"Well, there's no reason it should be kept a secret. I'll give you the facts as short as I can make them. If you came from Kansas I would not need to explain to you who Alexander Hamilton Garrideb was. He made his money in real estate, and afterwards in the wheat pit at Chicago, but he spent it in buying up as much land as would make one of your counties, lying along the Arkansas River, west of Fort Dodge. It's grazing-land and lumber-land and arable land and mineralized land, and just every sort of land that brings dollars to the man that owns it.

"He had no kith nor kin — or, if he had, I never heard of it. But he took a kind of pride in the queerness of his name. That was what brought us together. I was in the law at Topeka, and one day I had a visit from the old man, and he was tickled to death to meet another man with his own name. It was his pet fad, and he was dead set to find out if there were any more Garridebs in the world. 'Find me another!' said he. I told him I was a busy man and could not spend my life hiking round the world in search of Garridebs. 'None the less,' said he, 'that is just what you will do if things pan out as I planned them.' I thought he was joking, but there was a powerful lot of meaning in the words, as I was soon to discover.

"For he died within a year of saying them, and he left a will behind him. It was the queerest will that has ever been filed in the State of Kansas. His property was divided into three parts, and I was to have one on condition that I found two Garridebs who would share the remainder. It's five million dollars for each if it is a cent, but we can't lay a finger on it until we all three stand in a row.

"It was so big a chance that I just let my legal practice slide and I set forth looking for Garridebs. There is not one in the United States. I went through it, sir, with a fine-toothed comb and never a Garrideb could I catch. Then I tried the old country. Sure enough there was the name in the London Telephone Directory. I went after him two days ago and explained the whole matter to him. But he is a lone man, like myself, with some women relations, but no men. It says three adult men in the will. So you see we still have a vacancy, and if you can help to fill it we will be very ready to pay your charges."

"Well, Watson," said Holmes, with a smile, "I said it was rather whimsical, did I not? I should have thought, sir, that your obvious way was to advertise in the agony columns of the papers."

"I have done that, Mr. Holmes. No replies."

"Dear me! Well, it is certainly a most curious little problem. I may take a glance at it in my leisure. By the way, it is curious that you should have come from Topeka. I used to have a correspondent — he is dead now — old Dr. Lysander Starr, who was Mayor in 1890."

"Good old Dr. Starr!" said our visitor. "His name is still honored. Well, Mr. Holmes, I suppose all we can do is to report to you and let you know how we progress. I reckon you will hear within a day or two." With this assurance our American bowed and departed.

Holmes had lit his pipe, and he sat for some time with a curious smile upon his face.

"Well?" I asked at last.

"I am wondering, Watson — just wondering!"

"At what?"

Holmes took his pipe from his lips.

"I was wondering, Watson, what on earth could be the object of this man in telling us such a rigmarole of lies. I nearly asked him so — for there are times when a brutal frontal attack is the best policy — but I judged it better to let him think he had fooled us. Here is a man with an English coat frayed at the elbow and trousers bagged at the knee with a year's wear, and yet by this document and by his own account he is a provincial American lately landed in London. There have been no advertisements in the agony columns. You know that I miss nothing there. They are my favorite covert for putting up a bird, and I would never have overlooked such a cock pheasant as that. I never knew a Dr. Lysander Starr of Topeka. Touch him where you would he was false. I think the fellow is really an American, but he has worn his accent smooth with years of London. What is his game, then, and what motive lies behind this preposterous search for Garridebs? It's worth our attention, for, granting that the man is a rascal, he is certainly a complex and ingenious one. We must now find out if our other correspondent is a fraud also. Just ring him up, Watson."

I did so, and heard a thin, quavering voice at the other end of the line.

"Yes, yes, I am Mr. Nathan Garrideb. Is Mr. Holmes there? I should very much like to have a word with Mr. Holmes."

My friend took the instrument and I heard the usual syncopated dialogue.

"Yes, he has been here. I understand that you don't know him. . . . How long? . . . Only two days! . . . Yes, yes, of course, it is a most captivating prospect. Will you be at home this evening? I suppose your namesake will not be there? . . . Very good, we will come then, for I would rather have a chat without him. . . . Dr. Watson will come with me. . . . I understood from your note that you did not go out often. . . . Well, we shall be round about six. You need not mention it to the American lawyer. . . . Very good. Good-bye!"

It was twilight of a lovely spring evening, and even Little Ryder Street, one of the smaller offshoots from the Edgware Road, within a stone-cast of old Tyburn Tree of evil memory, looked golden and wonderful in the slanting rays of the setting sun. The particular house to which we were directed was a large, old-fashioned, Early Georgian edifice with a flat brick face broken only by two deep bay windows on the ground floor. It was on this ground floor that our client lived, and, indeed, the low windows proved to be the front of the huge room in which he spent his waking hours. Holmes pointed as we passed to the small brass plate which bore the curious name.

"Up some years, Watson," he remarked, indicating its discolored surface. "It's *his* real name, anyhow, and that is something to note."

The house had a common stair, and there were a number of names painted in the hall, some indicating offices and some private chambers. It was not a collection of residential flats, but rather the abode of Bohemian bachelors. Our client opened the door for us himself and apologized by saying that the woman in charge left at four o'clock. Mr. Nathan Garrideb proved to be a very tall, loose-jointed, round-backed person, gaunt and bald, some sixty-odd years of age. He had a cadaverous face, with the dull dead skin of a man to whom exercise was unknown. Large round spectacles and a small projecting goat's beard combined with his stooping attitude to give him an expression of peering curiosity. The general effect, however, was amiable, though eccentric.

The room was as curious as its occupant. It looked like a small museum. It was both broad and deep, with cupboards and cabinets all round, crowded with specimens, geological and anatomical. Cases of butterflies and moths flanked each side of the entrance. A large table in the center was littered with all sorts of débris, while the tall brass tube of a powerful microscope bristled up amongst them. As I glanced round I was surprised at the universality of the man's interests. Here was a case of ancient coins. There was a cabinet of flint instruments. Behind his central table was a large cupboard of fossil bones. Above was a line of plaster skulls with such names as "Neanderthal," "Heidelberg," "Cromagnon" printed beneath them. It was clear that he was a student of many subjects. As he stood in front of us now, he held a piece of chamois leather in his right hand with which he was polishing a coin.

"Syracusan — of the best period," he explained, holding it up. "They degenerated greatly toward the end. At their best I hold them supreme, though some prefer the Alexandrian school. You will find a chair here, Mr. Holmes. Pray allow me to clear these bones. And you, sir — ah, yes, Dr. Watson — if you would have the goodness to put the Japanese vase to one side. You see round me my little interests in life. My doctor lectures me about never going out, but why should I go out when I have so much to hold me here? I can assure you that the adequate cataloguing of one of those cabinets would take me three good months."

Holmes looked round him with curiosity.

"But do you tell me that you *never* go out?" he said.

"Now and again I drive down to Sotheby's or Christie's. Otherwise I very seldom leave my room. I am not too strong, and my researches are very absorbing. But you can imagine, Mr. Holmes, what a terrific shock — pleasant, but terrific — it was for me when I heard of this unparalleled good fortune. It only needs one more Garrideb to complete the matter, and surely we can find one. I had a brother, but he is dead, and female relatives are disqualified. But there must surely be others in the world. I had heard that you handled strange cases, and that was why I sent to you. Of course, this American gentleman is quite right, and I should have taken his advice first, but I acted for the best."

"I think you acted very wisely indeed," said Holmes. "But are you really anxious to acquire an estate in America?"

"Certainly not, sir. Nothing would induce me to leave my collection. But this gentleman has assured me that he will buy me out as soon as we have established our claim. Five million dollars was the sum named. There are a dozen specimens in the market at the present moment which fill gaps in my collection, and which I am unable to purchase for want of a few hundred pounds. Just think what I could do with five million dollars. Why, I have the nucleus of a national collection. I shall be the Hans Sloane of my age."

His eyes gleamed behind his great spectacles. It was very clear that no pains would be spared by Mr. Nathan Garrideb in finding a namesake.

"I merely called to make your acquaintance, and there is no reason why I should interrupt your studies," said Holmes. "I prefer to establish personal touch with those with whom I do business. There are few questions I need ask, for I have your very clear narrative in my pocket, and I filled up the blanks when this American gentleman called. I understand that up to this week you were unaware of his existence."

"That is so. He called last Tuesday."

"Did he tell you of our interview today?"

"Yes, he came straight back to me. He had been very angry."

"Why should he be angry?"

"He seemed to think it was some reflection on his honor. But he was quite cheerful again when he returned."

"Did he suggest any course of action?"

"No, sir, he did not."

"Has he had, or asked for, any money from you?"

"No, sir, never!"

"You see no possible object he has in view?"

"None, except what he states."

"Did you tell him of our telephone appointment?"

"Yes, sir, I did."

Holmes was lost in thought. I could see that he was puzzled.

"Have you any articles of great value in your collection?"

"No, sir. I am not a rich man. It is a good collection, but not a very valuable one."

"You have no fear of burglars?"

"Not the least."

"How long have you been in these rooms?"

"Nearly five years."

Holmes's cross-examination was interrupted by an imperative knocking at the door. No sooner had our client unlatched it than the American lawyer burst excitedly into the room.

"Here you are!" he cried, waving a paper over his head.
"I thought I should be in time to get you. Mr. Nathan Garrideb, my congratulations! You are a rich man, sir. Our business is happily finished and all is well. As to you, Mr. Holmes,
we can only say we are sorry if we have given you any useless
trouble."

He handed over the paper to our client, who stood staring
at a marked advertisement. Holmes and I leaned forward and
read it over his shoulder. This is how it ran:

HOWARD GARRIDEB

Constructor of Agricultural Machinery
Binders, reapers, steam and hand plows,
drills, harrows, farmers' carts, buckboards,
and all other appliances
Estimates for Artesian Wells
Apply Grosvenor Buildings, Aston

"Glorious!" gasped our host. "That makes our third man."

"I had opened up inquiries in Birmingham," said the American, "and my agent there has sent me this advertisement
from a local paper. We must hustle and put the thing through.
I have written to this man and told him that you will see him
in his office tomorrow afternoon at four o'clock."

"You want *me* to see him?"

"What do you say, Mr. Holmes? Don't you think it would
be wiser? Here am I, a wandering American with a wonderful
tale. Why should he believe what I tell him? But you are a
Britisher with solid references, and he is bound to take notice
of what you say. I would go with you if you wished, but I
have a very busy day tomorrow, and I could always follow
you if you are in any trouble."

"Well, I have not made such a journey for years."

"It is nothing, Mr. Garrideb. I have figured out your con-
nections. You leave at twelve and should be there soon after
two. Then you can be back the same night. All you have to
do is to see this man, explain the matter, and get an affidavit
of his existence. By the Lord!" he added hotly, "considering
I've come all the way from the center of America, it is surely

little enough if you go a hundred miles in order to put this matter through."

"Quite so," said Holmes. "I think what this gentleman says is very true."

Mr. Nathan Garrideb shrugged his shoulders with a disconsolate air. "Well, if you insist, I shall go," said he. "It is certainly hard for me to refuse you anything, considering the glory of hope that you have brought into my life."

"Then that is agreed," said Holmes, "and no doubt you will let me have a report as soon as you can."

"I'll see to that," said the American. "Well," he added, looking at his watch, "I'll have to get on. I'll call tomorrow, Mr. Nathan, and see you off to Birmingham. Coming my way, Mr. Holmes? Well, then, good-bye, and we may have good news for you tomorrow night."

I noticed that my friend's face cleared when the American left the room, and the look of thoughtful perplexity had vanished.

"I wish I could look over your collection, Mr. Garrideb," said he. "In my profession all sorts of odd knowledge comes useful, and this room of yours is a storehouse of it."

Our client shone with pleasure and his eyes gleamed from behind his big glasses.

"I had always heard, sir, that you were a very intelligent man," said he. "I could take you round now, if you have the time."

"Unfortunately, I have not. But these specimens are so well labelled and classified that they hardly need your personal explanation. If I should be able to look in tomorrow, I presume that there would be no objection to my glancing over them?"

"None at all. You are most welcome. The place will, of course, be shut up, but Mrs. Saunders is in the basement up to four o'clock and would let you in with her key."

"Well, I happen to be clear tomorrow afternoon. If you would say a word to Mrs. Saunders it would be quite in order. By the way, who is your house-agent?"

Our client was amazed at the sudden question.

"Holloway and Steele, in the Edgware Road. But why?"

"I am a bit of an archæologist myself when it comes to houses," said Holmes, laughing. "I was wondering if this was Queen Anne or Georgian."

"Georgian, beyond doubt."

"Really. I should have thought a little earlier. However, it is easily ascertained. Well, good-bye, Mr. Garrideb, and may you have every success in your Birmingham journey."

The house-agent's was close by, but we found that it was closed for the day, so we made our way back to Baker Street. It was not till after dinner that Holmes reverted to the subject.

"Our little problem draws to a close," said he. "No doubt you have outlined the solution in your own mind."

"I can make neither head nor tail of it."

"The head is surely clear enough and the tail we should see tomorrow. Did you notice nothing curious about that advertisement?"

"I saw that the word 'plough' was misspelt."

"Oh, you did notice that, did you? Come, Watson, you improve all the time. Yes, it was bad English but good American. The printer had set it up as received. Then the buckboards. That is American also. And artesian wells are commoner with them than with us. It was a typical American advertisement, but purporting to be from an English firm. What do you make of that?"

"I can only suppose that this American lawyer put it in himself. What his object was I fail to understand."

"Well, there are alternative explanations. Anyhow, he wanted to get this good old fossil up to Birmingham. That is very clear. I might have told him that he was clearly going on a wild-goose chase, but, on second thoughts, it seemed better to clear the stage by letting him go. Tomorrow, Watson — well, tomorrow will speak for itself."

Holmes was up and out early. When he returned at lunch-time I noticed that his face was very grave.

"This is a more serious matter than I had expected, Watson," said he. "It is fair to tell you so, though I know it will only be an additional reason to you for running your head into danger. I should know my Watson by now. But there *is* danger, and you should know it."

"Well, it is not the first we have shared, Holmes. I hope it may not be the last. What is the particular danger this time?"

"We are up against a very hard case. I have identified Mr. John Garrideb, Counsellor at Law. He is none other than 'Killer' Evans, of sinister and murderous reputation."

"I fear I am none the wiser."

"Ah, it is not part of your profession to carry about a portable Newgate Calendar in your memory. I have been down to see friend Lestrade at the Yard. There may be an occasional want of imaginative intuition down there, but they lead the world for thoroughness and method. I had an idea that we might get on the track of our American friend in their records. Sure enough, I found his chubby face smiling up at me from the Rogues' Portrait Gallery. James Winter, *alias* Morecroft, *alias* Killer Evans, was the inscription below." Holmes drew an envelope from his pocket. "I scribbled down a few points from his dossier. Aged forty-four. Native of Chicago. Known to have shot three men in the States. Escaped from penitentiary through political influence. Came to London in 1893. Shot a man over cards in a night club in the Waterloo Road in January, 1895. Man died, but he was shown to have been the aggressor in the row. Dead man was identified as Rodger Prescott, famous as forger and coiner in Chicago. Killer Evans released in 1901. Has been under police supervision since, but so far as known has led an honest life. Very dangerous man, usually carries arms and is prepared to use them. That is our bird, Watson — a sporting bird, as you must admit."

"But what is his game?"

"Well, it begins to define itself. I have been to the house-agents. Our client, as he told us, has been there five years. It was unlet for a year before. The previous tenant was a gentleman-at-large named Waldron. Waldron's appearance was well remembered at the office. He had suddenly vanished and nothing more been heard of him. He was a tall, bearded man with very dark features. Now, Prescott, the man whom Killer Evans had shot, was, according to Scotland Yard, a tall, dark man with a beard. As a working hypothesis, I think we may take it that Prescott, the American criminal, used to live in the very room which our innocent friend now devotes to his museum. So at last we get a link, you see."

"And the next link?"

"Well, we must go now and look for that."

He took a revolver from the drawer and handed it to me.

"I have my old favorite with me. If our Wild West friend tries to live up to his nickname, we must be ready for him. I'll give you an hour for siesta, Watson, and then I think it will be time for our Ryder Street adventure."

It was just four o'clock when we reached the curious apartment of Nathan Garrideb. Mrs. Saunders, the caretaker, was about to leave, but she had no hesitation in admitting us, for the door shut with a spring lock and Holmes promised to see that all was safe before we left. Shortly afterward the outer door closed, her bonnet passed the bow window, and we knew that we were alone in the lower floor of the house. Holmes made a rapid examination of the premises. There was one cupboard in a dark corner which stood out a little from the wall. It was behind this that we eventually crouched, while Holmes in a whisper outlined his intentions.

"He wanted to get our amiable friend out of his room — that is very clear, and, as the collector never went out, it took some planning to do it. The whole of this Garrideb invention was apparently for no other end. I must say, Watson, that there is a certain devilish ingenuity about it, even if the queer name of the tenant did give him an opening which he could hardly have expected. He wove his plot with remarkable cunning."

"But what did he want?"

"Well, that is what we are here to find out. It has nothing whatever to do with our client, so far as I can read the situation. It is something connected with the man he murdered —

the man who may have been his confederate in crime. There is some guilty secret in the room. That is how I read it. At first I thought our friend might have something in his collection more valuable than he knew — something worth the attention of a big criminal. But the fact that Rodger Prescott of evil memory inhabited these rooms points to some deeper reason. Well, Watson, we can but possess our souls in patience and see what the hour may bring."

That hour was not long in striking. We crouched closer in the window as we heard the outer door open and shut. Then came the sharp, metallic snap of a key, and the American was in the room. He closed the door softly behind him, took a sharp glance around him to see that all was safe, threw off his overcoat, and walked up to the central table with the brisk manner of one who knows exactly what he has to do and how to do it. He pushed the table to one side, tore up the square of carpet on which it rested, rolled it completely back, and then, drawing a jimmy from his inside pocket, he knelt down and worked vigorously upon the floor. Presently we heard the sound of sliding boards, and an instant later a square had opened in the planks. Killer Evans struck a match, lit a stump of candle, and vanished from our view.

Clearly our moment had come. Holmes touched my wrist as a signal, and together we stole across to the open trapdoor. Gently as we moved, however, the old floor must have creaked under our feet, for the head of our American, peering anxiously round, emerged suddenly from the open space. His face turned upon us with a glare of baffled rage, which gradually softened into a rather shamefaced grin as he realized that two pistols were pointed at his head.

"Well, well!" said he, coolly, as he scrambled to the surface. "I guess you have been one too many for me, Mr. Holmes. Saw through my game, I suppose, and played me for a sucker from the first. Well, sir, I hand it to you; you have me beat and ——"

In an instant he had whisked out a revolver from his breast and had fired two shots. I felt a sudden hot sear as if a red-hot iron had been pressed to my thigh. There was a crash as Holmes's pistol came down on the man's head. I had a vision of him sprawling upon the floor with blood running down his face while Holmes rummaged him for weapons. Then my friend's wiry arms were round me and he was leading me to a chair.

"You're not hurt, Watson? For God's sake, say that you are not hurt!"

It was worth a wound — it was worth many wounds — to know the depth of loyalty and love which lay behind that cold mask. The clear, hard eyes were dimmed for a moment, and the firm lips were shaking. For the one and only time I caught a glimpse of a great heart as well as of a great brain. All my years of humble but single-minded service culminated in that moment of revelation.

"It's nothing, Holmes. It's a mere scratch."

He had ripped up my trousers with his pocket-knife.

"You are right," he cried, with an immense sigh of relief. "It is quite superficial." His face set like flint as he glared at our prisoner, who was sitting up with a dazed face. "By the Lord, it is as well for you. If you had killed Watson, you would not have got out of this room alive. Now, sir, what have you to say for yourself?"

He had nothing to say for himself. He only lay and scowled. I leaned on Holmes's arm, and together we looked down into the small cellar which had been disclosed by the secret flap. It was still illuminated by the candle which Evans had taken down with him. Our eyes fell upon a mass of rusted machinery, great rolls of paper, a litter of bottles, and, neatly arranged upon a small table, a number of neat little bundles.

"A printing press — a counterfeiter's outfit," said Holmes.

"Yes, sir," said our prisoner, staggering slowly to his feet and then sinking into the chair. "The greatest counterfeiter London ever saw. That's Prescott's machine, and those bundles on the table are two thousand of Prescott's notes worth a hundred each and fit to pass anywhere. Help yourselves, gentlemen. Call it a deal and let me beat it."

Holmes laughed.

"We don't do things like that, Mr. Evans. There is no bolt-hole for you in this country. You shot this man Prescott, did you not?"

"Yes, sir, and got five years for it, though it was he who pulled me. Five years — when I should have had a medal the size of a soup plate. No living man could tell a Prescott from a Bank of England, and if I hadn't put him out he would have flooded London with them. I was the only one in the world who knew where he made them. Can you wonder that I wanted to get to the place? And can you wonder that when I found this crazy boob of a bug-hunter with the queer name squatting right on the top of it, and never quitting his room, I had to do the best I could to shift him? Maybe I would have been wiser if I had put him away. It would have been easy enough, but I'm a soft-hearted guy that can't begin shooting unless the other man has a gun also. But say, Mr. Holmes, what have I done wrong, anyhow? I've not used this plant. I've not hurt this old stiff. Where do you get me?"

"Only attempted murder, so far as I can see," said Holmes. "But that's not our job. They take that at the next stage. What we wanted at present was just your sweet self. Please give the Yard a call, Watson. It won't be entirely unexpected."

So those were the facts about Killer Evans and his remarkable invention of the three Garridebs. We heard later that our poor old friend never got over the shock of his dissipated dreams. When his castle in the air fell down, it buried him beneath the ruins. He was last heard of at a nursing-home in Brixton. It was a glad day at the Yard when the Prescott outfit was discovered, for, though they knew that it existed, they had never been able, after the death of the man, to find out where it was. Evans had indeed done great service and caused several worthy C. I. D. men to sleep the sounder, for the counterfeiter stands in a class by himself as a public danger. They would willingly have subscribed to that soup-plate medal of which the criminal had spoken, but an unappreciative Bench took a less favorable view, and the Killer returned to those shades from which he had just emerged.

QUESTIONS

1. How does the author awaken the reader's interest at the very beginning of the story?
2. What evidence does Dr. Watson bring in incidentally to prove to the reader the fame and the cleverness of Sherlock Holmes?
3. Did you understand the title before you read the story? Did it arouse your curiosity?
4. What do you think of the American in the story? Would he really have spoken as the author makes him speak?
5. What touches can you find in the story that make Sherlock Holmes seem human?
6. Why did Holmes wish to see Nathan Garrideb without the American's knowledge?
7. Why did Holmes encourage Nathan Garrideb to go to Birmingham?
8. Does the story keep the promise made by its first paragraph?
9. *Word Study.* — What do the following words mean as they are used in the story: *digression, preposterous, ingenious, hypothesis, ingenuity?*

Problem: POINT OF VIEW
(See page 25.)

1. Who tells the story? Does he tell you what he thought about the case as it developed? Does he tell you how he felt? Think of other detective stories you have read. Who tells them?
2. Why does not the great detective tell the story? Does he suspect the solution of the mystery before the reader does? Would the reader be held in as much suspense if he were told the detective's theories as they were formed?
3. Can you find another reason for not having Sherlock Holmes tell the story? Re-read the second paragraph as if Sherlock Holmes were telling the story; let him refer to himself as "I" and to Dr. Watson by name. Would the reader feel as much confidence in the great detective if he told his own story?
4. Look back at the other stories you have studied in this book, and try to determine why they are told as they are. Why, for instance, does the doctor tell the story of "The Siege of Berlin"? Why does not one of the characters tell a story in "A Service of Love"?

The Damned Thing *

Ambrose Bierce (1842–1914?)

A neglected genius of the nineteenth century, Ambrose Bierce, was born in Meigs County, Ohio, on June 24, 1842. He ran away from the farm, where he had lived all his life, to join the Union army, in which he served with distinction in the Civil War. He tried his hand at many things and was during his life, farmer, soldier, journalist, topographical engineer, ranch superintendent, and author.

Bierce was a lonely figure who kept aloof from the world. One writer has described him as being neither friendly nor happy. In 1913 he went to Illinois to visit his daughter, and a year later told a friend that he was going to Mexico to look about, and then go on to the country of the Incas. He was last heard of from Chihuahua, Mexico. Although several rumors of his death have reached the United States from time to time, no one knows what really became of him.

Bierce, a brilliant writer, with great natural gifts, has been ranked by the critics as one of the most original of American writers. He was especially noted for his powerful and unusual short stories. He wrote many striking stories of the horrible and the supernatural, among them "An Occurrence at Owl Creek Bridge," "The Snake," and "The Horseman in the Sky." His works have been much neglected of late, but an interested student will usually be able to find some of his stories in the Public Library.

"The Damned Thing" is a story of the supernatural told in a manner that forces the reader to accept the strange happenings as actual facts. After a dramatic introduction, the author unfolds his story rapidly, maintaining the suspense until the very end. Although not as important as the plot, the characters are well drawn, while the setting and atmosphere are in harmony with the story.

* From *Can Such Things Be?* by Ambrose Bierce. Reprinted by permission of the publishers, Albert & Charles Boni, Inc.

I

ONE DOES NOT ALWAYS EAT WHAT IS ON THE TABLE

BY THE light of a tallow candle which had been placed on one end of a rough table a man was reading something written in a book. It was an old account book, greatly worn; and the writing was not, apparently, very legible, for the man sometimes held the page close to the flame of the candle to get a stronger light on it. The shadow of the book would then throw into obscurity a half of the room, darkening a number of faces and figures; for besides the reader, eight men were present. Seven of them sat against the rough log walls, silent, motionless, and the room being small, not very far from the table. By extending an arm any one of them could have touched the eighth man, who lay on the table, face upward, partly covered by a sheet, his arms at his sides. He was dead.

The man with the book was not reading aloud, and no one spoke; all seemed to be waiting for something to occur; the dead man only was without expectation. From the blank darkness outside came in, through the aperture that served for a window, all the ever unfamiliar noises of night in the wilderness — the long nameless note of a distant coyote; the stilly pulsing thrill of tireless insects in trees; strange cries of night birds, so different from those of the birds of days; the drone of great blundering beetles, and all that mysterious chorus of small sounds that seem always to have been but half heard when they have suddenly ceased, as if conscious of an indiscretion. But nothing of all this was noted in that company; its members were not overmuch addicted to idle interest in matters of no practical importance; that was obvious in every line of their rugged faces — obvious even in the dim light of the single candle. They were evidently men of the vicinity — farmers and woodsmen.

The person reading was a trifle different; one would have said of him that he was of the world, worldly, albeit there was that in his attire which attested a certain fellowship with the organisms of his environment. His coat would hardly have passed muster in San Francisco; his foot-gear was not of urban origin, and the hat that lay by him on the floor (he was the only one uncovered) was such that if one had considered it as an article of mere personal adornment, he would have missed its meaning. In countenance the man was rather prepossessing, with just a hint of sternness; though that he may have assumed or cultivated, as appropriate to one in authority. For he was a coroner. It was by virtue of his office that he had possession of the book in which he was reading; it had been found among the dead man's effects — in his cabin, where the inquest was now taking place.

When the coroner had finished reading he put the book into his breast pocket. At that moment the door was pushed open and a young man entered. He, clearly, was not of mountain birth and breeding: he was clad as those who dwell in cities. His clothing was dusty, however, as from travel. He had, in fact, been riding hard to attend the inquest.

The coroner nodded; no one else greeted him.

"We have waited for you," said the coroner. "It is necessary to have done with this business tonight."

The young man smiled. "I am sorry to have kept you," he said. "I went away, not to evade your summons, but to post to my newspaper an account of what I suppose I am called back to relate."

The coroner smiled.

"The account that you posted to your newspaper," he said, "differs, probably, from that which you will give here under oath."

"That," replied the other, rather hotly and with a visible flush, "is as you please. I used manifold paper and have a copy of what I sent. It was not written as news, for it is incredible, but as fiction. It may go as a part of my testimony under oath."

"But you say it is incredible."

"That is nothing to you, sir, if I also swear that it is true."

The coroner was silent for a time, his eyes upon the floor. The men about the sides of the cabin talked in whispers, but seldom withdrew their gaze from the face of the corpse. Presently the coroner lifted his eyes and said: "We will resume the inquest."

The men removed their hats. The witness was sworn.

"What is your name?" the coroner asked.

"William Harker."

"Age?"

"Twenty-seven."

"You knew the deceased, Hugh Morgan?"

"Yes."

"You were with him when he died?"

"Near him."

"How did that happen — your presence, I mean?"

"I was visiting him at this place to shoot and fish. A part of my purpose, however, was to study him and his odd solitary way of life. He seemed a good model for a character in fiction. I sometimes write stories."

"I sometimes read them."

"Thank you."

"Stories in general — not yours."

Some of the jurors laughed. Against a somber background humor shows high lights. Soldiers in the intervals of battle laugh easily, and a jest in the death chamber conquers by surprise.

"Relate the circumstances of this man's death," said the coroner. "You may use any notes or memoranda that you please."

The witness understood. Pulling a manuscript from his breast pocket he held it near the candle and turning the leaves until he found the passage that he wanted, began to read.

II

WHAT MAY HAPPEN IN A FIELD OF WILD OATS

". . . The sun had hardly risen when we left the house. We were looking for quail, each with a shotgun, but we had only one dog. Morgan said that our best ground was beyond a certain ridge that he pointed out, and we crossed it by a trail through the *chaparral*. On the other side was comparatively level ground, thickly covered with wild oats. As we emerged from the *chaparral* Morgan was but a few yards in advance. Suddenly we heard, at a little distance to our right and partly in front, a noise as of some animal thrashing about in the bushes, which we could see were violently agitated.

"'We've started a deer,' I said, 'I wish we had brought a rifle.'

"Morgan, who had stopped and was intently watching the agitated *chaparral*, said nothing, but had cocked both barrels of his gun and was holding it in readiness to aim. I thought him a trifle excited, which surprised me, for he had a reputation for exceptional coolness, even in moments of sudden and imminent peril.

"'Oh, come,' I said. 'You are not going to fill up a deer with quail-shot, are you?'

"Still he did not reply; but catching a sight of his face as he turned it slightly toward me I was struck by the intensity of his look. Then I understood that we had serious business in hand and my first conjecture was that we had 'jumped' a grizzly. I advanced to Morgan's side, cocking my piece as I moved.

"The bushes were now quiet and the sounds had ceased, but Morgan was as attentive to the place as before.

"'What is it? What the devil is it?' I asked.

"'That Damned Thing!' he replied, without turning his head. His voice was husky and unnatural. He trembled visibly.

"I was about to speak further, when I observed the wild oats near the place of disturbance moving in the most inexplicable way. I can hardly describe it. It seemed as if stirred by a streak of wind, which not only bent it, but pressed it down — crushed it so that it did not rise; and this movement was slowly prolonging itself directly toward us.

"Nothing that I had ever seen had affected me so strangely

as this unfamiliar and unaccountable phenomenon, yet I am
unable to recall any sense of fear. I remember — and tell it
here because, singularly enough, I recollected it then — that
once in looking carelessly out of an open window I momen-
tarily mistook a small tree close at hand for one of a group
of larger trees at a little distance away. It looked the same
size as the others, but being more distinctly and sharply defined in mass and detail seemed out of harmony with them.
It was a mere falsification of the law of aërial perspective,
but it startled, almost terrified me. We so rely upon the orderly
operation of familiar natural laws that any seeming suspension
of them is noted as a menace to our safety, a warning of un-
thinkable calamity. So now the apparently causeless movement of the herbage and the slow, undeviating approach of
the line of disturbances were distinctly disquieting. My companion appeared actually frightened, and I could hardly credit
my senses when I saw him suddenly throw his gun to his
shoulder and fire both barrels at the agitated grain! Before
the smoke of the discharge had cleared away I heard a loud
savage cry — a scream like that of a wild animal — and fling-
ing his gun upon the ground Morgan sprang away and ran
swiftly from the spot. At the same instant I was thrown violently to the ground by the impact of something unseen in
the smoke — some soft, heavy substance that seemed thrown
against me with great force.

"Before I could get upon my feet and recover my gun,
which seemed to have been struck from my hands, I heard
Morgan crying out as if in mortal agony, and mingling with
his cries were such hoarse savage sounds as one hears from
fighting dogs. Inexpressibly terrified, I struggled to my feet
and looked in the direction of Morgan's retreat; and may
Heaven in mercy spare me from another sight like that! At
a distance of less than thirty yards was my friend, down upon
one knee, his head thrown back at a frightful angle, hatless,
his long hair in disorder and his whole body in violent movement from side to side, backward and forward. His right arm
was lifted and seemed to lack the hand — at least, I could

see none. The other arm was invisible. At times, as my memory now reports this extraordinary scene, I could discern but a part of his body; it was as if he had been partly blotted out — I cannot otherwise express it — then a shifting of his position would bring it all into view again.

"All this must have occurred within a few seconds, yet in that time Morgan assumed all the postures of a determined wrestler vanquished by superior weight and strength. I saw nothing but him, and him not always distinctly. During the entire incident his shouts and curses were heard, as if through an enveloping uproar of such sounds of rage and fury as I had never heard from the throat of man or brute!

"For a moment only I stood irresolute, then throwing down my gun I ran forward to my friend's assistance. I had a vague belief that he was suffering from a fit, or some form of convulsion. Before I could reach his side he was down and quiet. All sounds had ceased, but with a feeling of such terror as even these awful events had not inspired I now saw again the mysterious movement of the wild oats, prolonging itself from the trampled area about the prostrate man toward the edge of a wood. It was only when it had reached the wood that I was able to withdraw my eyes and look at my companion. He was dead."

III

A MAN THOUGH NAKED MAY BE IN RAGS

The coroner rose from his seat and stood beside the dead man. Lifting an edge of the sheet he pulled it away, exposing the entire body, altogether naked and showing in the candlelight a claylike yellow. It had, however, broad maculations of bluish black, obviously caused by extravasated blood from contusions. The chest and sides looked as if they had been beaten with a bludgeon. There were dreadful lacerations; the skin was torn in strips and shreds.

The coroner moved round to the end of the table and undid a silk handkerchief which had been passed under the chin and knotted on the top of the head. When the handkerchief was drawn away it exposed what had been the throat. Some of the jurors who had risen to get a better view repented their curiosity and turned away their faces. Witness Harker went to the open window and leaned out across the sill, faint and sick. Dropping the handkerchief upon the dead man's neck the coroner stepped to an angle of the room and from a pile of clothing produced one garment after another, each of which he held up a moment for inspection. All were torn, and stiff with blood. The jurors did not make a closer inspection. They seemed rather uninterested. They had, in truth, seen all this before; the only thing that was new to them being Harker's testimony.

"Gentlemen," the coroner said, "we have no more evidence, I think. Your duty has been already explained to you; if there is nothing you wish to ask you may go outside and consider your verdict."

The foreman rose — a tall, bearded man of sixty, coarsely clad.

"I should like to ask one question, Mr. Coroner," he said. "What asylum did this yer last witness escape from?"

"Mr. Harker," said the coroner, gravely and tranquilly, "from what asylum did you last escape?"

Harker flushed crimson again, but said nothing, and the seven jurors rose and solemnly filed out of the cabin.

"If you have done insulting me, sir," said Harker as soon as he and the officer were left alone with the dead man, "I suppose I am at liberty to go?"

"Yes."

Harker started to leave, but paused, with his hand on the door latch. The habit of his profession was strong in him — stronger than his sense of personal dignity. He turned about and said:

"The book that you have there — I recognize it as Morgan's diary. You seemed greatly interested in it; you read in it while I was testifying. May I see it? The public would like ——"

"The book will cut no figure in this matter," replied the official, slipping it into his coat pocket; "all the entries in it were made before the writer's death."

As Harker passed out of the house the jury reëntered and stood about the table, on which the now covered corpse showed under the sheet with sharp definition. The foreman seated himself near the candle, produced from his breast pocket a pencil and scrap of paper and wrote rather laboriously the following verdict, which with various degrees of effort all signed:

"We, the jury, do find that the remains come to their death at the hands of a mountain lion, but some of us thinks, all the same, they had fits."

IV

AN EXPLANATION FROM THE TOMB

In the diary of the late Hugh Morgan are certain interesting entries having, possibly, a scientific value as suggestions. At the inquest upon his body the book was not put in evidence; possibly the coroner thought it not worth while to confuse the jury. The date of the first of the entries mentioned cannot be ascertained; the upper part of the leaf is torn away; the part of the entry remaining follows:

". . . would run in a half-circle, keeping his head turned always toward the center, and again he would stand still, barking furiously. At last he ran away into the brush as fast as he could go. I thought at first that he had gone mad, but on returning to the house found no other alteration in his manner than what was obviously due to fear of punishment.

"Can a dog see with his nose? Do odors impress some cerebral center with images of the thing that emitted them? . . .

"*Sept. 2.* — Looking at the stars last night as they rose above the crest of the ridge east of the house, I observed them successively disappear — from left to right. Each was eclipsed but an instant, and only a few at the same time, but along the entire length of the ridge all that were within a degree or two of the crest were blotted out. It was as if something had passed along between me and them; but I could not see it, and the stars were not thick enough to define its outline. Ugh! I don't like this." ...

Several weeks' entries are missing, three leaves being torn from the book.

"*Sept. 27.* — It has been about here again — I find evidences of its presence every day. I watched again all last night in the same cover, gun in hand, double-charged with buckshot. In the morning the fresh footprints were there, as before. Yet I would have sworn that I did not sleep — indeed, I hardly sleep at all. It is terrible, insupportable! If these amazing experiences are real I shall go mad; if they are fanciful I am mad already.

"*Oct. 3.* — I shall not go — it shall not drive me away. No, this is *my* house, *my* land. God hates a coward. . .

"*Oct. 5.* — I can stand it no longer; I have invited Harker to pass a few weeks with me — he has a level head. I can judge from his manner if he thinks me mad.

"*Oct. 7.* — I have the solution of the mystery; it came to me last night — suddenly, as by revelation. How simple — how terribly simple!

"There are sounds that we cannot hear. At either end of the scale are notes that stir no chord of that imperfect instrument, the human ear. They are too high or too grave. I have observed a flock of blackbirds occupying an entire tree-top — the tops of several trees — and all in full song. Suddenly — in a moment — at absolutely the same instant — all spring into the air and fly away. How? They could not all see one another — whole tree-tops intervened. At no point could a leader have been visible to all. There must have been a signal of warning or command, high and shrill above the din, but by me unheard. I have observed, too, the same simultaneous flight when all were silent, among not only blackbirds, but other birds — quail, for example, widely separated by bushes — even on opposite sides of a hill.

"It is known to seamen that a school of whales basking or

sporting on the surface of the ocean, miles apart, with the convexity of the earth between, will sometimes dive at the same instant — all gone out of sight in a moment. The signal has been sounded — too grave for the ear of the sailor at the masthead and his comrades on the deck — who nevertheless feel its vibrations in the ship as the stones of a cathedral are stirred by the bass of the organ.

"As with sounds, so with colors. At each end of the solar spectrum the chemist can detect the presence of what are known as 'actinic' rays. They represent colors — integral colors in the composition of light — which we are unable to discern. The human eye is an imperfect instrument; its range is but a few octaves of the real 'chromatic scale.' I am not mad; there are colors that we cannot see.

"And, God help me! the Damned Thing is of such a color!"

QUESTIONS

1. Where in the story did you receive your first shock? Were you prepared for it?
2. Why was the coroner made a different kind of man from his jurors?
3. How did the mountaineers receive the newspaperman's story? Do you think the coroner believed him?
4. What was the verdict of the jury? Was it justified?
5. Why did the coroner refuse to have the dead man's diary read at all?
6. What methods does the author employ to make the reader accept the supernatural? Why does he have the news-writer ask permission to read the diary?
7. Is the story easier to believe because it is told by two different men?
8. Is Hugh Morgan's explanation of the mystery satisfactory to you? Can you offer any other explanation?
9. *Word Study.* — What do the following words mean as they are used in the story: *urban, prepossessing, laceration, indiscretion, environment, imminent?*

Problem: TONE OR ATMOSPHERE
(See page 27.)

1. Describe the tone or atmosphere of this story. Notice the three different points of view used by the author. Are they all accounted

for in the story? Do the changes in point of view have any connection with the tone of the story?

2. What does the first paragraph do for the story? What is unusual about the paragraph? What is its purpose in the story?

3. What part does the setting play in fixing the tone of the story? Could the story have been written with the scene laid in a city? In a village? How do you account for the time of day at which the story takes place?

4. Would the effect of the story have been heightened by having Hugh Morgan's diary read to the coroner's jury? Explain.

5. Find special sentences in the story that help to give the story its atmosphere.

5. Are the sub-titles in harmony with the atmosphere of the story? What is their effect upon the reader before he understands them? Do you think you would enjoy the story more without sub-titles?

The Pack *

John Galsworthy (1867–1933)

Very rarely there is a writer who does two types of writing so well that it is hard to decide in which of them lies his chief claim to recognition. Such a man was the English author, John Galsworthy. For years critics mentioned him as a dramatist, insisting that his novels did not reach the level of his plays; then, in 1922, when "The Forsyte Saga" was published, everyone admitted that interesting as are "Justice," "Strife," "The Silver Box," "Loyalties," and his other plays, his great cycle of novels has far surpassed them in interest and in literary value.

Mr. Galsworthy belonged to a well-to-do English family. His education, at Harrow and Oxford, was the best that England provides. Like many another writer, he studied for the bar — and practised very little. His most important work was done in in the first quarter of the twentieth century.

In all of his books Mr. Galsworthy is deeply concerned with the moral aspect of human action. He cries out against injustice and cruelty, deploring the hardness of the world's heart, and explaining how men come to be hard-hearted.

The few short stories by John Galsworthy carry out the general trend of his plays and novels. "The Pack" is typical in its insistence on an idea. It does not contain the human portraits to be found in his novels, but it does present in a clear and memorable form a common human failing.

"IT'S ONLY," said H., "when men run in packs that they lose their sense of decency. At least that's my experience. Individual man — I'm not speaking of savages — is more given to generosity than meanness, rarely brutal, inclines in fact to be a gentleman. It's when you add three or four more to him that his sense of decency, his sense of per-*son al* —

---

* From *A Motley:* Copyright, 1910, by Charles Scribner's Sons. Reprinted by permission of the publishers.

sonal responsibility, his private standards, go by the board. I am not at all sure that he does not become the victim of a certain infectious fever. Something physical takes place, I fancy . . . I happen to be a trustee, with three others, and we do a deal of cheeseparing in the year, which as private individuals we should never dream of."

"That's hardly a fair example," said D., "but on the whole, I quite agree. Single man is not an angel, collective man is a bit of a brute."

The discussion was carried on for several minutes, and then P., who had not yet spoken, said: "They say a pinch of illustration is worth a pound of argument. When I was at the 'Varsity there was a man at the same college with me called Chalkcroft, the son of a high ecclesiastic, a perfectly harmless, well-mannered individual, who had the misfortune to be a Radical, or, as some even thought, a Socialist — anyway, he wore a turn-down collar, a green tie, took part in Union debates on the shady side, and no part in college festivities. He was, in fact, a "smug" — a man, as you know, who, through some accident of his early environment, incomprehensibly fails to adopt the proper view of life. He was never drunk, not even pleasantly, played no games connected with a ball, was believed to be afraid of a horse or a woman, took his exercise in long walks with a man from another college, or solitarily in a skiff upon the river; he also read books, and was prepared to discuss abstract propositions. Thus, in one way or another he disgusted almost every self-respecting under-graduate. Don't imagine, of course, that his case was unusual; we had many such at M— in my time; but about this Chalkcroft there was an unjustifiable composure, a quiet sarcasm, which made him conspicuously intolerable. He was thought to be a "bit above himself," or, rather, he did not seem conscious, as any proper "smug" should, that he was a bit below his fellows; on the contrary, his figure, which was slim, and slightly stooping, passed in and about college with serene assurance; his pale face with its traces of reprehensible whisker wore a faint smile above his detested green tie; besides, he showed no signs

of that poverty which is, of course, some justification to
"smugs" for their lack of conformity. And as a matter of
fact, he was *not* poor, but had some of the best rooms in college,
which was ever a remembered grievance against him. For these
reasons, then," went on P., "it was decided one evening to
bring him to trial. This salutary custom had originated in
the mind of a third-year man named Jefferies, a dark person
with a kind of elephant-like unwieldiness in his nose and walk,
a biting, witty tongue, and very small eyes with a lecherous
expression. He is now a Scottish baronet. This gentleman in
his cups had quite a pretty malice, and a sense of the dignity
of the law. Wandering of a night in the quadrangles, he never
had any difficulty in gathering a troop of fellows in search of
distraction, or animated by public and other spirits; and,
with them whooping and crowing at his heels, it was his bene-
ficial practice to enter the rooms of any person, who for good
and sufficient reasons merited trial, and thereupon to conduct
the same with all the ceremony due to the dispensation of
British justice. I had attended one of these trials before, on
a chuckle-headed youth whose buffoonery was really offensive.
The ceremony was funny enough, nor did the youth seem to
mind, grinning from ear to ear, and ejaculating continually,
'Oh! I say, Jefferies!'

"The occasion of which I am going to speak now was a different sort of affair altogether. We found the man Chalkcroft
at home, reading before his fire by the light of three candles.
The room was panelled in black oak, and the yellow candle
flames barely lit up the darkness as we came whooping in.

"'Chalkcroft,' said Jefferies, 'we are going to try you.'
Chalkcroft stood up and looked at us. He was in a Norfolk
jacket, with his customary green tie, and his face was pale.

"He answered: 'Yes, Jefferies? You forgot to knock.'

"Jefferies put out his finger and thumb and delicately
plucked Chalkcroft's tie from out of his waistcoat.

"'You wear a green tie, sir,' he said.

"Chalkcroft went the color of the ashes in the grate; then,
slowly, a white-hot glow came into his cheeks. ——

"'Don't look at me, sir,' said Jefferies; 'look at the jury!' and he waved his hand at us. 'We are going to try you for ——' He specified an incident of a scabrous character which served as the charge on all such humorous occasions, and was likely to be peculiarly offensive to 'smugs' who are usually, as you know, what is called 'pi.'

"We yelped, guffawed, and settled ourselves in chairs; Jefferies perched himself on a table and slowly swung his thin legs; he always wore very tight trousers. His little black eyes gleamed greedily above his unwieldy nose. Chalkcroft remained standing.

"It was then," pursued P., "that I had my first qualm. The fellow was so still and pale and unmoved; he looked at me, and, when I tried to stare back, his eyes passed me over, quiet and contemptuous. And I remember thinking: 'Why are we all here — we are not a bit the kind of men to do this sort of thing?' And really we were not. With the exception of Jefferies, who was, no doubt, at times inhabited by a devil, and one Anderson, a little man in a long coat, with a red nose and very long arms, always half-drunk — a sort of desperate character, and long since, of course, a schoolmaster — there wasn't one of us, who, left to himself, would have entered another man's rooms unbidden (however unpopular he might be, however much of a 'smug') and insulted him to his face. There was Beal, a very fair, rather good-looking man, with bowed legs and no expression to speak of, known as Boshy Beal; Dunsdale, a heavy, long-faced, freckled person, prominent in every college disturbance but with a reputation for respectability; Horden (called Jos), a big, clean-cut Kentish man with nice eyes, and fists like hammers; Stickland, fussy, with mild habits; Sevenoax, now in the house of Lords; little Holingbroke, the cox; and my old schoolfellow, Fosdyke, whose dignity even then would certainly have forbidden his presence had he not previously dined. Thus, as you see, we were all or nearly all from the 'best' schools in the country, in the 'best' set at M—, and naturally, as individuals, quite —— — oh! quite — incapable of an ungentlemanlike act. ——

"Jefferies appointed Anderson gaoler, Dunsdale Public Prosecutor, no one counsel for the defence, the rest of us jury, himself judge, and opened the trial. He was, as I have said, a witty young man, and, dangling his legs, fastening his malevolent black eyes on Chalkcroft, he usurped the functions of us all. The nature of the charge precludes me from recounting to you the details of the trial, and, in fact, I have forgotten them, but as if he were standing here before us, I remember, in the dim glow of those three candles, Chalkcroft's pale, unmoved, ironic face; his unvarying, 'Yes, Jefferies'; his one remonstrance: 'Are you a gentleman, Jefferies?' and our insane laughter at the answer: 'No, sir, a by-our-Lady judge.' As if he were standing here before us I remember the expression on his face at the question: 'Prisoner, are you guilty — yes or no?' the long pause, the slow, sarcastic: 'As you like, Jefferies.' As if he were standing here before us I remember his calm and his contempt. He was sentenced to drink a tumbler of his own port without stopping; whether the sentence was carried out I cannot tell you; for with one or two more I slipped away.

"The next morning I had such a sense of discomfort that I could not rest till I had sent Chalkcroft a letter of apology. I caught sight of him in the afternoon walking across the quad. with his usual pale assurance, and in the evening I received his answer. It contained, at the end, this sentence: 'I feel sure you would not have come if it hadn't been for the others.' It has occurred to me since that he may have said the same thing to us all — for anything I know, we may all of us have written."

There was a silence. Then H. said: "The Pack? Ah! What second-hand devil is it that gets into us when we run in packs?"

QUESTIONS

1. Explain the statement "When men run in packs they lose their sense of decency."
2. Do you agree or disagree with this statement? Explain.

3. Tell of any incident you may have observed in which the actions of "packs" or "crowds" were demonstrated.

4. Tell as briefly as possible the plot of the story.

5. Does "The Pack" contain "a story within a story?" Consider your answer carefully.

6. *Word Study.* — What do the following words mean as they are used in the story: *conspicuously, ecclesiastic, intolerable, lecherous, scabrous, radical?*

Problem: THEME
(See page 27.)

1. What is theme?

2. What is the theme of this story? What is the theme of "A Service of Love?" Was it O. Henry's main purpose to prove that idea true? Explain.

3. What is the author really trying to do in this story? Is his purpose the same as O. Henry's in "A Service of Love?" Can you find a story in this book in which the author's purpose is similar to Galsworthy's purpose here?

4. How do the introductory paragraphs show you what the author is trying to do? Does the introduction serve any other purpose?

5. Has this story a moral? Explain.

Where Love Is, There God Is Also *

Leo Tolstoi (1828–1910)

Few writers have been as altruistic and as interested in social problems as was Count Leo (Lyof) Nickolaievich Tolstoi. When the American social worker, Jane Addams, visited him a number of years ago, she found him toiling with the peasants upon his large estate and living the simple life of the Russian farmer. Not only did Count Tolstoi believe in the necessity and dignity of labor, he was willing to put his belief into actual practice.

Born in Yasnaya Polyanna on September 9, 1828, of a wealthy family, the boy was brought up with every possible cultural advantage. His family had been German originally but had migrated to Russia. Tolstoi was educated in the University of Kazan and later served for a time in the Russian army. It was during his military service that he wrote his first books, "Childhood," "Boyhood," and "Youth."

Interesting himself in the sad condition of the Russian serfs, he worked for their liberation even though his efforts made him unpopular with the ruling classes. As the years passed by, Tolstoi's sympathy for humanity grew and developed. He saw clearly many of the evil practices of the world and strove constantly to right wrongs and bring about better social conditions.

His writings show his philosophy and his beliefs. To Tolstoi the two greatest questions in the world were "Why do I live?" and "How should I live?" As a writer he is noted for his sincerity, his honesty, his sympathy for the poor and the oppressed, and his love of justice. Tolstoi wrote novels and philosophical essays as well as short stories. His two greatest novels are "War and Peace" and "Anna Karenina."

IN A certain city dwelt Martin Avdyeeich, the cobbler. He lived in a cellar, a wretched little hole with a

---

* Reprinted by permission of the editors of *The Outlook*.

single window. The window looked up toward the street, and through it Martin could just see the passers-by. It is true that he could see little more than their boots, but Martin Avdyeeich could read a man's character by his boots; so he needed no more. Martin Avdyeeich had lived long in that one place, and had many acquaintances. Few indeed were the boots in that neighborhood which had not passed through his hands at some time or other. On some he would fasten new soles, to others he would give side-pieces, others again he would stitch all round, and even give them new uppers if need be. And often he saw his own handiwork through the window. There was always lots of work for him, for Avdyeeich's hand was cunning and his leather good; he did not overcharge, and he always kept his word. He always engaged to do a job by a fixed time if he could; but if he could not, he said so at once, and deceived no man. So everyone knew Avdyeeich, and he had no lack of work. Avdyeeich had always been a pretty good man, but as he grew old he began to think more about his soul, and draw nearer to his God. While Martin was still a journeyman his wife had died; but his wife had left him a little boy — three years old. Their other children had not lived. All the eldest had died early. Martin wished at first to send his little child into the country to his sister, but afterward he thought better of it. "My Kapitoshka," thought he, "will feel miserable in a strange household. He shall stay here with me." And so Avdyeeich left his master, and took to living in lodgings alone with his little son. But God did not give Avdyeeich happiness in his children. No sooner had the little one begun to grow up and be a help and a joy to his father's heart, than a sickness fell upon Kapitoshka; the little one took to his bed, lay there in a raging fever for a week, and then died. Martin buried his son in despair — so desperate was he that he began to murmur against God. Such disgust of life overcame him that he more than once begged God that he might die; and he reproached God for taking not him, an old man, but his darling, his only son, instead. And after that Avdyeeich left off going to church.

And, lo! one day there came to Avdyeeich from the Troitsa Monastery an aged peasant-pilgrim — it was already the eighth year of his pilgrimage. Avdyeeich fell a-talking with him, and began to complain of his great sorrow. "As for living any longer, thou man of God," said he, "I desire it not. Would only that I might die! That is my sole prayer to God. I am now a man who has no hope."

And the old man said to him: "Thy speech, Martin, is not good. How shall we judge the doings of God? God's judgments are not our thoughts. God willed that thy son shouldst die, but that thou shouldst live. Therefore 'twas the best thing both for him and for thee. It is because thou wouldst fain have lived for thy own delight that thou dost now despair."

"But what then *is* a man to live for?" asked Avdyeeich.

And the old man answered: "For God, Martin! He gave thee life, and for Him therefore must thou live. When thou dost begin to live for Him, thou wilt grieve about nothing more, and all things will come easy to thee."

Martin was silent for a moment, and then he said: "And how must one live for God?"

"Christ hath shown us the way. Thou knowest thy letters. Buy the Gospels and read; there thou wilt find out how to live for God. There everything is explained."

These words made the heart of Avdyeeich burn within him, and he went the same day and bought for himself a New Testament printed in very large type, and began to read.

Avdyeeich set out with the determination to read it only on holidays; but as he read it, it did his heart so much good that he took to reading it every day. And the second time he read until all the kerosene in the lamp had burnt itself out, and for all that he could not tear himself away from the book. And so it was every evening. And the more he read, the more clearly he understood what God wanted of him, and how it behooved him to live for God; and his heart grew lighter and lighter continually. Formerly, whenever he lay down to sleep he would only sigh and groan, and think of nothing but Kapitoshka, but now he would only say to himself: "Glory to Thee! Glory to Thee, O Lord! Thy will be done!"

Henceforth the whole life of Avdyeeich was changed. Formerly, whenever he had a holiday, he would go to the tavern to drink tea, nor would he say "no" to a drop of brandy now and again. He would tipple with his comrades, and though not actually drunk would, for all that, leave the inn a bit merry, babbling nonsense and talking loudly and censoriously. He had done with all that now. His life became quiet and joyful. With the morning light he sat down to his work, worked out his time, then took down his lamp from the hook, placed it on the table, took down his book from the shelf, bent over it, and sat him down to read. And the more he read the more he understood, and his heart grew brighter and happier.

It happened once that Martin was up reading till very late. He was reading St. Luke's Gospel. He was reading the sixth chapter, and as he read he came to the words: "And to him that smiteth thee on the one cheek, offer also the other." This passage he read several times, and presently he came to that place where the Lord says: "And why call ye me Lord, Lord, and do not the things which I say? Whosoever cometh to Me, and heareth My sayings, and doeth them, I will show you whom he is like. He is like a man which built an house, and dug deep, and laid the foundations on a rock. And when the flood arose, the storm beat vehemently upon that house, and could not shake it, for it was founded upon a rock. But he that heareth, and doeth not, is like a man that without a foundation built an house upon the sand, against which the storm did beat vehemently, and immediately it fell, and the ruin of that house was great."

Avdyeeich read these words through and through, and his heart was glad. He took off his glasses, laid them on the book, rested his elbow on the table, and fell a-thinking. And he began to measure his own life by these words. And he thought to himself, "Is my house built on the rock or on the sand? How good to be as on a rock! How easy it all seems to thee

sitting alone here! It seems as if thou wert doing God's will
to the full, and so thou takest no heed and fallest away again.
And yet thou wouldst go on striving, for so it is good for thee.
O Lord, help me!" Thus thought he, and would have laid
him down, but it was a grief to tear himself away from the
book. And so he began reading the seventh chapter. He read
all about the Centurion, he read all about the Widow's Son,
he read all about the answer to the disciples of St. John; and
so he came to that place where the rich Pharisee invited our
Lord to be his guest. And he read all about how the woman
who was a sinner anointed His feet and washed them with
her tears, and how He justified her. And so he came at last
to the forty-fourth verse, and there he read these words, "And
He turned to the woman and said to Simon, Seest thou this
woman? I entered into thine house, thou gavest Me no water
for My feet; but she has washed My feet with tears and wiped
them with the hairs of her head. Thou gavest Me no kiss, but
this woman, since the time I came in, hath not ceased to kiss
My feet. Mine head with oil thou didst not anoint." And
again Avdyeeich took off his glasses and laid them on the
book, and fell a-thinking.

"So it is quite plain that I, too, have something of the
Pharisee about me. Am I not always thinking of myself?
Am I not always thinking of drinking tea, and keeping myself as warm and cosy as possible, without thinking at all
about the guest? Simon thought about himself, but did not
give the slightest thought to his guest. But who was his guest?
The Lord Himself. And suppose He were to come to me,
should I treat Him as the Pharisee did?"

And Avdyeeich leaned both his elbows on the table and,
without perceiving it, fell a-dozing.

"Martin!" — it was as the voice of someone close to his ear.
Martin started up from his nap. "Who's there?"

He turned round, he gazed at the door, but there was no
one. Again he dozed off. Suddenly he heard quite plainly:

"Martin, Martin, I say! Look tomorrow into the street. I
am coming."

Martin awoke, rose from his chair, and began to his rub eyes. And he did not know himself whether he had heard these words asleep or awake. He turned down the lamp and laid him down to rest.

At dawn next day Avdyeeich arose, prayed to God, lit his stove, got ready his gruel and cabbage soup, filled his samovar, put on his apron, and sat him down by his window to work. There Avdyeeich sits and works, and thinks of nothing but the things of yesternight. His thoughts were divided. He thought at one time that he must have gone off dozing, and then again he thought he really must have heard that voice. It might have been so, thought he.

Martin sits at the window and looks as much at his window as at his work, and whenever a strange pair of boots passes by, he bends forward and looks out of the window, so as to see the face as well as the feet of the passers-by. The house porter passed by in new felt boots, the water-carrier passed by, and after that there passed close to the window an old soldier, one of Nicholas's veterans, in tattered old boots, with a shovel in his hands. Avdyeeich knew him by his boots. The old fellow was called Stepanuich, and lived with the neighboring shopkeeper, who harbored him of his charity. His duty was to help the porter. Stepanuich stopped before Avdyeeich's window to sweep away the snow. Avdyeeich cast a glance at him, and then went on working as before.

"I'm not growing sager as I grow older," thought Avdyeeich, with some self-contempt. "I make up my mind that Christ is coming to me, and, lo! 'tis only Stepanuich clearing away the snow. Thou simpleton thou! thou art wool-gathering!" Then Avdyeeich made ten more stitches, and then he stretched his head once more toward the window. He looked through the window again, and there he saw that Stepanuich had placed the shovel against the wall, and was warming himself and taking breath a bit.

"The old man is very much broken," thought Avdyeeich to himself. "It is quite plain that he has scarcely strength enough to scrape away the snow. Suppose I make him drink a little tea! the samovar, too, is just on the boil." Avdyeeich put down his awl, got up, placed the samovar on the table, put some tea in it, and tapped on the window with his fingers. Stepanuich turned round and came to the window. Avdyeeich beckoned to him, and then went and opened the door.

"Come in and warm yourself a bit," cried he. "You're a bit chilled, eh?"

"Christ requite you! Yes, and all my bones ache, too," said Stepanuich. Stepanuich came in, shook off the snow, and began to wipe his feet so as not to soil the floor, but he tottered sadly.

"Don't trouble about wiping your feet. I'll rub it off myself. It's all in the day's work. Come in and sit down," said Avdyeeich. "Here, take a cup of tea."

And Avdyeeich filled two cups, and gave one to his guest, and he poured his own tea out into the saucer and began to blow it.

Stepanuich drank his cup, turned it upside down, put a gnawed crust on the top of it, and said, "Thank you." But it was quite plain that he wanted to be asked to have some more.

"Have a drop more. Do!" said Avdyeeich, and poured out fresh cups for his guest and himself, and as Avdyeeich drank his cup, he could not help glancing at the window from time to time.

"Dost thou expect anyone?" asked his guest.

"Do I expect anyone? Well, honestly, I hardly know. I am expecting, and I am not expecting, and there's a word which has burnt itself right into my heart. Whether it was a vision or no, I know not. Look now, my brother! I was reading yesterday about our little Father Christ, how He suffered, how He came on earth. Hast thou heard of Him, eh?"

"I have heard, I have heard," replied Stepanuich, "but we poor ignorant ones know not our letters."

"Anyhow, I was reading about this very thing — how He came down upon earth. I was reading how He went to the Pharisee, and how the Pharisee did not receive Him at all. Thus I thought, and so, about yesternight, little brother mine, I read that very thing, and bethought me how the Honorable did not receive our little Father Christ honorably. But suppose, I thought, if He came to one like me — would I receive Him? Simon, at any rate, did not receive Him at all. Thus I thought, and so thinking, fell asleep. I fell asleep, I say, little brother mine, and I heard my name called. I started up. A voice was whispering at my very ear. 'Look out tomorrow!' it said, 'I am coming.' And so it befell twice. Now look! wouldst thou believe it? the idea stuck to me — I scold myself for my folly, and yet I look for Him, our little Father Christ!"

Stepanuich shook his head and said nothing, but he drank his cup dry and put it aside. Then Avdyeeich took up the cup and filled it again.

"Drink some more. 'Twill do thee good. Now it seems to me that when our little Father went about on earth, He despised no one, but sought unto the simple folk most of all. He was always among the simple folk. Those disciples of His, too, He chose most of them from amongst our brother-laborers, sinners like unto us. He that exalteth himself, He says, shall be abased, and he that abaseth himself shall be exalted. Ye, says He, call me Lord, and I, says He, wash your feet. He who would be the first among you, He says, let him become the servant of all. And therefore it is that He says, Blessed are the lowly, the peacemakers, the humble, and the long-suffering."

Stepanuich forgot his tea. He was an old man, soft-hearted, and tearful. He sat and listened, and the tears rolled down his cheeks.

"Come, drink a little more," said Avdyeeich. But Stepanuich crossed himself, expressed his thanks, pushed away his cup, and got up.

"I thank thee, Martin Avdyeeich," said he. "I have fared well at thy hands, and thou hast refreshed me both in body and soul."

"Thou wilt show me a kindness by coming again. I am very glad to have a guest," said Avdyeeich. Stepanuich departed, and Martin poured out the last drop of tea, drank it, washed up, and again sat down by the window to work — he had some back stitching to do. He stitched and stitched, and now and then cast glances at the window — he was looking for Christ, and could think of nothing but Him and His works. And the divers sayings of Christ were in his head all the time.

Two soldiers passed by, one in regimental boots, the other in boots of his own making; after that, the owner of the next house passed by in nicely brushed goloshes. A baker with a basket also passed by. All these passed by in turn, and then there came alongside the window a woman in worsted stockings and rustic shoes, and as she was passing by she stopped short in front of the partition wall. Avdyeeich looked up at her from his window, and he saw that the woman was a stranger and poorly clad, and that she had a little child with her. She was leaning up against the wall with her back to the wind, and tried to wrap the child up, but she had nothing to wrap it up with. The woman wore summer clothes, and thin enough they were. And from out of his corner Avdyeeich heard the child crying and the woman trying to comfort it, but she could not. Then Avdyeeich got up, went out of the door and on to the steps, and cried, "My good woman! my good woman!"

The woman heard him and turned round.

"Why dost thou stand out in the cold there with the child? Come inside! In the warm room thou wilt be better able to tend him. This way!"

The woman was amazed. What she saw was an old fellow in an apron and with glasses on his nose, calling to her. She came toward him.

They went down the steps together — they went into the room. The old man led the woman to the bed. "There," said he, "sit down, gossip, nearer to the stove, and warm and feed thy little one. . . ."

He went to the table, got some bread and a dish, opened the oven door, put some cabbage soup into the dish, took out a pot of gruel, but it was not quite ready, so he put some cabbage soup only into the dish, and placed it on the table. Then he fetched bread, took down the cloth from the hook, and spread it on the table.

"Sit down and have something to eat, gossip," said he, "and I will sit down a little with the youngster. I have had children of my own, and know how to manage them."

The woman crossed herself, sat down at the table, and began to eat, and Avdyeeich sat down on the bed with the child. Avdyeeich smacked his lips at him again and again, but his lack of teeth made it a clumsy joke at best. And all the time the child never left off shrieking. Then Avdyeeich hit upon the idea of shaking his finger at him, so he snapped his fingers up and down, backwards and forwards, right in front of the child's mouth, because his finger was black and sticky with cobbler's wax. And the child stared at the finger and was silent, and presently it began to laugh. And Avdyeeich was delighted. But the woman went on eating, and told him who she was and whence she came.

"I am a soldier's wife," she said. "My eight months' husband they drove right away from me, and nothing has been heard of him since. I took a cook's place till I became a mother. They could not keep me and the child. It is now three months since I have been drifting about without any fixed resting-place. I have eaten away my all. I wanted to be a wet-nurse, but people wouldn't have me: 'Thou art too thin,' they said. I have just been to the merchant's wife where our grandmother lives, and there they promised to take me in. I thought it was all right, but she told me to come again in a week. But she lives a long way off. I am chilled to death, and he is quite tired out. But, God be praised! our landlady has compassion on us, and gives us shelter for Christ's sake. But for that I don't know how we could live through it all."

Avdyeeich sighed, and said, "And have you no warm clothes?"

"Ah, kind friend! this is indeed warm-clothes time, but yesterday I pawned away my last shawl for two *grivenki*."

The woman went to the bed and took up the child, but Avdyeeich stood up, went to the wall cupboard, rummaged about a bit, and then brought back with him an old jacket.

"Look!" said he, "'Tis a shabby thing, 'tis true, but it will do to wrap up in."

The woman looked at the old jacket, then she gazed at the old man, and, taking the jacket, fell a-weeping. Avdyeeich also turned away, crept under the bed, drew out a trunk, and seemed to be very busy about it, whereupon he again sat down opposite the woman.

Then the woman said: "Christ requite thee, dear little father! It is plain that it was He who sent me by thy window. When I first came out it was warm, and now it has turned very cold. And He it was, little father, who made thee look out of the window and have compassion on wretched me."

Avdyeeich smiled slightly, and said: "Yes, He must have done it, for I looked not out of the window in vain, dear gossip!"

And Avdyeeich told his dream to the soldier's wife also, and how he had heard a voice promising that the Lord should come to him that day.

"All things are possible," said the woman. Then she rose up, put on the jacket, wrapped it round her little one, and then began to curtsy and thank Avdyeeich once more.

"Take this for Christ's sake," said Avdyeeich, giving her a two-*grivenka* piece, "and redeem your shawl." The woman crossed herself, Avdyeeich crossed himself, and then he led the woman to the door.

The woman went away. Avdyeeich ate up the remainder of the cabbage soup, washed up, and again sat down to work. He worked on and on, but he did not forget the window, and whenever the window was darkened he immediately looked up to see who was passing. Acquaintances passed, strangers passed, but there was no one in particular.

But now Avdyeeich sees how, right in front of his window, an old woman, a huckster, has taken her stand. She carries a basket of apples. Not many now remained; she had evidently sold them nearly all. Across her shoulder she carried a sack full of shavings. She must have picked them up near some new building, and was taking them home with her. It was plain that the sack was straining her shoulder. She wanted to shift it on to the other shoulder, so she rested the sack on the pavement, placed the apple-basket on a small post, and set about shaking down the shavings in the sack. Now while she was shaking down the sack, an urchin in a ragged cap suddenly turned up, goodness knows from whence, grabbed at one of the apples in the basket, and would have made off with it, but the wary old woman turned quickly round and gripped the youth by the sleeve. The lad fought and tried to tear himself loose, but the old woman seized him with both hands, knocked his hat off, and tugged hard at his hair. The lad howled, and the old woman reviled him. Avdyeeich ran out into the street.

The old woman was tugging at the lad's hair and wanted to drag him off to the police, while the boy fought and kicked.

"I didn't take it," said he. "What are you whacking me for? Let me go!"

Avdyeeich came up and tried to part them. He seized the lad by the arm and said: "Let him go, little mother! Forgive him for Christ's sake!"

"I'll forgive him so that he sha'n't forget the taste of fresh birch-rods. I mean to take the rascal to the police station."

Avdyeeich began to entreat with the old woman.

"Let him go, little mother; he will not do so any more. Let him go for Christ's sake."

The old woman let him go. The lad would have bolted, but Avdyeeich held him fast.

"Beg the little mother's pardon," said he, "and don't do such things any more. I saw thee take them."

Then the lad began to cry and beg pardon.

"Well, that's all right! And now, there's an apple for thee." And Avdyeeich took one out of the basket and gave it to the boy. "I'll pay thee for it, little mother," he said to the old woman.

"Thou wilt ruin them that way, the blackguards," said the

old woman. "If I had the rewarding of him, he should not be able to sit down for a week."

"Oh, little mother, little mother!" cried Avdyeeich, "that is our way of looking at things, but it is not God's way. If he ought to be whipped so for the sake of one apple, what do we deserve for our sins?"

The old woman was silent.

And Avdyeeich told the old woman about the parable of the master who forgave his servant a very great debt, and how that servant immediately went out and caught his fellow-servant by the throat because he was his debtor. The old woman listened to the end, and the lad listened, too.

"God bade us forgive," said Avdyeeich, "otherwise He will not forgive us. We must forgive everyone, especially the thoughtless."

The old woman shook her head and sighed.

"That's all very well," she said, "but they are spoiled enough already."

"Then it is for us old people to teach them better," said Avdyeeich.

"So say I," replied the old woman. "I had seven of them at one time, and now I have but a single daughter left." And the old woman began telling him where and how she lived with her daughter, and how many grandchildren she had. "I'm not what I was," she said, "but I work all I can. I am sorry for my grandchildren, and good children they are, too. No one is so glad to see me as they are. Little Aksyutka will go to none but me. 'Grandma dear! darling grandma!'" and the old woman was melted to tears. "As for him," she added, pointing to the lad, "boys will be boys, I suppose. Well, God be with him!"

Now just as the old woman was about to hoist the sack on to her shoulder, the lad rushed forward and said:

"Give it here and I'll carry it for thee, granny! It is all in my way."

The old woman shook her head, but she did put the sack on the lad's shoulder.

And so they trudged down the street together side by side. And the old woman forgot to ask Avdyeeich for the money for the apple. Avdyeeich kept standing and looking after them, and heard how they talked to each other, as they went, about all sorts of things.

Avdyeeich followed them with his eyes till they were out of sight, then he turned homeward and found his glasses on the steps (they were not broken), picked up his awl, and sat down to work again. He worked away for a little while, but soon he was scarcely able to distinguish the stitches, and saw the lamplighter going round to light the lamps. "I see it is time to light up," thought he, so he trimmed his little lamp, lighted it, and again sat down to work. He finished one boot completely, turned it round and inspected it. "Good!" he cried. He put away his tools, swept up the cuttings, removed the brushes and tips, put away the awl, took down the lamp, placed it on the table, and took down the Gospels from the shelf. He wanted to find the passage where he had last evening placed a strip of morocco leather by way of marker, but he lit upon another place. And just as Avdyeeich opened the Gospels, he recollected his dream of yesterday evening. And no sooner did he call it to mind than it seemed to him as if some persons were moving about and shuffling with their feet behind him. Avdyeeich glanced round and saw that somebody was indeed standing in the dark corner — yes, someone was really there, but who he could not exactly make out. Then a voice whispered in his ear:

"Martin! Martin! dost thou not know me?"

"Who art thou?" cried Avdyeeich.

"'Tis I," cried the voice, "lo, 'tis I!" And forth from the dark corner stepped Stepanuich. He smiled, and it was as though a little cloud were breaking, and he was gone.

"It is I!" cried the voice, and forth from the corner stepped a woman with a little child; and the woman smiled and the child laughed, and they also disappeared.

"And it is I!" cried the voice, and the old woman and the

lad with the apple stepped forth, and both of them smiled, and they also disappeared.

And the heart of Avdyeeich was glad. He crossed himself, put on his glasses, and began to read the Gospels at the place where he had opened them. And at the top of the page he read these words: "And I was an hungered and thirsty, and ye gave Me to drink. I was a stranger, and ye took Me in."

And at the bottom of the page he read this: "Inasmuch as ye have done it to the least of these My brethren, ye have done it unto Me."

And Avdyeeich understood that his dream had not deceived him, and that the Saviour had really come to him that day, and he had really received Him.

QUESTIONS

1. What is the meaning of the title? What has it to do with the story?
2. What gave Avdyeeich the idea that he would be visited by Christ?
3. What had prepared his mind for this idea?
4. What was Avdyeeich's vision after his visitors had left? How does the vision strike the keynote of the story?
5. From a careful reading of the story, what ideas do you get about the author?
6. Should you classify this story as probable, improbable, or impossible? Explain.
7. Notice the number of shoes described in the story. Why are they described?
8. *Word Study.* — What do the following words mean as they are used in the story: *rustic, censoriously, vehemently, requite?*

Problem: THEME
(See page 27.)

1. Which is most important in this story — plot, setting, theme, or character? Which is next most important?
2. Where is the theme of the story stated? How is it demonstrated?
3. Explain what is meant by the theme of a story. Does a story always have a theme? Does a story always have a moral?

The Blue Serge Suit *

John Langdon (1913–)

Born in 1913 in Sawtelle, now a part of Los Angeles, California, John Langdon was educated in the public schools and was graduated from the University High School during the great depression, which began in the fall of 1929 and lasted through the early and middle thirties. As he expressed it: "After high school, I knocked around and held a variety of jobs during the depression — dishwasher, sideshow barker, and actor. I was in CCC camps and on the road as a drifter. . . . My most lasting occupation has been that of electrician, at sea during World War II, ashore in plants, and out on the Gulf of Mexico on oil rigs and power barges." While serving as a seaman, the author visited the Pacific Islands, the Orient, Australia, Mexico, and some parts of South America. Indeed, it was his experience as a sailor which gave him the literary material for numerous short stories and his first novel, "Vicious Circuit," as well as his book "S.S. Silverspray," which tells the story of a merchant-marine freighter on a voyage from San Francisco to Manila. For a short time, John Langdon, with his wife and their three children, lived in a trailer in New Orleans while he was completing a novel.

"The Blue Serge Suit" and another story were both ranked first in a recent "Paris Review" short-story contest, and Mr. Langdon's story was later included in both "Prize Stories 1957: the O. Henry Awards" and "The Best American Short Stories 1957." It presents a vivid, realistic picture of some of the problems which a teen-ager — the child of divorced parents — has to meet and solve. More specifically, the story portrays a turning point in young Neal's life — when he begins to change from a boy into a man. Written with grim realism, the story, neverthe-

* Reprinted by permission of The Paris Review, Inc. and Mr. Langdon's agent, Toni Strassman, New York 3, N. Y.

*less, is warm, human, understanding, and — to most readers —
satisfying.*

FATHER was still drinking on Saturday, a few days
before the junior high-school graduation. He hadn't worked
in over a month and he had been drinking nearly two weeks.
He looked terrible. His face, which was a lean hard brown
when he wasn't drinking, was puffed and red. His eyes were
bloodshot, his one popeye stuck out more than ever, and he
needed a shave. But his hands shook too bad to use his straight
razor and ordinarily he wouldn't use a safety razor.

He hardly ever came home before midnight and he always
woke me up with the noise he made in the next room. He
would sit on the edge of his bed and roll brown-paper cigarettes
with tobacco from the pound can that Grandpop, his father,
gave him each month and put the cigarettes on the chair beside the bed. He would smoke and drink and talk to himself,
always getting ready to fight someone. He was good with his
fists, but he could last only a few minutes because of his
asthma. After a while he would quiet down and go to sleep,
but he snored loudly, and his coughing shook the whole house.
He coughed a lot at night, and there was a tearing sound about
it as if he were trying to drag something down inside him,
something that wouldn't come loose. He wheezed and gasped
and choked and spit into a cardboard box that was filled with
strips of torn newspaper. And in the morning when I looked
in at him before going to school, he would be asleep, his head
and shoulders propped up on two pillows so he was almost
sitting. There were always ten or twelve cigarette butts in
the ash tray and two or three whole cigarettes on the chair,
and an empty pint bottle of whiskey on the floor beside the bed.

I hadn't talked to him all week. I hadn't wanted to wake
him up just to tell him I was on my way to school, and he
had been gone every afternoon when I got home. But I couldn't
wait any longer. Wednesday night the graduation was going to
be held in the high school and the Junior High School audi-

torium, which was also the gymnasium, with the stage at one end of the gym, and we were going to have a dress rehearsal on Tuesday afternoon.

I went in and shook Father. After a while he woke up, swung his legs over the side of the bed and sat on the edge of it, smoking a cigarette and rubbing his face with both hands. I told him about the suit.

"But why blue serge?" he asked. "Why wouldn't a grey suit or a brown one do just as well?" Those were the only two suits he owned.

I told him what Miss Harmann, our science teacher and class advisor, had said about graduation being an important event in our lives, and how all the boys were going to wear blue serge suits, or dark suits, and how all the girls were going to have on white flannel skirts and dark jackets.

"Sounds pretty fancy," Father said. "You figure the kids will all be there and rigged up like that?"

I said I hadn't heard any of them say they wouldn't be dressed that way.

"I guess they wouldn't say anything at that," Father said. "They'd just stay home if they didn't have the clothes. You'd pass into high school if you hadn't nothing but overalls to wear wouldn't you?"

"I don't think they'd keep me out," I said. Father made the whole thing sound kind of silly somehow and I didn't know if I could explain to him how it was because I was already different enough, being the biggest kid in class and a couple of years older than most of them from having missed so much school.

After Mother and Father were divorced when I was nine, I had lived part of the time with Mother and part with my father. Mother moved around a lot, and whenever I stayed with her it was always in some new city or town, and I had a new school to go to. Some of the schools had been strict and made me start over when I came in near the middle or the end of a term. And besides that, I had been going to this school not quite two months now, and I hadn't made any real friends among the kids yet. I didn't think I ever would, either, unless I could be more like the rest of them. There were more kids there whose folks were rich or well-to-do, than at any school I'd ever been to; kids who came from fine homes around Brentwood Heights and Westwood, and whose fathers and mothers worked in the movies and a couple who were movie stars' kids.

Father said, "Your grades all right, Neal?"

"They're all right," I said.

"Well, what's the important thing — the grades or the clothes?"

"The grades," I said. That was what he wanted me to say. He had gone only as far as the fifth grade himself and he really wanted me to get an education. He always said that an education was the most valuable thing in the world and the one thing nobody could take away from me.

"All right, Neal," he said. "I'll see what I can do."

He would stop drinking now, I was sure. But he was still too sick to work, even if he could have found a job.

He was a good shingler. How much he made depended upon how many 'squares' or hundred square feet of roof he covered. But he had got into a fight on his last job. And in the fight the superintendent of the construction company that was building a lot of big homes around Westwood, Beverly Hills and Brentwood Heights was hurt. He blamed Father for it and I guess he told the other companies because none of them would give Father a job.

That had been over a month ago; and after a couple of weeks of looking for work and getting turned down everywhere, Father had started to drink.

I didn't know how he was able to keep on drinking without money. Grandpop was the only one who might have lent him some. But Grandpop didn't have very much either — just a little house of his own three blocks up the street in the direction of school, and the pension he drew from the Soldiers' Home twice a month. It wasn't a very big pension and he had already helped us out several times. He was a nice old guy always doing things like once in a while giving me a dollar for spending money, or buying Father a shirt or a necktie, or giving him the pound can of tobacco each month. Father was his only son and I was his only grandson.

Father put on his pants and slippers and went into the kitchen and made a pot of coffee. He could hardly pour it into the cups and he could hardly get his cup to his mouth. He had to use both hands. He drank two cups; then he rubbed the bristle on his face.

"Think I need to prune my whiskers?" he asked. I said he would look a lot better if he did. He held out his right hand and studied it. "I don't think I could use the old stand-by," he said. "Okay if I use your safety?"

I said it was okay with me, but there was only the one blade that was in it and I had been using it over a month. Father grinned.

"It should still have a pretty fine edge, then," he said.

I went out on the back screen-porch with him while he soaped-up and shaved. It smelled good out there, of shaving-lather and the pepper trees that hung down over the sidewalk. Across the street behind the fence of the Soldiers' Home grounds were rows of tall, smooth-trunked eucalyptus trees with patches of papery, peeling bark. They had dusty silver-blue leaves and young green leaves and crackling yellow-brown leaves that had dried on the ground along with the acorn-like pods. They smelled like medicine. And the peppers had white beads of gummy sap on their trunks and branches, and lines of little black ants crawling on them.

When he had finished shaving, he put on his grey suit and a shirt and a necktie. He looked a lot better. He had cut himself only twice.

"Well," he said, "I guess we might as well go and see Grandpop first."

I said I guessed so, but what Grandpop could do about a blue serge suit, I didn't know. The only clothes I had ever seen him wear were the khakis that were given out to the soldiers in the Soldiers' Home.

It was a beautiful day, the sun not too hot and there was just a little wind. It rustled the tops of the eucalyptus trees and it made me think of the bright copper in the gutters of the roofs the Saturdays and sometimes Sundays I worked with Father when he needed extra money. If he was working now I might have gone with him and earned enough to make a down-payment on a suit. He paid me five cents a bundle to carry shingles up to the roof and put them around where he needed them, and a couple of times I had made as much as five dollars.

Father worked fast, sitting on a little board platform that had the points of nails sticking out of the bottom to keep it from sliding off the steep roofs, his mouth full of shingle nails. He set shingles in place and drove nails with two blows so close together they sounded almost like one single quick *tat-tat, tat-tat*, his blue-steel hatchet rising and falling and glittering and winking in the sunlight.

Sometimes I brought him a drink of water and sometimes he sat up on a roof and rolled and smoked a brown-paper cigarette — to take the taste of the nails out of his mouth, he said. He took good care of his two hatchets, whetting their blades and finishing up with the same stone on which he honed his straight razors. He did this every evening after supper when he was working and more than ever I wished he hadn't got into that fight. But I didn't want to say anything to him about it as we walked toward Grandpop's place.

In the middle of the second block Father got to coughing and had to stop. He held onto the fork of a small pepper tree and clawed at his lungs with those raking coughs. Tears ran down his face.

"Damn' asthma," he said when he could speak.

I didn't tell him it never seemed to bother him very much when he wasn't drinking.

"Do we owe Grandpop any money?" he asked.

I said as far as I knew, unless he had borrowed some, it was only six dollars. Father nodded and we went on, but more slowly.

The last three mornings on my way to school, Grandpop had been waiting for me, sitting in his wicker rocking-chair on his little front porch, and he'd had two one-dollar bills for me each time. He didn't like me to thank him, though I told him we would pay him back. He would frown, his bushy eyebrows pulling together so they almost hid his little blue eyes, clear his throat and say that his son, Jeff, was a good lad and would get back on his feet pretty soon. Then he would talk until I had to trot all the way to school to keep from being late. He would talk about his days of soldiering in the Philippine Islands and in Nicaragua. And before I left he would point his cigar at me and say, "Don't drink, Neal. Your father and I have nothing just because of the bottle. So remember that."

I promised him I would remember, but I knew he still drank. He allowed himself a fifth of Irish whiskey each week.

Grandpop was at home. He was sitting in the old leather rocker in the tiny living room that smelled of cigar smoke and of the way an old man lived alone. It was dim in there but after a minute my eyes got used to it. On the wall back of him was a photograph of himself and my grandmother, who had died when I was five years old. There was another picture on the wall above the stand that had on it an old-fashioned gramaphone with a big shiny brass horn. It was a picture of a company of soldiers. Grandpop was among them. And over this picture two long crossed palm fronds were tacked to the wall. They were varnished and yellow and dried out, and I always expected them to fall apart.

Grandpop rocked and glared at Father.

"You don't look so good," he said. "How do you feel?"

Father said there had been times when he had felt a lot better and Grandpop said: "If it's about money, Jeff, I can't spare much. Only two or three dollars until payday."

"Money would help, Dad," Father said. "But it's mostly about Neal, here. He's got to have a suit to graduate in." Grandpop scowled at me.

"A blue serge suit," I said. "Or a dark one." I told him

what Miss Harmann had said and what the kids were going to wear. I might have laid it on a little thick about wanting to be more like the others. Grandpop stared out the front window at the yellow wooden frame buildings of the Soldiers' Home beyond the eucalyptus trees. Rows of palms lined both sides of the main road of the Home grounds, and some big black birds that were either crows or hawks, circled in the air above the buildings.

Grandpop's ragged grey moustache that was stained brown at the ends from cigar smoke twitched a few times and he mumbled something I couldn't quite catch about sheep, or sheepskin, and frowned at me.

"It mean a lot to you to be just like the others, Neal?" he asked.

I said I'd like to be part of something like this just once, anyway. Grandpop nodded. The knuckles of one hand gripping his cane-handle stood out large and white and there was a glint in his little, frosty blue eyes. He got up and went into the bedroom that opened off the living room. I heard him moving things around in there, and when he came back he held a suit out in front of him. It brought the smell of mothballs in with it.

It was a blue serge suit, glossy and heavy. Grandpop hung the hook of the hanger over the top of the bedroom door and stood there looking at the suit.

"Had it made for me years ago," he said.

Father came over and rubbed the cloth of the sleeve between his thumb and first two fingers. "A wonderful piece of goods, Dad," he said.

"Wear like iron," Grandpop said. "You can't match material and workmanship like that these days, not for any money."

"No," Father said. "You sure can't."

Grandpop stood straighter, his shoulders back, and leaned only a little on his cane.

"Let's see how it fits you, Neal," he said.

I took the suit into the bedroom and put it on. And when I had it on, I knew it was all wrong.

It wasn't such a bad fit; Grandpop and me were pretty near the same size. But the double-breasted coat with un-padded shoulders was kind of pinched-in at the waist and sort of flared out below the waist. It was longer than coats had been worn for at least thirty years and the pants had small tight cuffs that made my feet sticking out from under them seem enormous.

I thought Father was going to laugh when he saw me. His face became lopsided and red; his popeye watered; and he choked up and had a spell of coughing and gasping.

"Damn' asthma's getting worse," he said to Grandpop when he could speak. He looked me over. "It ain't so bad, Neal. You'll get by."

He sounded to me as if he had his mouth full of shingle-nails. I stared at his hands at the twisted little finger and the old healed cuts and the crushed left thumb that was spread out and had a thick ridged nail like a clamshell.

"There's one thing about Neal," he said to Grandpop after he'd given me a going-over. "No one can say the boy hasn't got a good understanding."

I had never thought my feet were small but I had never thought they were anything like this size, either. They just stuck a long way out ahead of me. I felt the sweat on my forehead and it seemed to me I couldn't turn around in the tiny living room without knocking something over.

Father must've seen that he was carrying things too far, because he said, "I don't know, Dad. It does seem kind of old-fashioned for a kid."

Grandpop drew himself up straighter.

"I was married in that there suit, Jeff."

"I know," Father said. "Forty-six years ago this Saint Patrick's day, wasn't it?"

"Forty-seven," Grandpop said.

"Well, that's what I mean, Dad. Styles've changed a little since then, and you know how kids are about these things —"

"Be damned if I see what you're getting at, Jeff!" Grandpop banged the floor once with the tip of his cane and the ends of his moustache quivered. "Are you saying the cut of a suit is more important than the quality of its material and workmanship?"

Father just shrugged and Grandpop said, "Besides, Neal's no longer a kid. He's reaching his manhood. That right, Neal?"

He glowered at me, his bushy eyebrows pulled together, and I couldn't tell if he was making fun of me, or not. I didn't know him well enough. But it seemed to me there was something — a twinkle or glint in his eyes that in spite of the fierceness of his scowl could have meant he was teasing.

I didn't know what to say. I couldn't wear this suit. I might as well quit going to school as to show up for graduation dressed in this outfit. But how could I tell him that? And while I was trying to think of some way, I saw the fierceness go out of his eyes. He squinted, trying to bring it back, but there was a film, like cobweb, over them. He bent his head and looked down at the floor.

"I ain't wore that suit since Ellen's funeral," he said, not very loud.

I knew Father was watching me but I couldn't look at him.

"I aimed to wear it only once more," Grandpop said. "When they laid me away alongside Ellen." His Adam's apple bobbed in his wrinkled throat.

There are times when all at once you stop being a kid and grow up. At least you take a long step toward it. And it hasn't anything to do with when you first shave, or wear long pants, or go out to work with your father on a job, either. It's something else, something that happens to you. And when it happens, you know it. I guess you don't stop feeling the way a kid feels about lots of things right then, and maybe not for a long time afterward. But you do what you know you have to do. Grandpop was doing the only thing he could do in letting me wear his suit; and the only thing I could do was to wear it to the graduation, and to hell with what the kids or anyone else thought about it.

Just the same, knowing all this didn't make me feel any better.

"It's a wonderful suit," I said. "Wonderful."

Grandpop raised his head and looked at me. For just a second his eyes were bright and hard. Then they clouded; his shoulders slumped; he leaned on his cane and was an old man again.

"It's yours, Neal," he said. "I reckon I'll find something else to wear when my time comes."

Before I could say anything more, he opened the front door and went out on the porch. He sat in his wicker rocking-chair and got a cigar out of his vest pocket. His hands shook so he could hardly open the blade of the penknife he carried on his watch chain, and he had trouble paring off the end of the cigar. And when he had the cigar going good, he rocked and stared toward the Soldiers' Home, waiting for someone to come down from the Home that he could talk to.

I still felt terrible about wearing this suit, kind of cold and sick inside. Just the same, I was going to wear it. But only on graduation night and not to the dress rehearsal on Tuesday afternoon.

I told Father this and he nodded. I knew he understood and I thought he seemed proud of me.

All day Tuesday I kept getting funny looks from some of the other kids who were already dressed in their graduation outfits while I had on only my old yellow corduroys and a blue shirt, and I was sure they talked about me. But also, I noticed that only the richer kids had snappy-looking and up-to-date blue serge suits. Quite a few of the poorer kids had dark suits that didn't seem to fit too well, and only two of those were blue serge. Still, none of them were going to look nearly as old-fashioned and out-of-date as I was going to look.

That afternoon in the gymnasium-aud, I told Miss Harmann I would have a suit tomorrow night, but she only nodded and said that would be all right. She was worried right then about how the rehearsal would go.

We went through the business of marching on stage and sitting in chairs, first a row of girls, then a row of boys, until all the seats were filled. Anna Hendrickson, the class valedictorian, gave her speech, and Colby Enos read his class poem. Miss Harmann and old Mr. Asbaugh, the Principal, skipped their speeches to make the rehearsal shorter. And during Anna's speech and Colby's poem, I looked around the empty gymnasium at the exercise rings and the parallel bars, the basketball court with its backboards, and at the high, dusty, arched windows, and thought about the girls. Every one of them looked so neat and pretty in a white flannel skirt and dark jacket.

After the speeches we stood up, first a row of girls, then a row of boys, marched off stage and turned around and came back, moving up as each name was called out so there were always about five of us standing at the side of the stage in sight of the audience. And when our name was called, we went across the stage, pretended to receive our diplomas, and sat down in the same seat we had been sitting in before. It all worked out fine.

Miss Harmann, who had been calling out the names and pretending to hand out diplomas, stopped me when the rehearsal was over.

"You won't have any trouble getting a dark suit, will you, Neal?" she asked me.

"No ma'am," I said. "I'll have it tomorrow night."

"That's fine," she said and smiled at me. "Because everything looks so nice now and we don't want to spoil it, do we?" She stopped smiling and frowned. "But if you can't — well, I mean, if you think you might not be able to get it — I mean, I think I might get you one."

I saw she meant it. She would get me a suit somehow, I was sure. All I had to do was to tell her that I didn't have one. And I wanted to do it. I wanted to so bad it made my face go hot and my lips dry and puffy. But I couldn't.

"No, ma'am," I said. "I have a suit. It's — it's just being cleaned and pressed."

"Very well, Neal." She went over to the Principal, who was talking to Anna Hendrickson, and the three of them walked off together.

The next night after supper I put the suit on. I had shined my shoes and Father let me have one of his white shirts and his best necktie. When it was time for me to leave, he asked if I wanted him to come along with me. He said he had planned to attend the graduation. I said no, I had to be alone and I needed the fifteen-block walk. Then he said I ought to stop by and let Grandpop see how I looked all dressed up in his suit. I said I had figured on doing that. Father put his arm around my shoulder and said, "All right, Neal. Good luck. And sometimes things ain't as bad as you think they're going to be."

I didn't think he knew what he was talking about but I didn't say so.

Grandpop was fixing supper when I got there. He looked me over and nodded, and there was a glow in his eyes.

"Wait a minute, Neal," he said. He went into his bedroom and when he came out he had a gold watch on a chain.

I knew that watch. It was a twenty-one jewel railroadman's watch and you had to unscrew the cover and pull out a little lever at the side to set the hands. It was a very good watch and he'd had it a long time and hardly ever wore it. I felt like crying and didn't want to take it.

"I was going to leave it to you some day, Neal," Grandpop said. "But you're a man now and I guess you can use it."

I wound it and set it and fixed it into my vest the way his other watch was fixed. Grandpop shook hands with me and wished me luck.

Outside, I began to shiver though the night wasn't cold. I had plenty of time, so I walked slow along the other side of the street from the Soldiers' Home grounds. There were blue-white arc lamps on each corner, not quite as high overhead as the tops of the biggest pepper trees, and their light cutting down through the eucalyptus trees across the street and the peppers on this side, filled the street and sidewalk with thick blue shadows. The old wooden houses of the town with lights behind their windows looked small and lonely.

I came to the gate in the steel-wire fence and went in and

started across the play field. I was shivering worse than ever, and the lights of the gymnasium seemed to jump at me from across the field.

About halfway there, I stopped. I stopped in the middle of the field and stood there a long time, shivering. My jaws ached from keeping my teeth clamped together, and I almost turned around and went back to the gate. But I thought about Grandpop giving me his suit and his good watch and I knew I couldn't back out now, so I crossed the field and walked around the gymnasium and up the gravelled path to the back of the stage where the double iron doors at the top of the concrete ramp were open.

There was a lot of talking going on and the kids were moving around, but I couldn't see them very well. The lights on the curtained-off stage were bright, but my eyes were kind of blurred. I got into a dark place between the front curtain and a piece of canvas stage scenery without anyone seeing me.

Miss Harmann looked different, somehow younger. She had on a long white dress and a dark wrap or jacket with some flowers pinned up near the shoulder. She was short and plump, but she didn't look so short and plump now, but more like one of the girls in class. She had done something to her hair that wasn't like she usually wore it because there didn't seem to be any grey in it. And she wasn't wearing her glasses which always made her nose look like a button beneath them.

She had been coming across the stage, checking up, I guess, on which kids were there yet and speaking a few words to some of them. She was quite near when she saw me.

"Is that you, Neal?" she asked.

"Yes, ma'am," I said. I had to step out then. I saw her blink four or five times real hard, and I thought she was going to laugh. But she didn't. She looked almost scared. Her mouth was open a little, and her eyes, which were small and blue-grey, got watery like Father's one popeye had the morning I had first worn the suit at Grandpop's. Then she closed her mouth and bent her head and I knew she was looking at my feet. When she raised her head, her face was red and her eyes shiny. Her mouth pressed together in a tight line. I wished then I had never promised to wear the suit, or that I had to graduate, or anything.

That wasn't all that was happening though. In those few seconds everyone had all of a sudden become very quiet, and I knew they were staring at me — even old Mr. Asbaugh, the Principal.

Then Fiesal Newbar, whose father owned the famous New-bar coffee company and who was the kind of fellow who always had to be wise-guy said, "What are you dressed up for, Neal? Going to a costume party?"

That got a laugh, and Fiesal said, "What're you supposed to be, Neal — old Abe Lincoln without his high hat?"

Nobody laughed that time and someone said, "Lay off, Fies."

Then, for the first time, I could see them all real clear — Miss Harmann, Mr. Asbaugh, the girls and the fellows, and Fiesal, whom I could've licked with one hand. They were all smiling. Even old Asbaugh, who was supposed never to have cracked a grin in his life, had a smile on his long horselike face. Miss Harmann, too, was smiling and trying not to, biting her lower lip as if she was ashamed of it. I saw her and Mr. Asbaugh look at each other. The Principal shook his head just a little and Miss Harmann gave a faint nod and pressed her lips together. I knew then she was going to ask me if I'd be willing to get my diploma later, or something like that.

But before she could say anything Raymond Dunbar, who was the most popular kid in class and such a good baseball pitcher that he was a cinch to start out right away pitching for the high school's first-string varsity, came up and put his hand on my shoulder and said, "How're things going, Neal?" or something like that. I couldn't remember what I answered, but I remember that he asked me if I was doing anything tonight after graduation was over, and when I said I wasn't, he said, "Well, how about coming over to my place? A bunch of us are going down to the beach for a wienie-roast and a swim."

I told him I didn't have any swimming trunks and he said he had an extra pair he would lend me since we were almost the same size.

After that, before the curtain went up, other kids whom I hadn't talked to since I'd been going to this school came up to me. All of them said something and nudged me in the ribs or slapped me on the back, and other guys flipped their hands at me in a kind of salute and grinned. It was all friendly and made me feel good. The girls, too, looked at me. But they turned away when I caught them at it, and Anna Hendrickson gave a smile. It wasn't as if she was laughing at me, either.

Old Asbaugh and Miss Harmann sort of shrugged while this was going on, and Miss Harmann got busy settling us down. And when the curtain went up, I sat there feeling warm and good until we had to stand up and march off stage. I had almost forgotten about the suit until I was near the curtain where I would have to stand in sight of the audience. Then my heart began to pound so hard I could barely hear the names being called out, and there was a flickering in front of my eyes.

What happened then, I guess I never will understand very well. As soon as I stepped out from behind the curtain and was in sight of the audience, there was a funny kind of stillness. I could hear Miss Harmann's voice real clear and even the breathing of people in the first rows of folding chairs.

The fellow in front of me went to get his diploma and I was the first in line. And as soon as I stood there at the head of the line, somebody, a man, guffawed. But he had hardly begun when someone said, "*Sh-h-h!*", and then a couple of others called out, "*Sh-h-h!*"

I heard Miss Harmann speak my name, and as I started across the stage, there was clapping. Someone clapped, and somebody else, and before I was all the way across and got my diploma, it seemed to me that nearly everybody in the place must be clapping.

It was the biggest surprise of my life. They hadn't clapped

for anyone but the speakers and the class poem, and they kept on clapping even after I had sat down.

It was the first time in my life anyone had ever clapped for me.

QUESTIONS

1. What did Neal mean by stating "I was already different enough"? State both the advantages and the dangers of always following the crowd. Do you believe teen-agers are too "herd-minded"? Why or why not?

2. How had the divorce affected Neal's life? Discuss the various effects that separation and divorce may have on the children in the family.

3. Is the father fair to consider grades are the thing of greatest importance; in other words, is the father right in asking, "What's the important thing — the grades or the clothes"? Discuss.

4. Why had Neal's father lost his job?

5. What are some of the reasons or excuses for excessive drinking? Discuss.

6. How can the reader tell where the story takes place? Mention several items which help to establish the local color.

7. What things show that Neal's father had a good sense of humor and possessed good qualities of character as well as bad?

8. What does Neal tell us of his father's skill as a roofer?

9. What was Neal's Grandpop like?

10. What did Grandpop tell Neal about drinking? Prove that he failed to follow his own counsel.

11. Explain how Grandpop tried to solve Neal's problem by making a real sacrifice. Why did he fail to do so?

12. What did Neal's father say and what did he think about the suit?

13. Why did Neal decide he couldn't wear the suit and why did he change his mind?

14. What did Neal mean by stating, "There are times when all at once you stop being a kid and grow up"? Do you agree? Discuss.

15. Give an interesting account of the graduation rehearsal.

16. What offer did Miss Harmann make Neal and why did he feel unable to accept it? Do you think he should have accepted the offer? Discuss.

17. What gift did Grandpop give Neal when the boy stopped to visit on his way to graduation?
18. Explain why Neal was shivering as he approached the school.
19. How did Fiesal Newbar add to Neal's embarrassment, and how did Ray Dunbar come to the rescue?
20. How did Neal's other classmates show they were friendly?
21. Give a brief account of the conclusion of the story.
22. Explain why the audience clapped for Neal.
23. *Word Study.* — What do the following words mean as they are used in the story: *asthma, dress rehearsal, gramaphone, frond, valedictorian, arc lamp, ramp* (n.), *guffaw* (v.)?

Problem: REALISM AND CHARACTER DRAWING

1. Give your reasons for believing (or not believing) that the story gives the reader a realistic picture of life.
2. Why, in your opinion, is realism less popular with readers than romanticism? Which type of writing do you prefer? Why?
3. Do you believe that the grim, unpleasant side of life should be pictured accurately, treated sketchily, or omitted entirely? Give your reasons for your opinion.
4. Do the main characters seem lifelike? Discuss.
5. The story is supposed to be narrated from the point of view of a teen-age boy. Give your reasons for believing (or not believing) that the author has been successful in maintaining this viewpoint.

The Bottle Imp *

Robert Louis Stevenson (1850–1894)

One of the greatest writers of the late nineteenth century was Robert Louis Stevenson, born in Edinburgh in 1850. At the age of seventeen he entered Edinburgh University, where he studied those subjects that appealed to him and neglected most of the rest. He was especially interested in English poetry and fiction and in Scottish history and legend. He was the descendant of two generations of lighthouse builders and during his vacations worked at lighthouse engineering. It was a great blow to his father that Stevenson finally decided that he did not care to continue the work. He studied law and was admitted to the bar, but soon turned to writing.

Stevenson's health was always delicate. During his whole life he traveled from place to place in search of a favorable climate. He lived at different times in Switzerland, in southern France, in the south of England, in the Adirondacks, in California, and in the South Sea Islands. He finally settled in the Samoan Islands and spent his last years there.

In 1880 Stevenson had been married in California to Mrs. Fanny Osbourne. Although at first the marriage did not please Stevenson's parents, they were later reconciled and made their son a small allowance.

Stevenson's first book, "An Inland Voyage," was published in 1878, and his first novel, "Treasure Island," was written a little later. It was not until he published "The Strange Case of Dr. Jekyll and Mr. Hyde" in 1886 that his reputation was firmly established.

Stevenson wrote novels, poetry, short stories, and essays. He is noted for his clarity of style, his keen sense of humor, his vivid imagination, and his delightful understanding of people. Primarily a writer of adventure, he believed that the action of the story was of supreme importance. Stevenson wrote with great care, slowly, and with much revision. Once he spent three weeks of

* Reprinted by arrangement with Charles Scribner's Sons.

hard labor in writing twenty-four pages — producing a little more than a page a day. One of his manuscripts was rewritten ten times before it was sent to the printer.

Although the author himself tells us in his introductory note that the idea of "The Bottle Imp" goes back to medieval legend, the story itself is fresh and the South Sea Island setting lends color to the story. It is interesting to see what a skillful author can do in modernizing a story that is doubtless centuries old. Stevenson is noted for the facility with which he plunges his heroes at once into mystery and adventure. The characters hold the reader's attention and interest, and the plot is cleverly planned.

This author was one of the greatest stylists of the nineteenth century, and the student should examine the story carefully for examples of especially fine description and happy choices of expression.

[*Note.* — Any student of that very unliterary product, the English drama of the early part of the century, will here recognize the name and the root idea of a piece once rendered popular by the redoubtable B. Smith. The root idea is there and identical, and yet I believe I have made it a new thing. And the fact that the tale has been designed and written for a Polynesian audience may lend it some extraneous interest nearer home.— R. L. S.]

THERE was a man of the island of Hawaii, whom I shall call Keawe; for the truth is, he still lives, and his name must be kept secret; but the place of his birth was not far from Honaunau, where the bones of Keawe the Great lie hidden in a cave. This man was poor, brave, and active; he could read and write like a schoolmaster; he was a first-rate mariner besides, sailed for some time in the island steamers, and steered a whale-boat on the Hamakua coast. At length it came in Keawe's mind to have a sight of the great world and foreign cities, and he shipped on a vessel bound to San Francisco.

This is a fine town, with a fine harbor, and rich people uncountable; and, in particular, there is one hill which is covered with palaces. Upon this hill Keawe was one day taking a walk, with his pocket full of money, viewing the great houses upon either hand with pleasure. "What fine houses there are!" he was thinking, "and how happy must these people be who dwell in them, and take no care for the morrow!" The thought was in his mind when he came abreast of a house that was smaller than some others, but all finished and beautified like a toy; the steps of that house shone like silver, and the borders of the garden bloomed like garlands, and the windows were bright like diamonds; and Keawe stopped and wondered at the excellence of all he saw. So stopping, he was aware of a man that looked forth upon him through a window, so clear, that Keawe could see him as you see a fish in a pool upon the reef. The man was elderly, with a bald head and a black beard; and his face was heavy with sorrow, and he bitterly sighed. And the truth of it is, that as Keawe looked in upon the man, and the man looked out upon Keawe, each envied the other.

All of a sudden the man smiled and nodded, and beckoned Keawe to enter, and met him at the door of the house.

"This is a fine house of mine," said the man, and bitterly sighed. "Would you not care to view the chambers?"

So he led Keawe all over it, from the cellar to the roof, and there was nothing there that was not perfect of its kind, and Keawe was astonished.

"Truly," said Keawe, "this is a beautiful house; if I lived in the like of it, I should be laughing all day long. How comes it, then, that you should be sighing?"

"There is no reason," said the man, "why you should not have a house in all points similar to this, and finer, if you wish. You have some money, I suppose?"

"I have fifty dollars," said Keawe; "but a house like this will cost more than fifty dollars."

The man made a computation. "I am sorry you have no more," said he, "for it may raise you trouble in the future; but it shall be yours at fifty dollars."

"The house?" asked Keawe.

"No, not the house," replied the man; "but the bottle. For, I must tell you, although I appear to you so rich and fortunate, all my fortune, and this house itself and its garden, came out of a bottle not much bigger than a pint. This is it."

And he opened a lockfast place, and took out a round-bellied bottle with a long neck; the glass of it was white like milk, with changing rainbow colors in the grain. Withinsides something obscurely moved, like a shadow and a fire.

"This is the bottle," said the man; and, when Keawe laughed. "You do not believe me?" he added. "Try, then, for yourself. See if you can break it."

So Keawe took the bottle up and dashed it on the floor till he was weary; but it jumped on the floor like a child's ball, and was not injured.

"This is a strange thing," said Keawe. "For by the touch of it, as well as by the look, the bottle should be of glass."

"Of glass it is," replied the man, sighing more heavily than ever; "but the glass of it was tempered in the flames of hell. An imp lives in it, and that is the shadow we behold there moving; or, so I suppose. If any man buy this bottle the imp is at his command; all that he desires — love, fame, money, houses like this house, ay, or a city like this city — all are his at the word uttered. Napoleon had this bottle, and by it he grew to be the king of the world; but he sold it at the last and fell. Captain Cook had this bottle, and by it he found his way to so many islands; but he, too, sold it, and was slain upon Hawaii. For, once it is sold, the power goes and the protection; and unless a man remain content with what he has, ill will befall him."

"And yet you talk of selling it yourself?" Keawe said.

"I have all I wish, and I am growing elderly," replied the man. "There is one thing the imp cannot do — he cannot prolong life; and it would not be fair to conceal from you there is a drawback to the bottle; for if a man die before he sells it, he must burn in hell forever."

"To be sure, that is a drawback and no mistake," cried Keawe. "I would not meddle with the thing. I can do without a house, thank God; but there is one thing I could not be doing with one particle, and that is to be damned."

"Dear me, you must not run away with things," returned the man. "All you have to do is to use the power of the imp in moderation, and then sell it to someone else, as I do to you, and finish your life in comfort."

"Well, I observe two things," said Keawe. "All the time you keep sighing like a maid in love, that is one; and, for the other, you sell this bottle very cheap."

"I have told you already why I sigh," said the man. "It is because I fear my health is breaking up; and, as you said yourself, to die and go to the devil is a pity for anyone. As for why I sell so cheap, I must explain to you there is a peculiarity about the bottle. Long ago, when the devil brought it first upon earth, it was extremely expensive, and was sold first of all to Prester John for many millions of dollars; but it cannot be sold at all, unless sold at a loss. If you sell it for as much as you paid for it, back it comes to you again like a homing pigeon. It follows that the price has kept falling in these centuries, and the bottle is now remarkably cheap. I bought it myself from one of my great neighbors on this hill, and the price I paid was only ninety dollars. I could sell it for as high as eighty-nine dollars and ninety-nine cents, but not a penny dearer, or back the thing must come to me. Now, about this there are two bothers. First, when you offer a bottle so singular for eighty-odd dollars, people suppose you to be jesting. And second — but there is no hurry about that — and I need not go into it. Only remember it must be coined money that you sell it for."

"How am I to know that this is all true?" asked Keawe.

"Some of it you can try at once," replied the man. "Give me your fifty dollars, take the bottle, and wish your fifty dollars back into your pocket. If that does not happen, I pledge you my honor I will cry off the bargain and restore your money."

"You are not deceiving me?" said Keawe.

The man bound himself with a great oath.

"Well, I will risk that much," said Keawe, "for that can do no harm," and he paid over his money to the man, and the man handed him the bottle.

"Imp of the bottle," said Keawe, "I want my fifty dollars

back." And sure enough, he had scarce said the word before his pocket was as heavy as ever.

"To be sure this is a wonderful bottle," said Keawe.

"And now good-morning to you, my fine fellow, and the devil go with you for me," said the man.

"Hold on," said Keawe, "I don't want any more of this fun. Here, take your bottle back."

"You have bought it for less than I paid for it," replied the man, rubbing his hands. "It is yours now; and, for my part, I am only concerned to see the back of you." And with that he rang for his Chinese servant, and had Keawe shown out of the house.

Now, when Keawe was in the street, with the bottle under his arm, he began to think. "If all is true about this bottle, I may have made a losing bargain," thinks he. "But, perhaps the man was only fooling me." The first thing he did was to count his money; the sum was exact — forty-nine dollars American money, and one Chili piece. "That looks like the truth," said Keawe. "Now I will try another part."

The streets in that part of the city were as clean as a ship's decks, and though it was noon, there were no passengers. Keawe set the bottle in the gutter and walked away. Twice he looked back, and there was the milky, round-bellied bottle where he left it. A third time he looked back, and turned a corner; but he had scarce done so when something knocked upon his elbow, and behold! it was the long neck sticking up; and as for the round belly, it was jammed into the pocket of his pilot-coat.

"And that looks like the truth," said Keawe.

The next thing he did was to buy a corkscrew in a shop, and go apart into a secret place in the fields. And there he tried to draw the cork, but as often as he put the screw in, out it came again, and the cork as whole as ever.

"This is some new sort of cork," said Keawe, and all at once he began to shake and sweat, for he was afraid of that bottle.

On his way back to port-side he saw a shop where a man

sold shells and clubs from the wild islands, old heathen deities, old coined money, pictures from China and Japan, and all manner of things that sailors bring in their sea-chests. And here he had an idea. So he went in and offered the bottle for a hundred dollars. The man of the shop laughed at him at first, and offered him five; but, indeed, it was a curious bottle, such glass was never blown in any human glassworks, so prettily the colors shone under the milky white, and so strangely the shadow hovered in the midst; so, after he had disputed awhile after the manner of his kind, the shopman gave Keawe sixty silver dollars for the thing and set it on a shelf in the midst of his window.

"Now," said Keawe, "I have sold that for sixty which I bought for fifty — or, to say truth, a little less, because one of my dollars was from Chili. Now I shall know the truth upon another point."

So he went back on board his ship, and when he opened his chest, there was the bottle, and had come more quickly than himself. Now Keawe had a mate on board whose name was Lopaka.

"What ails you," said Lopaka, "that you stare in your chest?"

They were alone in the ship's forecastle, and Keawe bound him to secrecy, and told all.

"This is a very strange affair," said Lopaka; "and I fear you will be in trouble about this bottle. But there is one point very clear — that you are sure of the trouble, and you had better have the profit in the bargain. Make up your mind what you want with it; give the order, and if it is done as you desire, I will buy the bottle myself; for I have an idea of my own to get a schooner, and go trading through the islands."

"That is not my idea," said Keawe; "but to have a beautiful house and garden on the Kona Coast, where I was born, the sun shining in at the door, flowers in the garden, glass in the windows, pictures on the walls, and toys and fine carpets on the tables, for all the world like the house I was in this day — only a story higher, and with balconies all about like the

King's palace; and to live there without care and make merry with my friends and relatives."

"Well," said Lopaka, "let us carry it back with us to Hawaii, and if all comes true, as you suppose, I will buy the bottle, as I said, and ask a schooner."

Upon that they were agreed, and it was not long before the ship returned to Honolulu, carrying Keawe and Lopaka and the bottle. They were scarce come ashore when they met a friend upon the beach, who began at once to condole with Keawe.

"I do not know what I am to be condoled about," said Keawe.

"Is it possible you have not heard," said the friend, "your uncle — that good old man — is dead, and your cousin — that beautiful boy — was drowned at sea?"

Keawe was filled with sorrow, and, beginning to weep and to lament, he forgot about the bottle. But Lopaka was thinking to himself, and presently, when Keawe's grief was a little abated, "I have been thinking," said Lopaka, "had not your uncle lands in Hawaii, in the district of Kau?"

"No," said Keawe, "not in Kau: they are on the mountain-side — a little be south Hookena."

"These lands will now be yours?" asked Lopaka.

"And so they will," says Keawe, and began again to lament for his relatives.

"No," said Lopaka, "do not lament at present. I have a thought in my mind. How if this should be the doing of the bottle? For here is the place ready for your house."

"If this be so," cried Keawe, "it is a very ill way to serve me by killing my relatives. But it may be, indeed; for it was in just such a station that I saw the house with my mind's eye."

"The house, however, is not yet built," said Lopaka.

"No, nor like to be!" said Keawe; "for though my uncle has some coffee and ava and bananas, it will not be more than will keep me in comfort; and the rest of that land is the black lava."

"Let us go to the lawyer," said Lopaka; "I have still this idea in my mind."

Now when they came to the lawyer's, it appeared Keawe's uncle had grown monstrous rich in the last days, and there was a fund of money.

"And here is the money for the house!" cried Lopaka.

"If you are thinking of a new house," said the lawyer, "here is the card of a new architect, of whom they tell me great things."

"Better and better!" cried Lopaka. "Here is all made plain for us. Let us continue to obey orders."

So they went to the architect, and he had drawings of houses on his table.

"You want something out of the way," said the architect. "How do you like this?" and he handed a drawing to Keawe.

Now, when Keawe set eyes on the drawing, he cried aloud, for it was the picture of his thought exactly drawn.

"I am in for this house," thought he. "Little as I like the way it comes to me, I am in for it now, and I may as well take the good along with the evil."

So he told the architect all that he wished, and how he would have that house furnished, and about the pictures on the wall and the knick-knacks on the tables; and he asked the man plainly for how much he would undertake the whole affair.

The architect put many questions, and took his pen and made a computation; and when he had done he named the very sum that Keawe had inherited.

Lopaka and Keawe looked at one another and nodded.

"It is quite clear," thought Keawe, "that I am to have this house, whether or no. It comes from the devil and I fear I will get little good by that; and of one thing I am sure, I will make no more wishes as long as I have this bottle. But with the house I am saddled, and I may as well take the good along with the evil."

So he made his terms with the architect, and they signed a paper; and Keawe and Lopaka took ship again and sailed to

Australia; for it was concluded between them they should not interfere at all, but leave the architect and the bottle imp to build and to adorn that house at their own pleasure.

The voyage was a good voyage, only all the time Keawe was holding in his breath for he had sworn he would utter no more wishes, and take no more favors, from the devil. The time was up when they got back. The architect told them that the house was ready, and Keawe and Lopaka took a passage in the *Hall*, and went down Kona way to view the house, and see if all had been done fitly according to the thought that was in Keawe's mind.

Now, the house stood on the mountain-side, visible to ships. Above, the forest ran up into the clouds of rain; below, the black lava fell in cliffs, where the kings of old lay buried. A garden bloomed about that house with every hue of flowers; and there was an orchard of papaia on the one hand and an orchard of herdprint on the other, and right in front, toward the sea, a ship's mast had been rigged up and bore a flag. As for the house, it was three stories high, with great chambers and broad balconies on each. The windows were of glass, so excellent that it was as clear as water and as bright as day. All manner of furniture adorned the chambers. Pictures hung upon the wall in golden frames — pictures of ships, and men fighting, and of the most beautiful women, and of singular places; nowhere in the world are there pictures of so bright a color as those Keawe found hanging in his house. As for the knick-knacks they were extraordinarily fine: chiming clocks and musical boxes, little men with nodding heads, books filled with pictures, weapons of price from all quarters of the world, and the most elegant puzzles to entertain the leisure of a solitary man. And as no one would care to live in such chambers, only to walk through and view them, the balconies were made so broad that a whole town might have lived upon them in delight; and Keawe knew not which to prefer, whether the back porch, where you got the land-breeze, and looked upon the orchards and the flowers, or the front balcony, where you could drink the wind of the sea, and look down the steep wall of the mountain and see the *Hall* going by once a week or so between Hookena and the hills of Pele, or the schooners plying up the coast for wood and ava and bananas.

When they had viewed all, Keawe and Lopaka sat on the porch.

"Well," asked Lopaka, "is it all as you designed?"

"Words cannot utter it," said Keawe. "It is better than I dreamed, and I am sick with satisfaction."

"There is but one thing to consider," said Lopaka, "all this may be quite natural, and the bottle imp have nothing whatever to say to it. If I were to buy the bottle, and got no schooner after all, I should have put my hand in the fire for nothing. I gave you my word, I know; but yet I think you would not grudge me one more proof."

"I have sworn I would take no more favors," said Keawe. "I have gone already deep enough."

"This is no favor I am thinking of," replied Lopaka. "It is only to see the imp himself. There is nothing to be gained by that, and so nothing to be ashamed of, and yet, if I once saw him, I should be sure of the whole matter. So indulge me so far, and let me see the imp; and, after that, here is the money in my hand, and I will buy it."

"There is only one thing I am afraid of," said Keawe. "The imp may be very ugly to view, and if you once set eyes upon him you might be very undesirous of the bottle."

"I am a man of my word," said Lopaka. "And here is the money betwixt us."

"Very well," replied Keawe, "I have a curiosity myself. So come, let us have one look at you, Mr. Imp."

Now as soon as that was said, the imp looked out of the bottle, and in again, swift as a lizard; and there sat Keawe and Lopaka turned to stone. The night had quite come before either found a thought to say or voice to say it with; and then Lopaka pushed the money over and took the bottle.

"I am a man of my word," said he, "and had need to be so, or I would not touch this bottle with my foot. Well, I shall get my schooner and a dollar or two for my pocket; and then I will be rid of this devil as fast as I can. For to tell you the plain truth, the look of him has cast me down."

"Lopaka," said Keawe, "do not you think any worse of me than you can help; I know it is night, and the roads bad, and the pass by the tombs an ill place to go by so late, but I declare since I have seen that little face, I cannot eat or sleep or pray till it is gone from me. I will give you a lantern, and a basket to put the bottle in, and any picture or fine thing in all my house that takes your fancy; and be gone at once, and go sleep at Hookena with Nahinu."

"Keawe," said Lopaka, "many a man would take this ill; above all, when I am doing you a turn so friendly, as to keep my word and buy the bottle; and for that matter, the night and the dark, and the way by the tombs, must be all tenfold more dangerous to a man with such a sin upon his conscience, and such a bottle under his arm. But for my part, I am so extremely terrified myself, I have not the heart to blame you. Here I go, then; and I pray God you may be happy in your house and I fortunate with my schooner, and both get to heaven in the end in spite of the devil and his bottle."

So Lopaka went down the mountain; and Keawe stood in his front balcony, and listened to the clink of the horse's shoes, and watched the lantern go shining down the path, and along the cliff of caves where the old dead are buried; and all the time he trembled and clasped his hands, and prayed for his friend, and gave glory to God that he himself was escaped out of that trouble.

But the next day came very brightly, and that new house of his was so delightful to behold that he forgot his terrors. One day followed another, and Keawe dwelt there in perpetual joy. He had his place on the back porch; it was there he ate and lived, and read the stories in the Honolulu newspapers; but when anyone came by they would go in and view the chambers and the pictures. And the fame of the house went far and wide; it was called Ka-Hale-Nui — the Great House — in all Kona; and sometimes the Bright House, for

Keawe kept a Chinaman, who was all day dusting and furbishing; and the glass, and the gilt, and the fine stuffs, and
the pictures, shone as bright as morning. As for Keawe himself, he could not walk in the chambers without singing, his
heart was so enlarged; and when ships sailed by upon the
sea, he would fly his colors on the mast.

So time went by, until one day Keawe went upon a visit
as far as Kailua to certain of his friends. There he was well
feasted; and left as soon as he could the next morning, and
rode hard, for he was impatient to behold his beautiful house;
and, besides, the night then coming on was the night in which
the dead of old days go abroad in the sides of Kona; and
having already meddled with the devil, he was the more
chary of meeting with the dead. A little beyond Honaunau,
looking far ahead, he was aware of a woman bathing in the
edge of the sea; and she seemed a well-grown girl, but he
thought no more of it. Then he saw her white shift flutter as
she put it on, and then her red holoku; and by the time he
came abreast of her she was done with her toilet, and she had
come up from the sea, and stood by the trackside in her red
holoku, and she was all freshened with the bath, and her eyes
shone and were kind. Now Keawe no sooner beheld her than
he drew rein.

"I thought I knew every one in this country," said he.
"How comes it that I do not know you?"

"I am Kokua, daughter of Kiano," said the girl, "and I
have just returned from Oahu. Who are you?"

"I will tell you who I am in a little," said Keawe, dismount-
ing from his horse, "but not now. For I have a thought in
my mind, and if you knew who I was, you might have heard
of me, and would not give me a true answer. But tell me,
first of all, one thing: are you married?"

At this Kokua laughed out loud. "It is you who ask questions," she said. "Are you married yourself?"

"Indeed, Kokua, I am not," replied Keawe, "and never
thought to be until this hour. But here is the plain truth. I
have met you here at the roadside, and I saw your eyes, which

are like the stars, and my heart went to you as swift as a bird. And so now, if you want none of me, say so, and I will go on to my own place; but if you think me no worse than any other young man, say so, too, and I will turn aside to your father's for the night, and tomorrow I will talk with the good man."

Kokua said never a word, but she looked at the sea and laughed.

"Kokua," said Keawe, "if you say nothing, I will take that for the good answer; so let us be stepping to your father's door."

She went on ahead of him, still without speech; only sometimes she glanced back and glanced away again, and she kept the strings of her hat in her mouth.

Now, when they had come to the door, Kiano came out on his veranda, and cried out and welcomed Keawe by name. At that the girl looked over, for the fame of the great house had come to her ears; and, to be sure, it was a great temptation. All that evening they were very merry together; and the girl was as bold as brass under the eyes of her parents, and made a mark of Keawe, for she had a quick wit. The next day he had a word with Kiano, and found the girl alone.

"Kokua," said he, "you made a mark of me all the evening; and it is still time to bid me go. I would not tell you who I was, because I have so fine a house, and I feared you would think too much of that house and too little of the man that loves you. Now you know all, and if you wish to have seen the last of me, say so at once."

"No," said Kokua, but this time she did not laugh, nor did Keawe ask for more.

This was the wooing of Keawe; things had gone quickly; but so an arrow goes, and the ball of a rifle swifter still, and yet both may strike the target. Things had gone fast, but they had gone far also, and the thought of Keawe rang in the maiden's head; she heard his voice in the breach of the surf upon the lava, and for this young man that she had seen but twice she would have left father and mother and her native islands. As for Keawe himself, his horse flew up the path of the mountain under the cliff of tombs, and the sound of the hoofs, and the sound of Keawe singing to himself for pleasure, echoed in the caverns of the dead. He came to the Bright House, and he was still singing. He sat and ate in the broad balcony, and the Chinaman wondered at his master to hear how he sang between the mouthfuls. The sun went down into the sea, and the night came; and Keawe walked the balconies by lamplight, high on the mountains, and the voice of his singing startled men on ships.

"Here am I now upon my high place," he said to himself. "Life may be no better; this is the mountain-top; and all shelves about me toward the worse. For the first time I will light up the chambers, and bathe in my fine bath with the hot water and the cold, and sleep above in the bed of my bridal chamber."

So the Chinaman had word, and he must rise from sleep and light the furnaces; and as he walked below, beside the boilers, he heard his master singing and rejoicing above him in the lighted chambers. When the water began to be hot the Chinaman cried to his master; and Keawe went into the bathroom; and the Chinaman heard him sing as he filled the marble basin; and heard him sing, and the singing broken, as he undressed; until of a sudden, the song ceased. The Chinaman listened, and listened; he called up the house to Keawe to ask if all were well, and Keawe answered him "Yes," and bade him go to bed; but there was no more singing in the Bright House; and all night long the Chinaman heard his master's feet go round and round the balconies without repose.

Now, the truth of it was this: as Keawe undressed for his bath, he spied upon his flesh a patch like a patch of lichen on a rock, and it was then that he stopped singing. For he knew the likeness of that patch, and knew that he was fallen in the Chinese Evil.

Now, it is a sad thing for any man to fall into this sickness. And it would be a sad thing for anyone to leave a house so beautiful and so commodious, and depart from all his friends to the north coast of Molokai, between the mighty cliff and the sea-breakers. But what was that to the case of the man Keawe, he who had met his love but yesterday, and won her but that morning, and now saw all his hopes break, in a moment, like a piece of glass?

Awhile he sat upon the edge of the bath, then sprang, with a cry, and ran outside; and to and fro, to and fro, along the balcony, like one despairing.

"Very willingly could I leave Hawaii, the home of my fathers," Keawe was thinking. "Very lightly could I leave my house, the high-placed, the many-windowed, here upon the mountains. Very bravely could I go to Molokai, to Kalaupapa by the cliffs, to live with the smitten and to sleep there, far from my fathers. But what wrong have I done, what sin lies upon my soul, that I should have encountered Kokua coming cool from the sea-water in the evening? Kokua, the soul ensnarer! Kokua, the light of my life! Her may I never wed, her may I look upon no longer, her may I no more handle with my loving hand; and it is for this, it is for you, O Kokua! that I pour my lamentations!"

Now you are to observe what sort of a man Keawe was, for he might have dwelt there in the Bright House for years, and no one been the wiser of his sickness; but he reckoned nothing of that, if he must lose Kokua. And again he might have wed Kokua even as he was; and so many would have done, because they have the souls of pigs; but Keawe loved the maid manfully, and he would do her no hurt and bring her in no danger.

A little beyond the midst of the night, there came in his mind the recollection of that bottle. He went around to the back porch, and called to memory the day when the devil had looked forth; and at the thought ice ran in his veins.

"A dreadful thing is the bottle," thought Keawe, "and dreadful is the imp, and it is a dreadful thing to risk the flames of hell. But what other hope have I to cure my sickness or to wed Kokua? What!" he thought, "would I beard the devil once, only to get me a house, and not face him again to win Kokua?"

Thereupon he called to mind it was the next day the *Hall* went by on her return to Honolulu. "There must I go first," he thought, "and see Lopaka. For the best hope that I have now is to find that same bottle I was so pleased to be rid of."

Never a wink could he sleep; the food stuck in his throat; but he sent a letter to Kiano, and about the time when the steamer would be coming, rode down beside the cliff of the tombs. It rained; his horse went heavily; he looked up at the black mouths of the caves, and he envied the dead that slept there and were done with trouble; and called to mind how he had galloped by the day before, and was astonished. So he came down to Hookena, and there was all the country gathered for the steamer as usual. In the shed before the store they sat and jested and passed the news; but there was no matter of speech in Keawe's bosom, and he sat in their midst and looked without on the rain falling on the houses, and the surf beating among the rocks, and the sighs arose in his throat.

"Keawe of the Bright House is out of spirits," said one to another. Indeed, and so he was, and little wonder.

Then the *Hall* came, and the whale-boat carried him on board. The afterpart of the ship was full of Haoles — whites — who had been to visit the volcano, as their custom is; and the midst was crowded with Kanakas, and the fore-part with wild bulls from Hilo and horses from Kau: but Keawe sat apart from all in his sorrow, and watched for the house of Kiano. There it sat low upon the shore in the black rocks, and shaded by the cocoa-palms, and there by the door was a red holoku, no greater than a fly, and going to and fro, with a fly's busyness. "Ah, queen of my heart," he cried, "I'll venture my dear soul to win you!"

Soon after, darkness fell and the cabins were lit up, and the Haoles sat and played at the cards and drank whisky as their custom is; but Keawe walked the deck all night; and all the next day, as they steamed under the lee of Maui or of Molokai, he was still pacing to and fro like a wild animal in a menagerie.

Toward evening they passed Diamond Head, and came to the pier of Honolulu. Keawe stepped out among the crowd and began to ask for Lopaka. It seemed he had become the owner of a schooner — none better in the islands — and was gone upon an adventure as far as Pola-Pola or Kakhiki; so there was no help to be looked for from Lopaka. Keawe called to mind a friend of his, a lawyer in the town (I must not tell his name), and inquired of him. They said he was grown suddenly rich, and had a fine new house upon Waikiki shore; and this put a thought in Keawe's head, and he called a hack and drove to the lawyer's house.

The house was all brand new, and the trees in the garden no greater than walking-sticks, and the lawyer, when he came, had the air of a man well pleased.

"What can I do to serve you?" said the lawyer.

"You are a friend of Lopaka's," replied Keawe, "and Lopaka purchased from me a certain piece of goods that I thought you might enable me to trace."

The lawyer's face became very dark. "I do not profess to misunderstand you, Mr. Keawe," said he, "though this is an ugly business to be stirring in. You may be sure I know nothing, but yet I have a guess, and if you would apply in a certain quarter I think you might have news."

And he named the name of a man, which, again, I had better not repeat. So it was for days, and Keawe went from one to another, finding everywhere new clothes and carriages, and fine new houses and men everywhere in great contentment, although, to be sure, when he hinted at his business their faces would cloud over.

"No doubt I am upon the track," thought Keawe. "These new clothes and carriages are all the gifts of the little imp, and these glad faces are the faces of men who have taken their profit and got rid of the accursed thing in safety. When I see pale cheeks and hear sighing, I shall know that I am near the bottle."

So it befell at last that he was recommended to a Haole in Beritania Street. When he came to the door, about the hour of the evening meal, there were the usual marks of the new house, and the young garden, and the electric light shining in the windows; but when the owner came, a shock of hope and fear ran through Keawe; for here was a young man, white as a corpse, and black about the eyes, the hair shedding from his head, and such a look in his countenance as a man may have when he is waiting for the gallows.

"Here it is, to be sure," thought Keawe, and so with this man he noways veiled his errand. "I am come to buy the bottle," said he.

At the word, the young Haole of Beritania Street reeled against the wall.

"The bottle!" he gasped. "To buy the bottle!" Then he seemed to choke, and seizing Keawe by the arm, carried him into a room and poured out wine in two glasses.

"Here is my respects," said Keawe, who had been much about Haoles in his time. "Yes," he added, "I am come to buy the bottle. What is the price by now?"

At the word the young man let his glass slip through his fingers, and looked upon Keawe like a ghost.

"The price," says he, "the price! You do not know the price?"

"It is for that I am asking you," returned Keawe. "But why are you so much concerned? Is there anything wrong about the price?"

"It has dropped a great deal in value since your time, Mr. Keawe," said the young man, stammering.

"Well, well, I shall have the less to pay for it," says Keawe. "How much did it cost you?"

The young man was as white as a sheet. "Two cents," said he.

"What?" cried Keawe, "two cents? Why, then, you can only sell it for one. And he who buys it——" The words died upon Keawe's tongue; he who bought could never sell it again, the bottle and the bottle imp must abide with him until he died, and when he died must carry him to the red end of hell.

The young man of Beritania Street fell upon his knees "For God's sake, buy it!" he cried. "You can have all my fortune in the bargain. I was mad when I bought it at that price. I had embezzled money at my store; I was lost else; I must have gone to jail."

"Poor creature," said Keawe, "you would risk your soul upon so desperate an adventure, and to avoid the proper punishment of your own disgrace, and you think I could hesitate with love in front of me. Give me the bottle, and the change which I make sure you have all ready. Here is a five-cent piece."

It was as Keawe supposed; the young man had the change ready in a drawer; the bottle changed hands, and Keawe's fingers were no sooner clasped upon the stalk than he had breathed his wish to be a clean man. And, sure enough, when he got home to his room, and stripped himself before a glass, his flesh was as whole as an infant's. And here was the strange thing: he had no sooner seen this miracle than his mind was changed with him, and he cared naught for the Chinese Evil, and little enough for Kokua; and had but the one thought, that here he was bound to the bottle imp for time and for eternity, and had no better hope but to be a cinder forever in the flames of hell. Away ahead of him he saw them blaze with his mind's eye, and his soul shrank, and darkness fell upon the light.

When Keawe came to himself a little, he was aware it was the night when the band played at the hotel. Thither he went, because he feared to be alone; and there, among happy faces, walked to and fro, and heard the tunes go up and down, and saw Berger beat the measure, and all the while he heard the flames crackle, and saw the red fire burning in the bottomless pit. Of a sudden the band played Hiki-ao-ao; that was a song that he had sung with Kokua, and at the strain courage returned to him.

"It is done now," he thought, "and once more let me take the good along with the evil."

So it befell that he returned to Hawaii by the first steamer, and as soon as it could be managed he was wedded to Kokua, and carried her up the mountainside to the Bright House.

Now it was so with these two, that when they were together

Keawe's heart was stilled; but as soon as he was alone he fell into a brooding horror, and heard the flames crackle, and saw the red fire burn in the bottomless pit. The girl, indeed, had come to him wholly; her heart leaped in her side at sight of him, her hand clung to his; and she was so fashioned, from the hair upon her head to the nails upon her toes, that none could see her without joy. She was pleasant in her nature. She had the good word always. Full of song she was, and went to and fro in the Bright House, the brightest thing in its three stories, carolling like the birds. And Keawe beheld and heard her with delight, and then must shrink upon one side, and weep and groan to think upon the price that he had paid for her; and then he must dry his eyes, and wash his face, and go and sit with her on the broad balconies, joining in her songs, and, with a sick spirit, answering her smiles.

There came a day when her feet began to be heavy and her songs more rare; and now it was not Keawe only that would weep apart, but each would sunder from the other and sit in opposite balconies with the whole width of the Bright House betwixt. Keawe was so sunk in his despair, he scarce observed the change, and was only glad he had more hours to sit alone and brood upon his destiny, and was not so frequently condemned to pull a smiling face on a sick heart. But one day, coming softly through the house, he heard the sound of a child sobbing, and there was Kokua rolling her face upon the balcony floor and weeping like the lost.

"You do well to weep in this house, Kokua," he said. "And yet I would give the head off my body that you (at least) might have been happy."

"Happy!" she cried. "Keawe, when you lived alone in your Bright House you were the word of the island for a happy man; laughter and song were in your mouth, and your face was as bright as the sunrise. Then you wedded poor Kokua; and the good God knows what is amiss in her — but from that day you have not smiled. Oh!" she cried, "what ails me? I thought I was pretty, and I knew I loved him. What ails me, that I throw this cloud upon my husband?"

"Poor Kokua," said Keawe. He sat down by her side, and sought to take her hand; but that she plucked away. "Poor Kokua," he said, again. "My poor child — my pretty. And I had thought all this while to spare you! Well, you shall know all. Then, at least, you will pity poor Keawe; then you will understand how much he loved you in the past — that he dared hell for your possession — and how much he loves you still (the poor condemned one), that he can yet call up a smile when he beholds you."

With that, he told her all, even from the beginning.

"You have done this for me?" she cried. "Ah, well, then what do I care!" and she clasped and wept upon him.

"Ah, child!" said Keawe, "and yet, when I consider of the fire of hell, I care a good deal!"

"Never tell me," said she, "no man can be lost because he loved Kokua, and no other fault. I tell you, Keawe, I shall save you with these hands, or perish in your company. What! you loved me and gave your soul, and you think I will not die to save you in return?"

"Ah, my dear, you might die a hundred times, and what difference would that make?" he cried, "except to leave me lonely till the time comes of my damnation?"

"You know nothing," said she. "I was educated in a school in Honolulu; I am no common girl. And I tell you I shall save my lover. What is this you say about a cent? But all the world is not American. In England they have a piece they call a farthing, which is about half a cent. Ah! sorrow!" she cried, "that makes it scarcely better for the buyer must be lost, and we shall find none so brave as my Keawe! But then, there is France; they have a small coin there which they call a centime, and these go five to the cent or thereabouts. We could not do better. Come, Keawe, let us go to the French islands; let us go to Tahiti, as fast as ships can bear us. There we have four centimes, three centimes, two centimes, one centime; four possible sales to come and go on; and two of us to push the bargain. Come, my Keawe! kiss me, and banish care. Kokua will defend you."

"Gift of God!" he cried. "I cannot think that God will punish me for desiring aught so good! Be it as you will, then, take me where you please; I put my life and my salvation in your hands."

Early the next day Kokua was about her preparations. She took Keawe's chest that he went with sailoring; and first she put the bottle in a corner, and then packed it with the richest of their clothes and the bravest of the knick-knacks in the house. "For," said she, "we must seem to be rich folks, or who will believe in the bottle!" All the time of her preparation she was as gay as a bird; only when she looked upon Keawe the tears would spring in her eye, and she must run and kiss him. As for Keawe, a weight was off his soul; now that he had his secret shared, and some hope in front of him, he seemed like a new man, his feet went lightly on the earth, and his breath was good to him again. Yet was terror still at his elbow; and ever and again, as the wind blows out a taper, hope died in him, and he saw the flames toss and the red fire burn in hell.

It was given out in the country they were gone pleasuring to the States, which was thought a strange thing, and yet not so strange as the truth, if any could have guessed it. So they went to Honolulu in the *Hall*, and thence in the *Umatilla* to San Francisco with a crowd of Haoles, and at San Francisco took their passage by the mail brigantine, the *Tropic Bird*, for Papeete, the chief place of the French in the south islands. Thither they came, after a pleasant voyage, on a fair day of the Trade wind, and saw the reef with the surf breaking and Motuiti with its palms, and the schooner riding withinside, and the white houses of the town low down along the shore among green trees, and overhead the mountains and the clouds of Tahiti, the wise island.

It was judged the most wise to hire a house, which they did accordingly, opposite the British Consul's, to make a great parade of money, and themselves conspicuous with carriage and horses. This it was very easy to do, so long as they had the bottle in their possession; for Kokua was more bold than Keawe, and, whenever she had a mind, called on the imp fo

twenty or a hundred dollars. At this rate they soon grew to
be remarked in the town; and the strangers from Hawaii,
their riding and their driving, the fine holokus, and the rich
lace of Kokua, became the matter of much talk.

They got on well after the first with the Tahitian language,
which is indeed like to the Hawaiian, with a change of certain
letters; and as soon as they had any freedom of speech, began
to push the bottle. You are to consider it was not an easy subject to introduce; it was not easy to persuade people you are
in earnest, when you offer to sell them for four centimes the
spring of health and riches inexhaustible. It was necessary
besides to explain the dangers of the bottle; and either people
disbelieved the whole thing and laughed, or they thought the
more of the darker part, became overcast with gravity, and
drew away from Keawe and Kokua, as from persons who had
dealings with the devil. So far from gaining ground, these two
began to find they were avoided in the town; the children ran
away from them screaming, a thing intolerable to Kokua;
Catholics crossed themselves as they went by; and all persons
began with one accord to disengage themselves from their
advances.

Depression fell upon their spirits. They would sit at night
in their house, after a day's weariness, and not exchange a
word, or the silence would be broken by Kokua bursting suddenly into sobs. Sometimes they would pray together; sometimes they would have the bottle out upon the floor, and sit
all evening watching how the shadow hovered in the midst.
At such times they would be afraid to go to rest. It was long
ere slumber came to them, and, if either dozed off, it would
be to wake and find the other silently weeping in the dark,
or perhaps to wake alone, the other having fled from the
house and the neighborhood of that bottle, to pace under
the bananas in the little garden, or to wander on the beach
by moonlight.

One night it was so when Kokua awoke. Keawe was gone.
She felt in the bed and his place was cold. Then fear fell upon
her, and she sat up in bed. A little moonshine filtered through

the shutters. The room was bright, and she could spy the bottle on the floor. Outside it blew high, the great trees of the avenue cried aloud, and the fallen leaves rattled in the veranda. In the midst of this Kokua was aware of another sound; whether of a beast or of a man she could scarce tell, but it was as sad as death, and cut her to the soul. Softly she arose, set the door ajar, and looked forth into the moonlit yard. There, under the bananas, lay Keawe, his mouth in the dust, and as he lay he moaned.

It was Kokua's first thought to run forward and console him; her second potently withheld her. Keawe had borne himself before his wife like a brave man; it became her little in the hour of weakness to intrude upon his shame. With the thought she drew back into the house.

"Heaven," she thought, "how careless have I been — how weak! It is he, not I, that stands in this eternal peril; it was he, not I, that took the curse upon his soul. It is for my sake, and for the love of a creature of so little worth and such poor help, that he now beholds so close to him the flames of hell — ay, and smells the smoke of it, lying without there in the wind and moonlight. Am I so dull of spirit that never till now I have surmised my duty, or have I seen it before and turned aside? But now, at least, I take up my soul in both the hands of my affection; now I say farewell to the white steps of heaven and the waiting faces of my friends. A love for a love, and let mine be equalled with Keawe's! A soul for a soul, and be it mine to perish!"

She was a deft woman with her hands, and was soon apparelled. She took in her hands the change — the precious centimes they kept ever at their side; for this coin is little used, and they had made provision at a government office. When she was forth in the avenue clouds came on the wind, and the moon was blackened. The town slept, and she knew not whither to turn till she heard one coughing in the shadow of the trees.

"Old man," said Kokua, "what do you here abroad in the cold night?"

The old man could scarce express himself for coughing, but she made out that he was old and poor, and a stranger in the island.

"Will you do me a service?" said Kokua. "As one stranger to another, and as an old man to a young woman, will you help a daughter of Hawaii?"

"Ah," said the old man. "So you are the witch from the Eight Islands, and even my old soul you seek to entangle. But I have heard of you, and defy your wickedness."

"Sit down here," said Kokua, "and let me tell you a tale." And she told him the story of Keawe from the beginning to the end.

"And now," said she, "I am his wife, whom he bought with his soul's welfare. And what should I do? If I went to him myself and offered to buy it, he will refuse. But if you go, he will sell it eagerly; I will await you here; you will buy it for four centimes, and I will buy it again for three. And the Lord strengthen a poor girl!"

"If you meant falsely," said the old man. "I think God would strike you dead."

"He would!" cried Kokua. "Be sure he would. I could not be so treacherous, God would not suffer it."

"Give me four centimes and await me here," said the old man.

Now, when Kokua stood alone in the street, her spirit died. The wind roared in the trees, and it seemed to her the rushing of the flames of hell; the shadows towered in the light of the street lamp, and they seemed to her the snatching hands of evil ones. If she had had the strength, she must have run away, and if she had had the breath, she must have screamed aloud; but, in truth, she could do neither, and stood and trembled in the avenue, like an affrighted child.

Then she saw the old man returning, and he had the bottle in his hand.

"I have done your bidding," said he, "I left your husband weeping like a child; tonight he will sleep easy." And he held the bottle forth.

"Before you give it to me," Kokua panted, "take the good with the evil — ask to be delivered from your cough."

"I am an old man," replied the other, "and too near the gate of the grave to take a favor from the devil. But what is this? Why do you not take the bottle? Do you hesitate?"

"Not hesitate!" cried Kokua. "I am only weak. Give me a moment. It is my hand resists, my flesh shrinks back from the accursed thing. One moment only!"

The old man looked upon Kokua kindly. "Poor child!" said he, "you fear: your soul misgives you. Well, let me keep it. I am old, and can never more be happy in this world, and as for the next ——"

"Give it to me!" gasped Kokua. "There is your money. Do you think I am so base as that? Give me the bottle."

"God bless you, child," said the old man.

Kokua concealed the bottle under her holoku, said farewell to the old man, and walked off along the avenue, she cared not whither. For all roads were now all the same to her, and led equally to hell. Sometimes she walked, and sometimes ran; sometimes she screamed out loud in the night, and sometimes lay by the wayside in the dust and wept. All that she had heard of hell came back to her; she saw the flames blaze, and she smelled the smoke, and her flesh withered on the coals.

Near day she came to her mind again, and returned to the house. It was even as the old man said — Keawe slumbered like a child. Kokua stood and gazed upon his face.

"Now, my husband," said she, "it is your turn to sleep. When you wake it will be your turn to sing and laugh. But for poor Kokua, alas! that meant no evil — for poor Kokua no more sleep, no more singing, no more delight, whether in earth or Heaven."

With that she lay down in the bed by his side, and her misery was so extreme that she fell into a deep slumber instantly.

Late in the morning her husband woke her and gave her the good news. It seemed he was silly with delight, for he paid no heed to her distress, ill though she dissembled it.

The words stuck in her mouth, it mattered not; Keawe did the speaking. She ate not a bite, but who was to observe it? For Keawe cleared the dish. Kokua saw and heard him, like some strange thing in a dream; there were times when she forgot or doubted, and put her hands to her brow; to know herself doomed and hear her husband babble seemed so monstrous.

All the while Keawe was eating and talking, and planning the time of their return, and thanking her for saving him, and fondling her, and calling her the true helper after all. He laughed at the old man that was fool enough to buy that bottle.

"A worthy old man he seemed," Keawe said. "But no one can judge by appearances. For why did the old reprobate require the bottle?"

"My husband," said Kokua, humbly, "his purpose may have been good."

Keawe laughed like an angry man.

"Fiddle-de-dee!" cried Keawe. "An old rogue, I tell you; and an old ass to boot. For the bottle was hard enough to sell at four centimes; and at three it will be quite impossible. The margin is not broad enough, the thing begins to smell of scorching — brrr!" said he, and shuddered. "It is true I bought it myself at a cent, when I knew not there were smaller coins. I was a fool for my pains; there will never be found another, and whoever has that bottle now will carry it to the pit."

"Oh, my husband!" said Kokua. "Is it not a terrible thing to save oneself by the eternal ruin of another? It seems to me I could not laugh. I would be humbled. I would be filled with melancholy. I would pray for the poor holder."

Then Keawe, because he felt the truth of what she said, grew the more angry. "Hoity-toity!" cried he. "You may be filled with melancholy if you please. It is not the mind of a good wife. If you thought at all of me, you would sit shamed."

Thereupon he went out, and Kokua was alone.

What chance had she to sell that bottle at two centimes?

None, she perceived. And if she had any, here was her husband hurrying her away to a country where there was nothing lower than a cent. And here — on the morrow of her sacrifice — was her husband leaving her and blaming her.

She would not even try to profit by what time she had, but sat in the house, and now had the bottle out and viewed it with unutterable fear, and now, with loathing, hid it out of sight.

By and by, Keawe came back, and would have her take a drive.

"My husband, I am ill," she said. "I am out of heart. Excuse me, I can take no pleasure."

Then was Keawe more wroth than ever. With her, because he thought she was brooding over the case of the old man; and with himself, because he thought she was right, and was ashamed to be so happy.

"This is your truth," cried he, "and this your affection! Your husband is just saved from eternal ruin, which he encountered for the love of you — and you can take no pleasure! Kokua, you have a disloyal heart."

He went forth again furious, and wandered in the town all day. He met friends, and drank with them; they hired a carriage and drove into the country, and there drank again. All the time Keawe was ill at ease, because he was taking this pastime while his wife was sad, and because he knew in his heart that she was more right than he; and the knowledge made him drink the deeper.

Now, there was an old brutal Haole drinking with him, one that had been a boatswain of a whaler — a runaway, a digger in gold mines, a convict in prisons. He had a low mind and a foul mouth; he loved to drink and to see others drunken; and he pressed the glass upon Keawe. Soon there was no more money in the company.

"Here, you!" said the boatswain, "you are rich, you have been always saying. You have a bottle or some foolishness."

"Yes," said Keawe, "I am rich; I will go back and get some money from my wife, who keeps it."

"That's a bad idea, mate," said the boatswain. "Never

you trust a petticoat with dollars. They're all as false as water; you keep an eye on her."

Now, this word struck in Keawe's mind; for he was muddled with what he had been drinking.

"I should not wonder but she was false, indeed," thought he. "Why else should she be so cast down at my release? But I will show her I am not the man to be fooled. I will catch her in the act."

Accordingly, when they were back in town, Keawe bade the boatswain wait for him at the corner, by the old calaboose, and went forward up the avenue alone to the door of his house. The night had come again; there was a light within, but never a sound; and Keawe crept about the corner, opened the back door softly, and looked in.

There was Kokua on the floor, the lamp at her side; before her was a milk-white bottle, with a round belly and a long neck; and as she viewed it, Kokua wrung her hands.

A long time Keawe stood and looked in the doorway. At first he was struck stupid; and then fear fell upon him that the bargain had been made amiss, and the bottle had come back to him as it came at San Francisco; and at that his knees were loosened, and the fumes of the wine departed from his head like mists off a river in the morning. And then he had another thought; and it was a strange one, that made his cheeks to burn.

"I must make sure of this," thought he.

So he closed the door, and went softly round the corner again, and then came noisily in, as though he were but now returned. And, lo! by the time he opened the front door no bottle was to be seen; and Kokua sat in a chair and started up like one awakened out of sleep.

"I have been drinking all day and making merry," said Keawe. "I have been with good companions, and now I only come back for money, and return to drink and carouse with them again."

Both his face and voice were as stern as judgment, but Kokua was too troubled to observe.

"You do well to use your own, my husband," said she, and her words trembled.

"Oh, I do well in all things," said Keawe, and he went straight to the chest and took out money. But he looked besides in the corner where they kept the bottle, and there was no bottle there.

At that the chest heaved upon the floor like a sea-billow, and the house span about him like a wreath of smoke, for he saw she was lost now, and there was no escape. "It is what I feared," he thought. "It is she who has bought it."

And then he came to himself a little and rose up; but the sweat streamed on his face as thick as the rain and as cold as the well-water.

"Kokua," said he, "I said to you today what ill became me. Now I return to house with my jolly companions," and at that he laughed a little quietly. "I will take more pleasure in the cup if you forgive me."

She clasped his knees in a moment; she kissed his knees with flowing tears.

"Oh," she cried, "I ask but a kind word!"

"Let us never one think hardly of the other," said Keawe, and was gone out of the house.

Now, the money that Keawe had taken was only some of that store of centime pieces they had laid in at their arrival. It was very sure he had no mind to be drinking. His wife had given her soul for him, now he must give his for hers; no other thought was in the world with him.

At the corner, by the old calaboose, there was the boatswain waiting.

"My wife has the bottle," said Keawe, "and unless you help me to recover it, there can be no more money and no more liquor tonight."

"You do not mean to say you are serious about that bottle?" cried the boatswain.

"There is the lamp," said Keawe. "Do I look as if I was jesting?"

"That is so," said the boatswain. "You look as serious as a ghost."

"Well, then," said Keawe, "here are two centimes; you must go to my wife in the house, and offer her these for the bottle, which (if I am not much mistaken) she will give to you instantly. Bring it to me here, and I will buy it back from you for one; for that is the law with this bottle, that it still must be sold for a less sum. But whatever you do, never breathe a word to her that you have come from me."

"Mate, I wonder are you making a fool of me?" asked the boatswain.

"It will do you no harm if I am," returned Keawe.

"That is so, mate," said the boatswain.

"And if you doubt me," added Keawe, "you can try. As soon as you are clear of the house, wish to have your pocket full of money, or a bottle of the best rum, or what you please, and you will see the virtue of the thing."

"Very well, Kanaka," says the boatswain. "I will try; but if you are having your fun out of me I will take my fun out of you with a belaying-pin."

So the whaler-man went off up the avenue; and Keawe stood and waited. It was near the same spot where Kokua had waited the night before; but Keawe was more resolved, and never faltered in his purpose; only his soul was bitter with despair.

It seemed a long time he had to wait before he heard a voice singing in the darkness of the avenue. He knew the voice to be the boatswain's; but it was strange how drunken it appeared upon a sudden.

Next the man himself came stumbling into the light of the lamp. He had the devil's bottle buttoned in his coat; another bottle was in his hand; and even as he came in view he raised it to his mouth and drank.

"You have it," said Keawe. "I see that."

"Hands off!" cried the boatswain, jumping back. "Take a step near me, and I'll smash your mouth. You thought you could make a cat's paw of me, did you?"

"What do you mean?" cried Keawe.

"Mean?" cried the boatswain. "This is a pretty good

bottle, this is; that's what I mean. How I got it for two centimes I can't make out; but I am sure you sha'n't have it for one."

"You mean you won't sell?" gasped Keawe.

"No, sir," cried the boatswain. "But I'll give you a drink of the rum, if you like."

"I tell you," said Keawe, "the man who has that bottle goes to hell."

"I reckon I'm going anyway," returned the sailor, "and this bottle's the best thing to go with I've struck yet. No, sir!" he cried again, "this is my bottle now, and you can go and fish for another."

"Can this be true?" Keawe cried. "For your own sake, I beseech you, sell it me!"

"I don't value any of your talk," replied the boatswain. "You thought I was a flat, now you see I'm not; and there's an end. If you won't have a swallow of the rum, I'll have one myself. Here's your health, and good-night to you!"

So off he went down the avenue toward town, and there goes the bottle out of the story.

But Keawe ran to Kokua light as the wind; and great was their joy that night; and great, since then, has been the peace of all their days in the Bright House.

QUESTIONS

1. What is the problem that holds the reader throughout the story?
2. What were the conditions governing the sale of the bottle? How did Keawe fail to keep the conditions after he sold the bottle to Lopaka?
3. By what devices does the author arouse in the reader's mind a feeling of horror toward the bottle and the bottle imp?
4. What is the true climax of the story?
5. Why is the sailor who last possesses the bottle presented as a man with no good qualities?
6. Stevenson was a great stylist. Find examples of especially good style in this story.
7. *Word Study.* — What do the following words mean as they are used in the story: *computation, condole, furbishing, lichen?*

Problem: ROMANCE
(See page 28.)

1. Is this story probable, improbable, or impossible? What kind of stories that children read does it remind you of?

2. What is romance? Is there anything realistic about this story? Did Stevenson try to make it like a story from real life?

3. We know that Keawe and Kokua were young and brave and that they loved each other. Do we need to know anything more about them for the purpose of this story?

4. Could this story be told in another setting? Does its present setting add anything to the story? Does the setting make the story seem real to you? Does it help the reader to accept the story? Explain your answers.

The Poison Ship *

Morgan Robertson (1861–1915)

Most readers are attracted by the mystery of the sea; they enjoy a good story with a sea setting. Morgan Robertson, author of a number of volumes of excellent sea stories, was born in Oswego, New York, on September 29, 1861. His father, a captain on one of the Great Lakes steamers, did not wish his son to follow in his footsteps; but young Robertson, barely sixteen, ran away from home and shipped before the mast. The only formal education that he obtained was received in the public schools of Oswego, and later in Cooper Institute in New York. For ten years Robertson followed the sea, making two trips around the world and filling nearly every possible position on shipboard. After leaving the sea, he learned the trade of watch-making and diamond-setting, but eight years later his sight failed and he was forced to give up the work. Looking about him for some other means of livelihood, he began to write short stories. It is said that he was first inspired to write by reading one of the sea stories of Kipling. Though he was not very successful at first he eventually gained recognition, and before his death, which occurred in a hotel in Atlantic City on March 4, 1915, he had published a number of volumes, among them "Where Angels Fear to Tread" (1899), "Masters of Men" (1901), "Shipmates" (1901), "Down to the Sea" (1905), and "Sinful Peck" (1905). A complete edition of his works was published in 1916, the year after his death.

Robertson wrote about the sea and the men who sailed the sea. He wrote dramatic, vivid tales, some of which have since made successful motion pictures. Taking nearly all of his plots from personal experiences, Robertson wrote of the life on the sailing ships before the day of palatial liners and steam freighters — of a period of marine history that is now past.

"The Poison Ship" is one of the last stories that Robertson wrote. It may be classed as a sea story although some critics

* Reprinted by permission of Alice M. Robertson, for the estate of Morgan Robertson.

maintain that there is really no such type and suggest that sea stories are either stories of plot, stories of character, or stories of setting. "The Poison Ship" is told in an original way, being revealed to the reader bit by bit. While the story has not a real surprise ending, most readers do not guess the outcome until the end. The chief interest is centered in the plot, but the setting is well done, there is a fair amount of local color, and the character of the American mate makes a firm impression upon the reader's memory. It is suggested that the student read other stories by the same author and compare them with "The Poison Ship."

OVER twenty years ago, broken in health, nerve, and spirit after a four years' fight to attain and retain a foothold on shore, I fell back upon "sailors' rights," and, backed up by my discharges and certificates, entered the Marine Hospital at Stapleton as a patient. Here I was pulled through in time, but against the back-pull, or down-drag, of a patient in the adjoining cot. Part of my trouble was insomnia; his was insanity, with occasional lucid remissions which gave me short intervals of sleep. But usually, night and day, he kept me awake with his ravings and mutterings, which, though of nautical character, were not understandable, for they were intermingled with terms, expressions, and phrasings having nothing to do with pure seamanship. He shouted vociferously about carbonic-acid gas and live steam as non-supporters of combustion. He voiced his belief that sleeping aloft in hammocks was wise and advisable. He begged, pleaded, and prayed to someone to paint the deck, and, if the paint gave out, to tar it — an unseamanly procedure. Insane himself, he called others insane, and would insanely order them to "wake up." I, for one, always obeyed this order, and it was in vain that I petitioned doctors and nurses for removal from his neighborhood. Despite the fact that the vast chain of Marine Hospitals in the country and the fund which supports them come from sailors' money, sailors who enter them are treated as charity patients. This man was surely a sailor. He was powerfully built, though emaciated, was suntanned to the color of a Moor, and when the maniacal glare left his deep-sunken eyes his face showed a degree of intelligence that marked him as a skipper or mate. He had been picked up in an open boat in the Strait of Magellan, taken to Montevideo, and then, still out of his mind, sent to New York by the American consul.

It ended at last when he had recovered the mental poise that usually precedes death, and when I was so exhausted and distracted that his words practically went into one ear and out the other. He died next day, and even before he died, the story he told, terrible though it was, had gone from my mind. But the wonderful subconscious memory that records every face, fact, and happening from the cradle to the grave held that story against the time — a few months ago — when, helped by another wonderful subconscious faculty, the association of ideas, I could dig it out of my soul and write it down.

The associated idea in this case was a picture — a full-page picture in a magazine, illustrating a story of the sea. The story was well told, and when I had finished reading I naturally examined the illustration. It was equally well done, but did not seem to belong to that story. The author had described the wrecking on a rock-bound lee shore of a square-rigged ship under lower topsails, main spenser, fore-topmast-staysail, and reefed spanker, with green seas breaking over her; but the picture, properly captioned from this part of the text, was of a *bark* under *all sail*, with little wind or sea to bother her, apparently drifting close to the rock-bound shore described. This shore was all that linked the picture with the story, and, marveling at the perversity of artists in refusing to read the stories they illustrate, I put the matter from my mind — or, rather, tried to.

For the picture persisted; it intruded itself at all times and places until finally I convinced myself that at some time I must have seen that bark and rocky coast, but was unable to recall just when and where. Yet this did not banish the obsession; it got into my dreams after a few restless nights.

Then, one morning, I wakened with the memory of that hospital experience and the story poured into my distressed ears by the dying man. Only a part of the story came back to me, but it was enough to explain the grip that picture had taken on me. I had not seen the bark; he had described her as she looked from the boat in which he had left her to drift until picked up, half-starved and deranged.

That day I did what I might have done before had I the slightest plausible excuse: I found the artist's address and called upon him at his studio. His name was Marlowe; he was a pleasant-faced young fellow of about twenty-five, but neither in years nor appearance did he give any indication of the sea-faring tutelage which had produced the admirable — though incongruous — technique of that picture. He was slight but symmetrically built, with sensitive mouth and expressive eyes, and with hands that showed no indications of any harder work than sharpening a lead-pencil. He received me cordially, and as I was not there to criticize, but merely to refresh my memory, I asked him bluntly if he had ever seen that bark and the rocky shore. The expression on his face startled me.

"Have *you* seen her?" he asked, excitedly.

"Not to my recollection," I answered, "but I think I heard of her, years ago, from a dying sailor. It came to me this morning; but all I can remember is the way she looked when he quit her. I thought you might know, inasmuch as you did not really illustrate the story, but seemed to have pictured something firmly fixed in your mind."

"It *is* fixed," he answered, mournfully, as he picked up the brushes he had put down on my entrance, "or, rather, has been: for since I got it off my chest I do not think of it so much. It is the first thing I can remember of my life. I was a baby, in a boat full of men, and we were leaving that bark. I cannot remember anything else for a few years of my childhood until I knew I was in an orphan-asylum. I do not know that my name is Marlowe, but that is the name I was called, and I remember being called Bennie; so I wear the name

Benjamin Marlowe, and when I took to art I studied marines, with that bark always in the back of my head. Who was that sailor?"

"I don't know. He might have been in that boat with you, but I have a dim recollection that he was picked up alone. If he told me his name, or the name of the bark, I have forgotten. It is twenty-three years ago."

"About the right time," he said. "I must have been about two years old, when consciousness — or, rather, memory — begins, and I must be about twenty-five now. If you remember any more of what he told you, please let me hear it. I want to find out who I am. But don't roast me about that misfit picture!"

I promised, and departed, not much easier in mind as far as mere curiosity was concerned. Only this much more had come to me: somewhere in the world, about twenty-three years before, there had been a debarkation from a craft in good condition, in fine weather, and on a smooth sea — possibly in the land-locked Magellan Strait. I went that day to the Maritime Exchange and the Hydrographic Office, but obtained no information. Government clerks are indifferent, impatient, and sometimes peevish.

The mental state continued; I could not disabuse my mind of that bark, the smooth sea beneath, the fair sky above, and the threatening rocks beyond. Intermingled, too, were transient memories of the distracting experience in the hospital, where I had listened to the ravings of the dying man and finally to a story which had escaped me. But the story came, in time — not as a whole, but in fragments. Each morning as I lay in the borderland between sleep and waking there would come to me something new — new, but old, something remembered out of the long-forgotten past. And finally it was complete save for two things: either I could not recall, or he had not told me, his own name and that of the bark. I waited for a week, searching my mind, then gave it up and called upon Marlowe. He received me in a condition of repressed excitement, but listened quietly while I reeled off the yarn which had come back to me from the realm of delirium and dreams.

It began with my fellow-patient asking me, after an hour of quiet, what hospital he was in, and when I had told him he lay for another hour, then muttered:

"Six thousand miles from that hell-hole! I must have been a long time out of my head. What month and year is it, mate?"

"April, 1890," I answered, weariedly; for I wanted to sleep.

"Two months, at least," he said. "I just remember a steamer coming toward me, but I don't know how long I was adrift."

I did not answer, but he evidently wanted to talk, and did so. I do not pretend to give his story with all his pauses and repetitions; but in substance, as I gave it to young Marlowe, it ran as follows:

I shipped second mate of her at a small port in New Zealand, where she had put in for fresh water and stores for the run home. Somewhere, out among the islands, she had filled up with a cargo of jute — she didn't get it in New Zealand, for it doesn't grow there — and this cargo was battened tight under hatches to keep the water away from it. But she was an iron ship, with a rotten wooden deck, and I always had a theory that with a cargo of jute or cotton, liable to spontaneous combustion, hatches should be open in fine weather to let air down, particularly in iron ships, which sweat. But I was only second mate, and, being an American among Englishmen, not supposed to know anything. So my advice was not taken. It made no difference at first, for we had fine weather, and it was Southern summer down there; but we sailed the Great Circle course to Cape Horn, and that took us down to nearly sixty south, where it was cold and stormy. The result was that, with decks wet all the time, water oozed through the leaky seams, and the chilled iron hull condensed the harmless watery vapor in the hold into solid, trickling water. Then we sailed up on the last leg into warmer weather, but the mischief was done. We smelled smoke one day, and after a thorough search realized that the jute was on fire, not blazing, you know, but smoldering.

Now, the customary thing to do with fire is to douse it with water, and, excepting in the presence of some chemicals, like potassium and calcium sulphide, it works first-rate — provided you know where the fire is. But we couldn't know. One part of the deck was as rotten and spongy as another, and she was iron, fore and aft. So all we could do was to keep battened down, keep all hands on deck and all windows and skylights closed, and trust that the fire would smother from lack of air. About this time we spoke a ship, but were not scared enough yet to ask for help, so we let her go on.

In spite of the fact that we carried a big crew — thirty-three all told — this lime-juice bark was equipped with one of these new-fangled donkey-engines — just a boiler in the after part of the forward house and a steam-winch outside. Well, that boiler could make steam, and I knew from my studies in physics — went through high-school before going to sea — that steam would replace air and, by depriving the fire of oxygen, kill it in no time. I suggested this to the skipper. I wanted him to set the donkey-man and the carpenter at work — to turn the main steam-pipe into a hole in the deck forward, open an aperture aft, and, by firing up the boiler, flood that smoldering jute with steam, driving out the air through the aperture in the stern. But he wouldn't have it. He argued that steam was nothing but water, after all, forgetting, or not knowing, that steam condensed to water has but the smallest fraction of its former volume, and the harm would be less than the benefit. I argued and swore, but it did no good. I was only an ignorant Yankee second mate, and he was skipper; so he had his way. He was a big, fine-looking Englishman, and was entitled to some brains, but God Almighty had limited him.

The first mate was an educated pig from Cardiff, and the less I say about him the better. The third mate was a passed apprentice, a gentleman's son in the way of a second mate's berth, and a fine young fellow. We had a big crew: there were four apprentices serving their time, a steward, cook, and cabin-boy, a carpenter, sailmaker, two bo'suns, a donkey-

man, and a butcher — for we carried about a dozen passengers, all men, except one small baby — and then we had
sixteen in the forecastle — thirty-three of a crew. Now, you
might think that in that crowd I'd have found a few with
sense enough to listen to me; but no — not one, not even the
third mate. They were all English or Scotch, insular as hell,
and the baby, a small toddler, while a good friend of mine,
was too young to know anything or have much influence. He
was an orphan, consigned to relatives in England, and his
name was Bennie. We had good times in my watch below.
As second mate I could have done something for that ship,
even with the passengers, who had paid their way, against
me: but I was blocked by the ignorance and stupidity of the
skipper and mate. Even with all hatches, windows, skylights,
and doors closed, we could not seal up the hold, and when I
suggested painting or tarring the deck I was laughed at.

Soon, and before it was warm enough to stand watch without an overcoat, we could see little spirals of smoke rising
from the seams in the deck, and it was evident that the fire
was spreading. Then the deck grew hot, and, provided we
kept out of the draught from over the rail, we did not want
our coats. We were over a furnace, and no one complained at
sleeping on deck. But this brought to the case a new danger.
It was hard to waken a man from sleep, and many a time I
had to go the rounds and rouse up the watch below at eight
bells with a belaying-pin, for nothing but a tap on the head
would stir them. I understood why it was: burning jute gives
off the soporific fumes of hashish, which is made from India
hemp, and which produces drowsiness, then wild dreams and
a waking ecstasy.

I am, or was, a pretty husky man, and didn't feel this as
quickly as some of the weaker men of the crowd. The passengers slept and wakened as they pleased; but I soon noticed
that they acted foolish — that they talked to themselves a
good deal, and that when they talked with me it was about
trees and flowers and fine spring weather. Think of it! — trees
and flowers and spring weather down in that wet, watery

wilderness near the Horn. The one to show it first, and hardest, was little Bennie. I found one day that, though I could get his eyes open, I couldn't get him to talk or move; so I rigged a kind of hammock for him out of a sailor's clothes-bag, and dressed him warmly, and whipped him aloft at the end of a cro'jack buntline. Up there he escaped the fumes somewhat, and whenever he'd yell I'd go aloft and comfort him. So I think I saved his life — that is, if the boat that took him away at the end was picked up. But it's doubtful; they were all crazy or stupefied, and, as all of them were passengers, not one could pull an oar, while the fellow that had charge of Bennie, a dull-witted uncle from Falmouth, was one of the first to go under. However, he managed to give me Bennie's last name. It was Derringer, and there was big money coming to him in England.

It was when Bennie's guardian, after a crazy day about the deck, was found dead in the scuppers that the captain realized the wisdom of rigging canvas hammocks aloft to sleep in; and we sprinkled the rigging with them as fast as we could make them. But they mainly benefited the passengers, as the crew had to be on deck half the time at least. So the next dead man was a sailor, who was too sleepy at the end of his watch to climb aloft. Then followed another, and another, and we buried them, sea-fashion, as fast as they died. The next to go were the steward, cook, and cabin-boy, whose duties required that they enter the closed cabin and galley.

We carried a 'midship bridge extending fore and aft from the poop-deck to the forecastle, and on this raised platform the skipper and mates had some immunity from the fumes; but even up there we felt the effects. I remember being wakened, flat on my back on the bridge, by the captain's boot, after a long dream about the country, with its green and yellow and red flowers and foliage; there were beautiful girls in that dream, and singing children, and it seemed like my idea of heaven. But it was only the hashish coming out of that smoldering jute, and it was a cold awakening. I protected Bennie from it; no matter how he yelled, I kept him aloft, only lowering him down to feed him and change his clothes.

All this time we were driving up the Horn before fresh, fair winds and half-gales that occasionally demanded the taking in of royals. I saw to it that the men took turns going aloft to furl, for this gave them their only breathing-spells; yet they weakened, one by one. I spent as much time as I could aloft with Bennie, but the skipper, first mate, and third mate had no such incentive; they remained on the bridge, as became their dignity, so all three went under in time. The skipper went first. He stayed too long in his room working out chronometer sights, and when he came up he was talking to his wife, his owners, and himself. When a man talks to himself he's beyond all reason, and nothing I could say to him would drive him aloft to clear out his brain. He stayed on the bridge, seeing things and telling us about them until the end, then we sewed him up in canvas for burial; but we never buried him. By this time the whole working force of the ship was more or less crazy, wandering around the deck, unable to understand an order, and finally, to a man, they dropped, though a few managed to climb to the bridge before giving up. It was pitiful to hear the third mate babbling to his mother and his sweetheart, telling them about the fine little cottage he was to put them in when he got command. But he went under in time, leaving things to me; for the first mate, as soon as he saw the skipper die, went below and returned with a bottle. He shared that bottle with the men, as many as could get to it, but they took it in the forward companion, and a few drinks sent them tumbling down into the cabin, where they remained.

Meanwhile I had taken my blankets, sextant, the chart, and the log into the mizzentop, where I also fixed up a bed for Bennie. The passengers stuck to their hammocks up the fore and main, and none of us went down except to grab something to eat. It was dangerous, for the whole deck was hazy with fumes, and a few that went down did not return. But one spot on the deck seemed fairly safe — aft near the wheel there seemed to be immunity, so that a man could steer for a while and find sanity to climb. There were no sailors left now, but I made the passengers take their turn at it, and, as the wind was fair and the yards square, they managed to keep the bark fairly on the course I gave them. I planned to make the Magellan Strait and stop at Punta Arenas, where there might be some way of putting out the fire, either by steam, or by burning coal on the dock and injecting the products of combustion — carbonic-acid gas, you know — into the hold. It will kill any fire.

Well, I made Cape Pillar, and, as the wind luckily hauled to the nor'west, we did not need to touch the braces, but sailed into the nest of tide-rips, currents, and uncharted shoals backed by high, mountainous cliffs. I don't know how far we got. I had lost all thought of Punta Arenas, and was in the green country again, hearing music. I suppose the rest were the same; but when a jar shook the bark we waked up. We were ashore, and there was not a sail, a town, nor a habitation in sight — nothing but high, rocky walls of a deep cove into which some vagrant current had drifted us; and the man at the wheel was asleep or dead.

There was mutiny and insurrection at once; and had things been normal I would have fought that frenzied handful of passengers and made them hold on until something came along to help. But, under the circumstances, I yielded; so, holding our breaths, and holding one another together, we lowered the starboard-quarter boat, and they all tumbled down, the last to go being Bennie, lowered by myself in a bowline. Then I thought of food and water, and, telling them to wait, I went below for a supply. But on coming up I found them a hundred feet away, pulling like farmers, each man in his turn. They would not come back, nor even answer my hail; so I took a short breathing-spell near the wheel, then, one end at a time, I lowered the port boat, got into her, and cast off before thinking of the food and water I had brought up. I was too hazy of mind, too, to see that there were no oars in the boat. So I drifted away — to seaward; for the tide, or current, seemed to have changed. About all I can remember after that, before I saw the steamer coming, is the sight of that poison ship, resting quietly, with all canvas set, and the background of rock behind her. Lord knows what became of her, or of that boat-load of passengers.

As I finished, Marlowe was crying.

"I was that child Bennie, I know," he said; "but I do not know how I was rescued nor what became of the rest. Look at this." He showed me a morning paper, and I read the following:

"SPECIAL CORRESPONDENCE TO THE ——

"*London, Oct. 26.* — A weird story of the sea has been briefly cabled from New Zealand. It is the story of the finding of the sailing-ship *Marlowe*, with twenty skeletons on board.

"The *Marlowe* — a Glasgow-owned bark — sailed from Lyttleton, New Zealand, with several passengers and a crew of thirty-three in January, 1890. She was homeward bound by the Cape Horn route, and was spoken in mid-ocean in the southern Pacific, after which no other word of her was ever heard.

"In April of that year she was posted as missing, and later on was given up as having been lost around the Horn, where the bones of many a good ship and many a hundred seamen lie. A government cruiser searched the rocky and tortuous coasts of Patagonia, but no trace of her was found. The *Marlowe* became just another of the thousand mysteries of the sea.

"A day or two ago another British sailing-ship arrived in Lyttleton with the story that she had found the *Marlowe* and the skeletons of twenty of her crew in one of the rocky coves near Punta Arenas (Sandy Point), in the Magellan Strait. The captain is quoted as telling the story in the following words:

"'We were off the rocky coves near Punta Arenas, keeping near the land for shelter. The coves are deep and silent, the sailing difficult and dangerous. We rounded a rocky point into a deep-cleft cove. Before us, a mile or more across the water, stood a sailing-vessel with the barest shreds of canvas fluttering in the breeze. We signaled and hove to. No answer came. We searched the stranger with our glasses. Not a soul could we see, not a movement of any sort. Masts and yards were picked out in green — the green of decay. At last we came up. There was no sign of life on board. After an interval our first mate and a member of the crew boarded her. The sight that met their gaze was thrilling. Below the wheel lay the skeleton of a man. Treading warily on the rotten deck, which cracked and broke in places as they walked, they encountered three skeletons in the hatchway. In the messroom were the remains of ten bodies, and six were found, one alone, possibly the captain, on the bridge. An uncanny stillness pervaded everything, and a dank smell of mold which made the flesh creep. A few remnants of books were found in the captain's cabin, and a rusty cutlass. Nothing more weird in the history of the sea can ever have been seen. The first mate examined the faint lettering on the bows and, after much trouble, read, *Marlowe*, Glasgow.'"

"Possibly," I said, when I had finished reading, "you were the child; and, as all English craft have their names on their boats, whoever found you called you Marlowe. What shall you do about it?"

"I'm going to England — to Falmouth. I shall investigate all families named Derringer."

He departed next day, and in a few weeks I received a letter written on crested paper which, in part, read as follows:

"I was right. I needed no story nor testimony. I am so much the image of my father as he was at my age that my grandparents received me and welcomed me at once. I shall return soon. Meanwhile, can you find the grave of that second mate?"

I found it easily; and there now stands over it a monument bearing no name — simply this:

A Seaman and a Man Who Stuck to His Ship

QUESTIONS

1. What hints of the plot are found in the introduction?
2. How does the author explain the effect of the magazine illustration upon the narrator?
3. Do you believe that the artist would have drawn, from memory, the same picture that the narrator would have remembered from a description? Explain.
4. What do you think of the manner in which the story is told? Should you have preferred a straight, unbroken narrative? Why did not the author write it as unbroken narrative?
5. Is Bennie's reunion with his family necessary to the story?
6. *Word Study.* — What do the following words mean as they are used in the story: *subconscious, remission, plausible, vociferously, combustion, perversity, tutelage, insular, incentive?*

Problem: ROMANCE
(See page 28.)

1. Is the plot of this story probable, improbable, or impossible?
2. Is this story anything like a fairy tale? Is it like a story of real life?
3. How has the author tried to make it seem real? How does the point of view help?
4. Find places where the author has tried to explain unusual statements.
5. What is the most important element in this story — setting, plot, character, or theme?
6. Why is the setting important to the story? Does the far-away setting help the reader to accept the story?
7. What makes the story romantic? What do you think are the characteristics of romantic stories?

Children of Loneliness *

Anzia Yezierska (1885–   )

Probably the best person to write stories of the dreams, the hopes, the disappointments, the fears, the aims, and the ideals of the foreigner who comes to our shores is one who has experienced these thoughts and emotions. Born in Russia in 1885, Anzia Yezierska came to the United States in 1901 and became a citizen eleven years later. She spent her first years here in a hard, bitter struggle for existence, now working as a servant in private families, now toiling in the factories and sweat shops — and always experiencing weariness, bitterness, and loneliness. By attending night schools, she learned the reading, speaking, and writing of English, and in 1918 — then in her thirties — began to write short stories about life on the East Side of New York City as it was in her youth, about fifty years ago. One year later, her story, "The Fat of the Land," was pronounced by Edward J. O'Brien the best short story of 1919. Anzia Yezierska wrote several books, among them "Salome of the Tenements," and eventually went to Hollywood, where she gained wealth and further literary success. Unfortunately, the author lost her fortune during the depression of the nineteen thirties. She then returned to New York City, where she has been living quietly and doing work for the New York "Times" and various magazines. Indeed, the only book which Miss Yezierska has written fairly recently is her autobiography, "Red Ribbon on a White Horse."

Typical of the author's individual, realistic style and life-like characterization, "Children of Loneliness" is more than an interesting, well-written story, for in it the author considers a problem that even today is still important in the social life of the United States. Anzia Yezierska makes the sensitive reader realize the sadness and grief in the heart of the child of immigrant parents when she realizes that she has grown away from the cus-toms and manners of the Old World and still feels that she does not really belong to the New.

I

"OH, MOTHER, can't you use a fork?" exclaimed Rachel as Mrs. Ravinsky took the shell of the baked potato in her fingers and raised it to her watering mouth.

"Here, Teacherin mine, you want to learn me in my old age how to put the bite in my mouth?" The mother dropped the potato back into her plate, too wounded to eat. Wiping her hands on her blue-checked apron, she turned her glance to her husband, at the opposite side of the table.

"Yankev," she said bitterly, "stick your bone on a fork. Our teacherin said you dassn't touch no eatings with the hands."

"All my teachers died already in the old country," retorted the old man. "I ain't going to learn nothing new no more from my American daughter." He continued to suck the marrow out of the bone with that noisy relish that was so exasperating to Rachel.

"It's no use," stormed the girl, jumping up from the table in disgust; "I'll never be able to stand it here with you people."

"'You people'? What do you mean by 'you people'?" shouted the old man, lashed into fury by his daughter's words. "You think you got a different skin from us because you went to college?"

"It drives me wild to hear you crunching bones like savages. If you people won't change, I shall have to move and live by myself."

Yankev Ravinsky threw the half-gnawed bone upon the table with such vehemence that a plate broke into fragments.

"You witch you!" he cried in a hoarse voice tense with rage. "Move by yourself! We lived without you while you was away in college, and we can get on without you further. God ain't going to turn his nose on us because we ain't got table manners from America. A hell she made from this house since she got home."

"Shah! Yankev leben," pleaded the mother, "the neighbors are opening the windows to listen to our hollering. Let us have a little quiet for a while till the eating is over."

But the accumulated hurts and insults that the old man had borne in the one week since his daughter's return from college had reached the breaking-point. His face was convulsed, his eyes flashed, and his lips were flecked with froth as he burst out in a volley of scorn:

"You think you can put our necks in a chain and learn us new tricks? You think you can make us over for Americans? We got through till fifty years of our lives eating in our own old way —— "

"Wo is me, Yankev leben!" entreated his wife. "Why can't we choke ourselves with our troubles? Why must the whole world know how we are tearing ourselves by the heads? In all Essex Street, in all New York, there ain't such fights like by us."

Her pleadings were in vain. There was no stopping Yankev Ravinsky once his wrath was roused. His daughter's insistence upon the use of a knife and fork spelled apostasy, Anti-Semitism, and the aping of the Gentiles.

Like a prophet of old condemning unrighteousness, he ran the gamut of denunciation, rising to heights of fury that were sublime and godlike, and sinking from sheer exhaustion to abusive bitterness.

"Pfui on all your American colleges! Pfui on the morals of America! No respect for old age. No fear for God. Stepping with your feet on all the laws of the holy Torah. A fire should burn out the whole new generation. They should sink into the earth, like Korah."

"Look at him cursing and burning! Just because I insist on their changing their terrible table manners. One would think I was killing them."

"Do you got to use a gun to kill?" cried the old man, little red threads darting out of the whites of his eyes.

"Who is doing the killing? Aren't you choking the life out of me? Aren't you dragging me by the hair to the darkness of past ages every minute of the day? I'd die of shame if one of my college friends should open the door while you people are eating."

"You — you ——"

The old man was on the point of striking his daughter when his wife seized the hand he raised.

"Mincha! Yankev, you forgot Mincha!"

This reminder was a flash of inspiration on Mrs. Ravinsky's part, the only thing that could have ended the quarreling instantly. Mincha was the prayer just before sunset of the orthodox Jews. This religious rite was so automatic with the old man that at his wife's mention of Mincha everything was immediately shut out, and Yankev Ravinsky rushed off to a corner of the room to pray.

"Ashrai Yoishwai Waisahuh!"

"Happy are they who dwell in Thy house. Ever shall I praise Thee. Selah! Great is the Lord, and exceedingly to be praised; and His greatness is unsearchable. On the majesty and glory of Thy splendor, and on Thy marvelous deeds, will I meditate."

The shelter from the storms of life that the artist finds in his art, Yankev Ravinsky found in his prescribed communion with God. All the despair caused by his daughter's apostasy, the insults and disappointments he suffered, were in his sobbing voice. But as he entered into the spirit of his prayer, he felt the man of flesh drop away in the outflow of God around him. His voice mellowed, the rigid wrinkles of his face softened, the hard glitter of anger and condemnation in his eyes was transmuted into the light of love as he went on:

"The Lord is gracious and merciful; slow to anger and of great loving-kindness. To all that call upon Him in truth He will hear their cry and save them."

Oblivious to the passing and repassing of his wife as she warmed anew the unfinished dinner, he continued:

"Put not your trust in princes, in the son of man in whom

there is no help." Here Reb Ravinsky paused long enough to make a silent confession for the sin of having placed his hope on his daughter instead of on God. His whole body bowed with the sense of guilt. Then in a moment his humility was transfigured into exaltation. Sorrow for sin dissolved in joy as he became more deeply aware of God's unfailing protection.

"Happy is he who hath the God of Jacob for his help, whose hope is in the Lord his God. He healeth the broken in heart, and bindeth up their wounds."

A healing balm filled his soul as he returned to the table, where the steaming hot food awaited him. Rachel sat near the window pretending to read a book. Her mother did not urge her to join them at the table, fearing another outbreak, and the meal continued in silence.

The girl's thoughts surged hotly as she glanced from her father to her mother. A chasm of four centuries could not have separated her more completely from them than her four years at Cornell.

"To think that I was born of these creatures! It's an insult to my soul. What kinship have I with these two lumps of ignorance and superstition? They're ugly and gross and stupid. I'm all sensitive nerves. They want to wallow in dirt."

She closed her eyes to shut out the sight of her parents as they silently ate together, unmindful of the dirt and confusion.

"How is it possible that I lived with them and like them only four years ago? What is it in me that so quickly gets accustomed to the best? Beauty and cleanliness are as natural to me as if I'd been born on Fifth Avenue instead of the dirt of Essex Street."

A vision of Frank Baker passed before her. Her last long talk with him out under the trees in college still lingered in her heart. She felt that she had only to be with him again to carry forward the beautiful friendship that had sprung up between them. He had promised to come shortly to New York. How could she possibly introduce such a born and bred American to her low, ignorant, dirty parents?

"I might as well tear the thought of Frank Baker out of my heart," she told herself. "If he just once sees the pigsty of a home I come from, if he just sees the table manners of my father and mother, he'll fly through the ceiling."

Timidly, Mrs. Ravinsky turned to her daughter.

"Ain't you going to give a taste the eating?"

No answer.

"I fried the lotkes special' for you ——"

"I can't stand your fried, greasy stuff."

"Ain't even my cooking good no more either?" Her gnarled, hard-worked hands clutched at her breast. "God from the world, for what do I need yet any more my life? Nothing I do for my child is no use no more."

Her head sank; her whole body seemed to shrivel and grow old with the sense of her own futility.

"How I was hurrying to run by the butcher before everybody else, so as to pick out the grandest, fattest piece of brust!" she wailed, tears streaming down her face. "And I put my hand away from my heart and put a whole fresh egg into the lotkes, and I stuffed the stove full of coal like a millionaire so as to get the lotkes fried so nice and brown; and now you give a kick on everything I done ——"

"Fool woman," shouted her husband, "stop laying yourself on the ground for your daughter to step on you! What more can you expect from a child raised up in America? What more can you expect but that she should spit in your face and make dirt from you?" His eyes, hot and dry under their lids, flashed from his wife to his daughter. "The old Jewish eating is poison to her; she must have trefa ham — only forbidden food."

Bitter laughter shook him.

"Woman, how you patted yourself with pride before all the neighbors, boasting of our great American daughter coming home from college! This is our daughter, our pride, our hope, our pillow for our old age that we were dreaming about! This is our American teacherin! A Jew-hater, an Anti-Semite we brought into the world, a betrayer of our race who hates her own father and mother like the Russian Czar once hated a Jew. She makes herself so refined, she can't stand it when we use the knife or fork the wrong way; but her heart is that of a brutal Cossack, and she spills her own father's and mother's blood like water."

Every word he uttered seared Rachel's soul like burning acid. She felt herself becoming a witch, a she-devil, under the spell of his accusations.

"You want me to love you yet?" She turned upon her father like an avenging fury. "If there's any evil hatred in my soul, you have roused it with your cursed preaching."

"Oi-i-i! Highest One! pity Yourself on us!" Mrs. Ravinsky wrung her hands. "Rachel, Yankev, let there be an end to this knife-stabbing! Gottuniu! my flesh is torn to pieces!"

Unheeding her mother's pleading, Rachel rushed to the closet where she kept her things.

"I was a crazy idiot to think that I could live with you people under one roof." She flung on her hat and coat and bolted for the door.

Mrs. Ravinsky seized Rachel's arm in passionate entreaty.

"My child, my heart, my life, what do you mean? Where are you going?"

"I mean to get out of this hell of a home this very minute," she said, tearing loose from her mother's clutching hands.

"Wo is me! My child! We'll be to shame and to laughter by the whole world. What will people say?"

"Let them say! My life is my own; I'll live as I please." She slammed the door in her mother's face.

"They want me to love them yet," ran the mad thoughts in Rachel's brain as she hurried through the streets, not knowing where she was going, not caring. "Vampires, bloodsuckers fastened on my flesh! Black shadow blighting every ray of light that ever came my way! Other parents scheme and plan and wear themselves out to give their child a chance, but they put dead stones in front of every chance I made for myself."

With the cruelty of youth to everything not youth, Rachel reasoned:

"They have no rights, no claims over me like other parents who do things for their children. It was my own brains, my own courage, my own iron will that forced my way out of the sweat-shop to my present position in the public schools. I owe them nothing, nothing, nothing."

II

Two weeks already away from home. Rachel looked about her room. It was spotlessly clean. She had often said to herself while at home with her parents: "All I want is an empty room, with a bed, a table, and a chair. As long as it is clean and away from them, I'll be happy." But was she happy?

A distant door closed, followed by the retreating sound of descending footsteps. Then all was still, the stifling stillness of a rooming-house. The white, empty walls pressed in upon her, suffocated her. She listened acutely for any stir of life, but the continued silence was unbroken save for the insistent ticking of her watch.

"I ran away from home burning for life," she mused, "and all I've found is the loneliness that's death." A wave of self-pity weakened her almost to the point of tears. "I'm alone! I'm alone!" she moaned, crumpling into a heap.

"Must it always be with me like this," her soul cried in terror, "either to live among those who drag me down or in the awful isolation of a hall bedroom? Oh, I'll die of loneliness among these frozen each-shut-in-himself Americans! It's one thing to break away, but, oh, the strength to go on alone! How can I ever do it? The love instinct is so strong in me; I cannot live without love, without people."

The thought of a letter from Frank Baker suddenly lightened her spirits. That very evening she was to meet him for dinner. Here was hope — more than hope. Just seeing him again would surely bring the certainty.

This new rush of light upon her dark horizon so softened her heart that she could almost tolerate her superfluous parents.

"If I could only have love and my own life, I could almost forgive them for bringing me into the world. I don't really hate them; I only hate them when they stand between me and the new America that I'm to conquer."

Answering her impulse, her feet led her to the familiar Ghetto streets. On the corner of the block where her parents lived she paused, torn between the desire to see her people and the fear of their nagging reproaches. The old Jewish proverb came to her mind: "The wolf is not afraid of the dog, but he hates his bark." "I'm not afraid of their black curses for sin. It's nothing to me if they accuse me of being an Anti-Semite or a murderer, and yet why does it hurt me so?"

Rachel had prepared herself to face the usual hailstorm of reproaches and accusations, but as she entered the dark hallway of the tenement, she heard her father's voice chanting the old familiar Hebrew psalm of "The Race of Sorrows":

"Hear my prayer, O Lord, and let my cry come unto Thee.

"For my days are consumed like smoke, and my bones are burned as an hearth.

"I am like a pelican of the wilderness.

"I am like an owl of the desert.

"I have eaten ashes like bread and mingled my drink with weeping."

A faintness came over her. The sobbing strains of the lyric song melted into her veins like a magic sap, making her warm and human again. All her strength seemed to flow out of her in pity for her people. She longed to throw herself on the dirty, ill-smelling tenement stairs and weep: "Nothing is real but love — love. Nothing so false as ambition."

Since her early childhood she remembered often waking up in the middle of the night and hearing her father chant this age-old song of woe. There flashed before her a vivid picture of him, huddled in the corner beside the table piled high with Hebrew books, swaying to the rhythm of his Jeremiad, the sputtering light of the candle stuck in a bottle throwing uncanny shadows over his gaunt face. The skull-cap, the sidelocks, and the long gray beard made him seem like some mystic stranger from a far-off world and not a father. The father of the daylight who ate with a knife, spat on the floor, and who was forever denouncing America and Americans was different from the mystic spirit stranger who could thrill with such impassioned rapture.

Thousands of years of exile, thousands of years of hunger, loneliness, and want swept over her as she listened to her father's voice. Something seemed to be crying out to her to run in and seize her father and mother in her arms and hold them close.

"Love, love — nothing is true between us but love," she thought.

But why couldn't she do what she longed to do? Why, with all her passionate sympathy for them, should any actual contact with her people seem so impossible? No, she couldn't go in just yet. Instead, she ran up on the roof, where she could be alone. She stationed herself at the air-shaft opposite their kitchen window, where for the first time since she had left in a rage she could see her old home.

Ach! what sickening disorder! In the sink were the dirty dishes stacked high, untouched, it looked, for days. The table still held the remains of the last meal. Clothes were strewn about the chairs. The bureau drawers were open, and their contents brimmed over in mad confusion.

"I couldn't endure it, this terrible dirt!" Her nails dug into her palms, shaking with the futility of her visit. "It would be worse than death to go back to them. It would mean giving up order, cleanliness, sanity, everything that I've striven all these years to attain. It would mean giving up the hope of my new world — the hope of Frank Baker."

The sound of the creaking door reached her where she crouched against the air-shaft. She looked again into the murky depths of the room. Her mother had entered. With arms full of paper bags of provisions, the old woman paused on the threshold, her eyes dwelling on the dim figure of her husband. A look of pathetic tenderness illumined her wrinkled features.

"I'll make something good to eat for you, yes?"

Reb Ravinsky only dropped his head on his breast. His eyes were red and dry, sandy with sorrow that could find no release in tears. Good God! never had Rachel seen such profound despair. For the first time she noticed the grooved tracings of withering age knotted on his face and the growing hump on her mother's back.

"Already the shadow of death hangs over them," she thought as she watched them. "They're already with one foot in the grave. Why can't I be human to them before they're dead? Why can't I?"

Rachel blotted away the picture of the sordid room with both hands over her eyes.

"To death with my soul! I wish I were a plain human being with a heart instead of a monster of selfishness with a soul."

But the pity she felt for her parents began now to be swept away in a wave of pity for herself.

"How every step in advance costs me my heart's blood! My greatest tragedy in life is that I always see the two opposite sides at the same time. What seems to me right one day seems all wrong the next. Not only that, but many things seem right and wrong at the same time. I feel I have a right to my own life, and yet I feel just as strongly that I owe my father and mother something. Even if I don't love them, I have no right to step over them. I'm drawn to them by something more compelling than love. It is the cry of their dumb, wasted lives."

Again Rachel looked into the dimly lighted room below. Her mother placed food upon the table. With a self-effacing stoop of humility, she entreated, "Eat only while it is hot yet."

With his eyes fixed almost unknowingly, Reb Ravinsky sat down. Her mother took the chair opposite him, but she only pretended to eat the slender portion of the food she had given herself. Rachel's heart swelled. Yes, it had always been like that. Her mother had taken the smallest portion of everything for herself. Complaints, reproaches, upbraidings, abuse, yes, all these had been heaped by her upon her mother; but always the juiciest piece of meat was placed on her plate, the thickest slice of bread; the warmest covering was given to her, while her mother shivered through the night.

"Ah, I don't want to abandon them!" she thought; "I only want to get to the place where I belong. I only want to get to the mountain-tops and view the world from the heights, and then I'll give them everything I've achieved."

Her thoughts were sharply broken in upon by the loud sound of her father's eating. Bent over the table, he chewed with noisy gulps a piece of herring, his temples working to the motion of his jaws. With each audible swallow and smacking of the lips Rachel's heart tightened with loathing.

"Their dirty ways turn all my pity into hate." She felt her toes and her fingers curl inward with disgust. "I'll never amount to anything if I'm not strong enough to break away from them once and for all." Hypnotizing herself into her line of self-defense, her thoughts raced on: "I'm only cruel to be kind. If I went back to them now, it would not be out of love, but because of weakness — because of doubt and unfaith in myself."

Rachel bluntly turned her back. Her head lifted. There was iron will in her jaws.

"If I haven't the strength to tear free from the old, I can never conquer the new. Every new step a man makes is a tearing away from those clinging to him. I must get tight and hard as rock inside of me if I'm ever to do the things I set out to do. I must learn to suffer and suffer, walk through blood and fire, and not bend from my course."

For the last time she looked at her parents. The terrible loneliness of their abandoned old age, their sorrowful eyes, the wrung-dry weariness on their faces, the whole black picture of her ruined, desolate home, burned into her flesh. She knew all the pain of one unjustly condemned, and the guilt of one with the spilt blood of helpless lives upon his hands. Then came tears, blinding, wrenching tears that tore at her heart until it seemed that they would rend her body into shreds.

"God! God!" she sobbed as she turned her head away from them, "if all this suffering were at least for something worth while, for something outside myself. But to have to break them and crush them merely because I have a fastidious soul that can't stomach their table manners, merely because I can't strangle my aching ambitions to rise in the world!"

She could no longer sustain the conflict which raged within her higher and higher at every moment. With a sudden tension of all her nerves she pulled herself together and stumbled blindly downstairs and out of the house. And she felt as if she had torn away from the flesh and blood of her own body.

III

Out in the street she struggled to get hold of herself again. Despite the tumult and upheaval that racked her soul, an intoxicating lure still held her up — the hope of seeing Frank Baker that evening. She was indeed a storm-racked ship, but within sight of shore. She need but throw out the signal, and help was nigh. She need but confide to Frank Baker of her break with her people, and all the dormant sympathy between them would surge up. His understanding would widen and deepen because of her great need for his understanding. He would love her the more because of her great need for his love.

Forcing back her tears, stepping over her heart-break, she hurried to the hotel where she was to meet him. Her father's impassioned rapture when he chanted the Psalms of David lit up the visionary face of the young Jewess.

"After all, love is the beginning of the real life," she thought as Frank Baker's dark, handsome face flashed before her. "With him to hold on to, I'll begin my new world."

Borne higher and higher by the intoxicating illusion of her great destiny, she cried:

"A person all alone is but a futile cry in an unheeding wilderness. One alone is but a shadow, an echo of reality. It takes two together to create reality. Two together can pioneer a new world."

With a vision of herself and Frank Baker marching side by side to the conquest of her heart's desire, she added:

"No wonder a man's love means so little to the American woman. They belong to the world in which they are born. They belong to their fathers and mothers; they belong to their relatives and friends. They are human even without a man's love. I don't belong; I'm not human. Only a man's love can save me and make me human again."

It was the busy dinner-hour at the fashionable restaurant. Pausing at the doorway with searching eyes and lips eagerly parted, Rachel's swift glance circled the lobby. Those seated in the dining-room beyond who were not too absorbed in one another noticed a slim, vivid figure of ardent youth, but with dark, age-old eyes that told of the restless seeking of her homeless race.

With nervous little movements of anxiety, Rachel sat down, got up, then started across the lobby. Halfway, she stopped, and her breath caught.

"Mr. Baker," she murmured, her hands fluttering toward him with famished eagerness. His smooth, athletic figure had a cock-sureness that to the girl's worshiping gaze seemed the perfection of male strength.

"You must be doing wonderful things," came from her admiringly. "You look so happy, so shining with life."

"Yes," — he shook her hand vigorously — "I've been living for the first time since I was a kid. I'm full of such interesting experiences. I'm actually working in an East Side settlement."

Dazed by his glamorous success, Rachel stammered soft phrases of congratulation as he led her to a table. But seated opposite him, the face of this untried youth, flushed with the health and happiness of another world than that of the poverty-crushed Ghetto, struck her as an insincerity.

"You in an East Side settlement?" she interrupted sharply. "What reality can there be in that work for you?"

"Oh," he cried, his shoulders squaring with the assurance of his master's degree in sociology, "it's great to get under the surface and see how the other half live. It's so picturesque! My conception of these people has greatly changed since I've been visiting their homes." He launched into a glowing account of the East Side as seen by a twenty-five-year-old college graduate.

"I thought them mostly immersed in hard labor, digging subways or slaving in sweat-shops," he went on. "But think of the poetry which the immigrant is daily living!"

"But they're so sunk in the dirt of poverty, what poetry do you see there?"

"It's their beautiful home life, the poetic devotion between parents and children, the sacrifices they make for one another ——"

"Beautiful home life? Sacrifices? Why, all I know of is the battle to the knife between parents and children. It's black tragedy that boils there, not the pretty sentiments that you imagine."

"My dear child" — he waved aside her objection — "you're too close to judge dispassionately. This very afternoon, on one of my friendly visits, I came upon a dear old man who peered up at me through horn-rimmed glasses behind his pile of Hebrew books. He was hardly able to speak English, but I found him a great scholar."

"Yes, a lazy old do-nothing, a bloodsucker on his wife and children."

Too shocked for remonstrance, Frank Baker stared at her.

"How else could he have time in the middle of the afternoon to pore over his books?" Rachel's voice was hard with bitterness. "Did you see his wife? I'll bet she was slaving for him in the kitchen. And his children slaving for him in the sweatshop."

"Even so, think of the fine devotion that the women and children show in making the lives of your Hebrew scholars possible. It's a fine contribution to America, where our tendency is to forget idealism."

"Give me better a plain American man who supports his wife and children and I'll give you all those dreamers of the Talmud."

He smiled tolerantly at her vehemence.

"Nevertheless," he insisted, "I've found wonderful material for my new book in all this. I think I've got a new angle on the social types of your East Side."

An icy band tightened about her heart. "Social types," her lips formed. How could she possibly confide to this man of the terrible tragedy that she had been through that very day? Instead of the understanding and sympathy that she had hoped to find, there were only smooth platitudes, the sightseer's surface interest in curious "social types."

Frank Baker talked on. Rachel seemed to be listening, but her eyes had a far-off, abstracted look. She was quiet as a spinning top is quiet, her thoughts and emotions revolving within her at high speed.

"That man in love with me? Why, he doesn't see me or feel me. I don't exist to him. He's only stuck on himself, blowing his own horn. Will he never stop with his 'I,' 'I,' 'I?' Why, I was a crazy lunatic to think that just because we took the same courses in college, he would understand me out in the real world."

All the fire suddenly went out of her eyes. She looked a thousand years old as she sank back wearily in her chair.

"Oh, but I'm boring you with all my heavy talk on sociology." Frank Baker's words seemed to come to her from afar. "I have tickets for a fine musical comedy that will cheer you up, Miss Ravinsky ——"

"Thanks, thanks," she cut in hurriedly. Spend a whole evening sitting beside him in a theater when her heart was breaking? No. All she wanted was to get away — away where she could be alone. "I have work to do," she heard herself say. "I've got to get home."

Frank Baker murmured words of polite disappointment and escorted her back to her door. She watched the sure swing of his athletic figure as he strode away down the street, then she rushed upstairs.

Back in her little room, stunned, bewildered, blinded with her disillusion, she sat staring at her four empty walls.

Hours passed, but she made no move, she uttered no sound. Doubled fists thrust between her knees, she sat there, staring blindly at her empty walls.

"I can't live with the old world, and I'm yet too green for the new. I don't belong to those who gave me birth or to those with whom I was educated."

Was this to be the end of all her struggles to rise in America, she asked herself, this crushing daze of loneliness? Her driving thirst for an education, her desperate battle for a little cleanliness, for a breath of beauty, the tearing away from her own flesh and blood to free herself from the yoke of her parents — what was it all worth now? Where did it lead to? Was loneliness to be the fruit of it all?

Night was melting away like a fog; through the open window the first lights of dawn were appearing. Rachel felt the sudden touch of the sun upon her face, which was bathed in tears. Overcome by her sorrow, she shuddered and put her hand over her eyes as though to shut out the unwelcome contact. But the light shone through her fingers.

Despite her weariness, the renewing breath of the fresh morning entered her heart like a sunbeam. A mad longing for life filled her veins.

"I want to live," her youth cried. "I want to live, even at the worst."

Live how? Live for what? She did not know. She only felt she must struggle against her loneliness and weariness as she had once struggled against dirt, against the squalor and ugliness of her Ghetto home.

Turning from the window, she concentrated her mind, her poor tired mind, on one idea.

"I have broken away from the old world; I'm through with it. It's already behind me. I must face this loneliness till I get to the new world. Frank Baker can't help me; I must hope for no help from the outside. I'm alone; I'm alone till I get there.

"But am I really alone in my seeking? I'm one of the millions of immigrant children, children of loneliness, wandering between worlds that are at once too old and too new to live in."

QUESTIONS

1. Why was Rachel Ravinsky alienated from her parents?
2. Do you think she was justified in leaving home? Explain.
3. How was the attitude of Rachel's mother different from that of her father?
4. Is it possible to consider that both parents and daughter were justified and that each member of the family was in the clutch of circumstances over which he had no control? Explain.
5. Why was Rachel not satisfied even after she had left her home?
6. Why was Rachel disappointed in Frank Baker? Did he really understand her problem? Explain.
7. Explain the meaning of Rachel's words, "I am one of the millions of immigrant children, children of loneliness, wandering between worlds that are at once too old and too new to live in."
8. Does the ending of the story satisfy you? What other ending could it have?
9. *Word Study.* — What do the following words mean as they are used in the story: *apostasy, denunciation, transmuted, oblivious, futility, avenging, humility, fastidious, dormant?*

Problem: REALISM
(See page 28.)

1. What was the author trying to do in this story? Did she succeed?
2. Which of the earlier stories in this book does this story most nearly resemble? How?
3. Do the characters in "Children of Loneliness" seem real to you? Are they heroic? Are they very wicked? Do you know persons who, given the same conditions, would have behaved as the characters in the story did? Can you find exaggeration in this story?
4. Is this a story from real life? Is there much action in it? Find details that would not have been put into a romantic story.
5. Look back to "A Village Singer." Is it romance or realism? Give reasons for your belief.

Pigs Is Pigs *

Ellis Parker Butler (1869–1937)

The oldest of eight children, Ellis Parker Butler was born in the Mississippi river town of Muscatine, Iowa, on December 5, 1869, and died in Flushing, Long Island, on September 13, 1937. As a small lad, young Ellis watched the rafts of pine logs floating down the Mississippi from the northern forests. Because the family was extremely poor, the boy lived for a time with his father's sister, a school teacher, who inspired in him an interest in good literature. Years later, the author wrote, "The three greatest influences in my work were my Aunt Lizzie Butler, my high-school English teacher, and my father." Young Ellis had only one year of high school before he left to go to work — first as a bill clerk and later as a salesman. In 1897, Butler — on the advice of three New York editors — left Iowa for New York City, where he wrote humor and did editorial work for two trade papers. He later became the founder of the Dutch Treat Club and of the Authors' League.

A writer and an editor for over forty years, Butler wrote chiefly short stories and articles. "I have tried writing novels," he once admitted, "but never with much success." Other good stories by the author are "The Jack-Knife Man," "Philo Gubb: Correspondence School Detective," "The Great American Pie Company," "Mike Flannery," and "Swatty."

Butler's reputation as an American humorist rests largely on "Pigs Is Pigs," published originally in "American Magazine" and as a small book a year later. This famous story, which has been read with pleasure by hundreds of thousands of people, furnishes a good illustration of the author's talent for inventing and developing surprising situations in an original manner; it is also an excellent example of the humor of exaggeration. The chief character, Mike Flannery, is an unschooled, practical philosopher, with a sound understanding of human nature, a

*rich fund of Irish humor, and a happy faculty for making the
best of things.*

MIKE FLANNERY, the Westcote agent of the
Interurban Express Company, leaned over the counter of
the express office and shook his fist. Mr. Morehouse, angry
and red, stood on the other side of the counter, trembling
with rage. The argument had been long and heated, and at
last Mr. Morehouse had talked himself speechless. The cause
of the trouble stood on the counter between the two men.
It was a soap box across the top of which were nailed a number
of strips, forming a rough but serviceable cage. In it two
spotted guinea-pigs were greedily eating lettuce leaves.

"Do as you loike, then!" shouted Flannery, "pay for thim
an' take thim, or don't pay for thim and leave thim be. Rules
is rules, Misther Morehouse, an' Mike Flannery's not goin'
to be called down fer breakin' of thim."

"But, you everlastingly stupid idiot!" shouted Mr. Morehouse, madly shaking a flimsy printed book beneath the
agent's nose, "can't you read it here — in your own plain
printed rates? 'Pets, domestic, Franklin to Westcote, if
properly boxed, twenty-five cents each.'" He threw the
book on the counter in disgust. "What more do you want?
Aren't they pets? Aren't they domestic? Aren't they properly
boxed? What?"

He turned and walked back and forth rapidly, frowning
ferociously.

Suddenly he turned to Flannery, and forcing his voice to an
artificial calmness spoke slowly but with intense sarcasm.

"Pets," he said, "P-e-t-s! Twenty-five cents each. There
are two of them. One! Two! Two times twenty-five are fifty!
Can you understand that? I offer you fifty cents."

Flannery reached for the book. He ran his hand through
the pages and stopped at page sixty-four.

"An' I don't take fifty cints," he whispered in mockery.
"Here's the rule for ut. 'Whin the agint be in anny doubt

regardin' which of two rates applies to a shipment, he shall charge the larger. The consign-ey may file a claim for the overcharge.' In this case, Misther Morehouse, I be in doubt. Pets thim animals may be, but pigs I'm blame sure they do be, an' me rules says plain as the nose on yer face, 'Pigs Franklin to Westcote, thirty cints each.' An' Mister Morehouse, by me arithmetical knowledge two time thurty comes to sixty cints."

Mr. Morehouse shook his head savagely. "Nonsense!" he shouted, "confounded nonsense, I tell you! Why, you poor ignorant foreigner, that rule means common pigs, domestic pigs, not guinea-pigs!"

Flannery was stubborn.

"Pigs is pigs," he declared firmly. "Guinea-pigs, or dago pigs or Irish pigs is all the same to the Interurban Express Company an' to Mike Flannery. Th' nationality of the pig creates no differentiality in the rate, Misther Morehouse! 'Twould be the same was they Dutch pigs or Rooshun pigs. Mike Flannery," he added, "is here to tind to the expriss business and not to hould conversation wid dago pigs in sivinteen languages fer to discover be they Chinese or Tipperary by birth an' nativity."

Mr. Morehouse hesitated. He bit his lip and then flung out his arms wildly.

"Very well!" he shouted, "you shall hear of this! Your president shall hear of this! It is an outrage! I have offered you fifty cents. You refuse it! Keep the pigs until you are ready to take the fifty cents, but, by George sir, if one hair of those pigs' heads is harmed I will have the law on you!"

He turned and stalked out, slamming the door. Flannery carefully lifted the soap box from the counter and placed it in a corner. He was not worried. He felt the peace that comes to a faithful servant who has done his duty and done it well.

Mr. Morehouse went home raging. His boy, who had been awaiting the guinea-pigs, knew better than to ask him for them. He was a normal boy and therefore always had a guilty conscience when his father was angry. So the boy slipped quietly around the house. There is nothing so soothing to a guilty conscience as to be out of the path of the avenger.

Mr. Morehouse stormed into the house. "Where's the ink?" he shouted at his wife as soon as his foot was across the doorsill.

Mrs. Morehouse jumped, guiltily. She never used ink. She had not seen the ink, nor moved the ink, nor thought of the ink, but her husband's tone convicted her of the guilt of having borne and reared a boy, and she knew that whenever her husband wanted anything in a loud voice the boy had been at it.

"I'll find Sammy," she said meekly.

When the ink was found Mr. Morehouse wrote rapidly, and he read the completed letter and smiled a triumphant smile.

"That will settle that crazy Irishman!" he exclaimed. "When they get that letter he will hunt another job, all right!"

A week later Mr. Morehouse received a long official envelope with the card of the Interurban Express Company in the upper left corner. He tore it open eagerly and drew out a sheet of paper. At the top it bore the number A6754. The letter was short. "Subject — Rate on guinea-pigs," it said, "Dr. Sir — We are in receipt of your letter regarding rate on guinea-pigs between Franklin and Westcote, addressed to the president of this company. All claims for overcharge should be addressed to the Claims Department."

Mr. Morehouse wrote to the Claims Department. He wrote six pages of choice sarcasm, vituperation, and argument, and sent them to the Claims Department.

A few weeks later he received a reply from the Claims Department. Attached to it was his last letter.

"Dr. Sir," said the reply. "Your letter of the 16th inst., addressed to this Department, subject rate on guinea-pigs from Franklin to Westcote, rec'd. We have taken up the matter with our agent at Westcote, and his reply is attached herewith. He informs us that you refused to receive the consignment or to pay the charges. You have therefore no claim against this company, and your letter regarding the proper rate on the consignment should be addressed to our Tariff Department."

Mr. Morehouse wrote to the Tariff Department. He stated his case clearly, and gave his arguments in full, quoting a page or two from the encyclopedia to prove that guinea-pigs were not common pigs.

With the care that characterizes corporations when they are systematically conducted, Mr. Morehouse's letter was numbered, O. K'd, and started through the regular channels. Duplicate copies of the bill of lading, manifest, Flannery's receipt for the package, and several other pertinent papers were pinned to the letter, and they were passed to the head of the Tariff Department.

The head of the Tariff Department put his feet on his desk and yawned. He looked through the papers carelessly.

"Miss Kane," he said to his stenographer, "take this letter. 'Agent, Westcote, N. J. Please advise why consignment referred to in attached papers was refused domestic pet rates.'"

Miss Kane made a series of curves and angles on her notebook and waited with pencil poised. The head of the department looked at the papers again.

"Huh! guinea-pigs!" he said. "Probably starved to death by this time! Add this to that letter: 'Give condition of consignment at present.'"

He tossed the papers on to the stenographer's desk, took his feet from his own desk and went out to lunch.

When Mike Flannery received the letter he scratched his head.

"Give prisint condition," he repeated thoughtfully. "Now what do thim clerks be wantin' to know, I wonder! 'Prisint condition,' is ut? Thim pigs, praise St. Patrick, do be in good health, so far as I know, but I niver was no veternairy surgeon to dago pigs. Mebby thim clerks wants me to call in the pig docther an' have their pulses took. Wan thing I do know, howiver, which is they've glorious appytites for pigs of their soize. Ate? They'd ate the brass padlocks off of a barn door! If the paddy pig, by the same token, ate as hearty as these dago pigs do, there'd be a famine in Ireland."

To assure himself that his report would be up to date, Flannery went to the rear of the office and looked into the cage. The pigs had been transferred to a larger box — a dry goods box.

"Wan — two — t'ree — four — foive — six — sivin — eight!" he counted. "Sivin spotted an' wan all black. All well an' hearty an' all eatin' loike ragin' hippypottymusses." He went back to his desk and wrote.

"Mr. Morgan, Head of Tariff Department," he wrote. "Why do I say dago pigs is pigs because they is pigs and will be til you say they ain't which is what the rule book says stop your jollying me you know it as well as I do. As to health they are all well and hoping you are the same. P. S. There are eight now the family increased all good eaters. P. S. I paid out so far two dollars for cabbage which they like shall I put in bill for same what?"

Morgan, head of the Tariff Department, when he received this letter, laughed. He read it again and became serious.

"By George!" he said. "Flannery is right, 'pigs is pigs.' I'll have to get authority on this thing. Meanwhile, Miss Kane, take this letter: 'Agent, Westcote, N. J. Regarding shipment guinea-pigs, File No. A6754. Rule 83, General Instruction to Agents, clearly states that agents shall collect from consignee all costs of provender, etc., etc., required for live stock while in transit or storage. You will proceed to collect same from consignee.'"

Flannery received this letter next morning, and when he read it he grinned.

"Proceed to collect," he said softly. "How thim clerks do loike to be talkin'! *Me* proceed to collect two dollars and twinty-foive cints off Misther Morehouse! I wonder do thim clerks *know* Misther Morehouse? I'll git it! Oh, yes! 'Misther Morehouse, two an' a quarter, plaze.' 'Cert'nly, me dear frind Flannery. Delighted!' *Not!*"

Flannery drove the express wagon to Mr. Morehouse's door. Mr. Morehouse answered the bell.

"Ah, ha!" he cried as soon as he saw it was Flannery. "So you've come to your senses at last, have you? I thought you would! Bring the box in."

"I hev no box," said Flannery coldly. "I hev a bill agin Misther John C. Morehouse for two dollars and twenty-foive cints for kebbages aten by his dago pigs. Wud you wish to pay ut?"

"Pay —— Cabbages —— !" gasped Mr. Morehouse. "Do you mean to say that two little guinea-pigs ——"

"Eight!" said Flannery. "Papa an' mamma an' six childer. Eight!"

For answer Mr. Morehouse slammed the door in Flannery's face. Flannery looked at the door reproachfully.

"I take ut the con-*sign*-y don't want to pay for thim kebbages," he said. "If I know signs of refusal, the con-*sign*-y refuses to pay for wan dang kebbage leaf an' be hanged to me!"

Mr. Morgan, the head of the Tariff Department, consulted the president of the Interurban Express Company regarding guinea-pigs, as to whether they were pigs or not pigs. The president was inclined to treat the matter lightly.

"What is the rate on pigs and on pets?" he asked.

"Pigs thirty cents, pets twenty-five," said Morgan.

"Then of course guinea-pigs are pigs," said the president.

"Yes," agreed Morgan, "I look at it that way, too. A thing that can come under two rates is naturally due to be classed as the higher. But are guinea-pigs, pigs? Aren't they rabbits?"

"Come to think of it," said the president, "I believe they are more like rabbits. Sort of halfway station between pig and rabbit. I think the question is this — are guinea-pigs of the domestic pig family? I'll ask Professor Gordon. He is authority on such things. Leave the papers with me."

The president put the papers on his desk and wrote a letter to Professor Gordon. Unfortunately the Professor was in

South America collecting zoölogical specimens, and the letter
was forwarded to him by his wife. As the Professor was in
the highest Andes, where no white man had ever penetrated,
the letter was many months in reaching him. The president
forgot the guinea-pigs, Morgan forgot them, Mr. Morehouse
forgot them, but Flannery did not. One-half of his time he
gave to the duties of his agency; the other half was devoted
to the guinea-pigs. Long before Professor Gordon received
the president's letter Morgan received one from Flannery.

"About them dago pigs," it said, "what shall I do they
are great in family life, no race suicide for them, there are
thirty-two now shall I sell them do you take this express
office for a menagerie, answer quick."

Morgan reached for a telegraph blank and wrote:

"Agent, Westcote. Don't sell pigs."

He then wrote Flannery a letter calling his attention to the
fact that the pigs were not the property of the company but
were merely being held during a settlement of a dispute regarding rates. He advised Flannery to take the best possible
care of them.

Flannery, letter in hand, looked at the pigs and sighed.
The dry-goods box cage had become too small. He boarded
up twenty feet of the rear of the express office to make a large
and airy home for them, and went about his business. He
worked with feverish intensity when out on his rounds, for
the pigs required attention and took most of his time. Some
months later, in desperation, he seized a sheet of paper and
wrote "160" across it and mailed it to Morgan. Morgan returned it asking for explanation. Flannery replied:

"There be now one hundred sixty of them dago pigs, for
heavens sake let me sell off some, do you want me to go crazy,
what."

"Sell no pigs," Morgan wired.

Not long after this the president of the express company
received a letter from Professor Gordon. It was a long and
scholarly letter, but the point was that the guinea-pig was
the *Cavia aparoea* while the common pig was the genus *Sus*

of the family *Suidae*. He remarked that they were prolific and multiplied rapidly.

"They are not pigs," said the president, decidedly, to Morgan. "Twenty-five-cent rate applies."

Morgan made the proper notation on the papers that had accumulated in File A6754, and turned them over to the Audit Department. The Audit Department took some time to look the matter up, and after the usual delay wrote Flannery that as he had on hand one hundred and sixty guinea-pigs, the property of consignee, he should deliver them and collect charges at the rate of twenty-five cents each.

Flannery spent a day herding his charges through a narrow opening in their cage so that he might count them.

"Audit Dept.," he wrote, when he had finished the count, "you are way off there may be was one hundred and sixty dago pigs once, but wake up don't be a back number. I've got even eight hundred, now shall I collect for eight hundred or what, how about sixty-four dollars I paid out for cabbages?"

It required a great many letters back and forth before the Audit Department was able to understand why the error had been made of billing one hundred and sixty instead of eight hundred, and still more time for it to get the meaning of the "cabbages."

Flannery was crowded into a few feet at the extreme front of the office. The pigs had all the rest of the room and two boys were employed constantly attending to them. The day after Flannery had counted the guinea-pigs there were eight more added to his drove, and by the time the Audit Department gave him authority to collect for eight hundred Flannery had given up all attempts to attend to the receipt or the delivery of goods. He was hastily building galleries around the express office, tier above tier. He had four thousand and sixty-four guinea-pigs to care for! More were arriving daily.

Immediately following its authorization the Audit Department sent another letter, but Flannery was too busy to open it. They wrote another and then they telegraphed:

"Error in guinea-pig bill. Collect for two guinea-pigs, fifty cents. Deliver all to consignee."

Flannery read the telegram and cheered up. He wrote out a bill as rapidly as his pencil could travel over paper and ran all the way to the Morehouse home. At the gate he stopped suddenly. The house stared at him with vacant eyes. The windows were bare of curtains and he could see into the empty rooms. A sign on the porch said, "To Let." Mr. Morehouse had moved! Flannery ran all the way back to the express office. Sixty-nine guinea-pigs had been born during his absence. He ran out again and made feverish inquiries in the village. Mr. Morehouse had not only moved, but he had left Westcote. Flannery returned to the express office and found that two hundred and six guinea-pigs had entered the world since he left it. He wrote a telegram to the Audit Department.

"Can't collect fifty cents for two dago pigs consignee has left town address unknown what shall I do? Flannery."

The telegram was handed to one of the clerks in the Audit Department, and as he read it he laughed.

"Flannery must be crazy. He ought to know that the thing to do is to return the consignment here," said the clerk. He telegraphed Flannery to send the pigs to the main office of the company at Franklin.

When Flannery received the telegram he set to work. The six boys he had engaged to help him also set to work. They worked with the haste of desperate men, making cages out of soap boxes, cracker boxes, and all kinds of boxes, and as fast as the cages were completed they filled them with guinea-pigs and expressed them to Franklin. Day after day the cages of guinea-pigs flowed in a steady stream from Westcote to Franklin, and still Flannery and his six helpers ripped and nailed and packed — relentlessly and feverishly. At the end of the week they had shipped two hundred and eighty cases of guinea-pigs, and there were in the express office seven hundred and four more pigs than when they began packing them.

"Stop sending pigs. Warehouse full," came a telegram to

Flannery. He stopped packing only long enough to wire back, "Can't stop," and kept on sending them. On the next train up from Franklin came one of the company's inspectors. He had instructions to stop the stream of guinea-pigs at all hazards. As his train drew up at Westcote station he saw a cattle-car standing on the express company's siding. When he reached the express office he saw the express wagon backed up to the door. Six boys were carrying bushel baskets full of guinea-pigs from the office and dumping them into the wagon. Inside the room Flannery, with his coat and vest off, was shoveling guinea-pigs into bushel baskets with a coal scoop. He was winding up the guinea-pig episode.

He looked up at the inspector with a snort of anger.

"Wan wagonload more an' I'll be quit of thim, an' niver will ye catch Flannery wid no more foreign pigs on his hands. No, sur! They near was the death o' me. Nixt toime I'll know that pigs of whativer nationality is domistic pets — an' go at the lowest rate.

He began shoveling again rapidly, speaking quickly between breaths.

"Rules may be rules, but you can't fool Mike Flannery twice wid the same thrick — whin ut comes to live stock, dang the rules. So long as Flannery runs this expriss office — pigs is pets — an' cows is pets — an' horses is pets — an' lions an' tigers an' Rocky Mountain goats is pets — an' the rate on thim is twinty-foive cints."

He paused long enough to let one of the boys put an empty basket in the place of the one he had just filled. There were only a few guinea-pigs left. As he noted their limited number his natural habit of looking on the bright side returned.

"Well, annyhow," he said cheerfully, "'tis not so bad as ut might be. What if thim dago pigs had been elephants!"

QUESTIONS

1. How does the title strike the keynote of the story?
2. What is the opening situation in the story? Would you expect a really serious story to follow such an opening? Explain.

3. Read Flannery's speeches. What do you think of his brogue?

4. Would the express agent's situation have been as funny if Mr. Morehouse had not moved away?

5. Estimate roughly how much of the story is given over to dialogue. Find passages where dialogue is used to advance the plot.

6. State the plot of the story as briefly as possible.

7. *Word Study.* — What do the following words mean as they are used in the story: *vituperation, manifest, provender, prolific?*

Problem: HUMOR
(See page 28.)

1. What is humor? What kinds of things seem funny to you? Try to explain why they are funny.

2. What is the funniest incident in this story? What is funny about it — the situation, the dialogue, a pointed contrast, exaggeration?

3. Find examples of humor achieved by a funny situation; funny dialogue; a contrast; exaggeration.

4. Is the plot of this story probable, improbable, or impossible? Does the probability of the plot have anything to do with the effect of the story?

Keeping Up Appearances *

William Wymark Jacobs (1863–1943)

William Wymark Jacobs, once described by the late Christopher Morley as "one of the most permanently delightful short-story writers who ever lived," was born in London, on September 8, 1863, and died there in a nursing home just one week before his eightieth birthday. As young William's father was the manager of South Devon Wharf, Wapping, London, the young son played about the dock many, many hours while he was growing up and observed with interest the skippers, the sailors, and the small boats which were then employed in coastwise traffic. Undoubtedly, the lad stored in his youthful mind the material which he used when he began to write; in later years, Jacobs remembered vividly the watchmen, the longshoremen, and the coast sailors who later peopled his short stories.

After completing his basic schooling (Jacobs was educated privately), he took and passed his Civil Service examinations and was then appointed to a position in the savings bank department of the British General Post Office. At first, writing was merely a pleasant hobby; Jacobs was thirty-three years old when his first book, "Many Cargoes," was published, but three years after this, in 1899, he gave up his position to devote himself entirely to writing.

Although the author was primarily a humorist, nevertheless, several of his stories (for example, "The Well," "The Toll House," and "The Monkey's Paw") are proof of his ability as a writer of dramatic fiction. In his stories, the realistic, clever dialogue and the natural development of most unusual situations seem to be entirely spontaneous. Actually, since the author was one of the most painstaking craftsmen of his day, this humor is the result of much thought and careful planning. Jacobs himself was taciturn, rather shy, and extremely modest. For the last

*fifteen years of his life, he wrote very little, and his last published
book (1931) was a collection of some of the finest stories he had
written years before.*

*"Keeping Up Appearances" is typical of the best in Jacob's
vein and contains one of the author's favorite characters, the
night-watchman of the wharf. In the story itself, the author blends
original situation, clever dialogue, humorous characters, and rich
local color in one harmonious whole. As usual in a Jacob's story,
the dialogue is excellent; it is indeed so subtle in spots that the
rapid reader is in danger of missing some of the best humor.
Pupils who would like to read more stories by this author should
consult the omnibus collection, "Snug Harbor."*

"EVERYBODY is superstitious," said the night-
watchman, as he gave utterance to a series of chirruping
endearments to a black cat with one eye that had just been
using a leg of his trousers as a serviette; "if that cat 'ad stole
some men's suppers they'd have acted foolish, and suffered
for it all the rest of their lives."

He scratched the cat behind the ear, and despite himself
his face darkened. "Slung it over the side, they would," he
said, longingly, "and chucked bits o' coke at it till it sank.
As I said afore, everybody is superstitious, and those that
ain't ought to be night-watchmen for a time — that 'ud cure
'em. I knew one man that killed a black cat, and arter that
for the rest of his life he could never get three sheets in the
wind without seeing its ghost. Spoilt his life for 'im, it did."

He scratched the cat's other ear. "I only left it a moment,
while I went round to the Bull's Head," he said, slowly filling
his pipe, "and I thought I'd put it out o' reach. Some men
——"

His fingers twined round the animal's neck; then, with a
sigh, he rose and took a turn or two on the jetty.

"Superstitiousness is right and proper, to a certain extent,"
he said, resuming his seat; "but, o' course, like everything
else, some people carry it too far — they'd believe anything.
Weak-minded they are, and if you're in no hurry I can tell

you a tale of a pal o' mine, Bill Burtenshaw by name, that'll prove my words."

His mother was superstitious afore 'im, and always knew when 'er friends died by hearing three loud taps on the wall. The on'y mistake she ever made was one night when, arter losing no less than seven friends, she found out it was the man next door hanging pictures at three o'clock in the morning. She found it out by 'im hitting 'is thumb-nail.

For the first few years arter he grew up Bill went to sea, and that on'y made 'im more superstitious than ever. Him and a pal named Silas Winch went several v'y'ges together, and their talk used to be that creepy that some o' the chaps was a'most afraid to be left on deck alone of a night. Silas was a long-faced, miserable sort o' chap, always looking on the black side o' things, and shaking his 'ead over it. He thought nothing o' seeing ghosts, and pore old Ben Huggins slept on the floor for a week by reason of a ghost with its throat cut that Silas saw in his bunk. He gave Silas arf a dollar and a neck-tie to change bunks with 'im.

When Bill Burtenshaw left the sea and got married he lost sight of Silas altogether, and the on'y thing he 'ad to remind him of 'im was a piece o' paper which they 'ad both signed with their blood, promising that the fust one that died would appear to the other. Bill agreed to it one evenin' when he didn't know wot he was doing, and for years arterwards 'e used to get the cold creeps down 'is back when he thought of Silas dying fust. And the idea of dying fust 'imself gave 'im creeps all over.

Bill was a very good husband when he was sober, but 'is money was two pounds a week, and when a man has all that an on'y a wife to keep out of it, it's natural for 'im to drink. Mrs. Burtenshaw tried all sorts o' ways and means of curing 'im, but it was no use. Bill used to think o' ways, too, knowing the 'arm the drink was doing 'im, and his fav'rite plan was for 'is missis to empty a bucket o' cold water over 'im every time he came 'ome the worse for licker. She did it once, but as she 'ad to spend the rest o' the night in the back yard, it wasn't tried again.

Bill got worse as he got older, and even made away with the furniture to get drink with. And then he used to tell 'is missis that he was drove to the pub because his 'ome was so uncomfortable.

Just at that time things was at their worst Silas Winch, who 'appened to be ashore and 'ad got Bill's address from a pal, called to see 'im. It was a Saturday arternoon when he called, and, o' course, Bill was out, but 'is missis showed him in, and, arter fetching another chair from the kitchen, asked 'im to sit down.

Silas was very perlite at fust, but arter looking round the room and seeing 'ow bare it was, he gave a little cough, and he ses, "I thought Bill was doing well?" he ses.

"So he is," ses Mrs. Burtenshaw.

Silas Winch coughed again.

"I suppose he likes room to stretch 'imself about in?" he ses, looking round.

Mrs. Burtenshaw wiped 'er eyes and then, knowing 'ow Silas had been an old friend o' Bill's, she drew 'er chair a bit closer and told him 'ow it was. "A better 'usband, when he's sober, you couldn't wish to see," she ses, wiping her eyes agin. "He'd give me anything — if he 'ad it."

Silas's face got longer than ever. "As a matter o' fact," he ses, "I'm a bit down on my luck, and I called round with the 'ope that Bill could lend me a bit, just till I can pull round."

Mrs. Burtenshaw shook her 'ead.

"Well, I s'pose I can stay and see 'im?" ses Silas. "Me and 'im used to be great pals at one time, and many's the good turn I've done him. Wot time'll he be 'ome?"

"Any time after twelve," ses Mrs. Burtenshaw; "but you'd better not be here then. You see, 'im being in that condition, he might think you was your own ghost come according to promise and be frightened out of 'is life. He's often talked about it."

Silas Winch scratched his head and looked at 'er thoughtful-like.

"Why shouldn't he mistake me for a ghost?" he ses at last; "the shock might do 'im good. And, if you come to that, why shouldn't I pretend to be my own ghost and warn 'im off the drink?"

Mrs. Burtenshaw got so excited at the idea she couldn't 'ardly speak, but at last, arter saying over and over agin she wouldn't do such a thing for worlds, she and Silas arranged that he should come in at about three o'clock in the morning and give Bill a solemn warning. She gave 'im her key, and Silas said he'd come in with his 'air and cap all wet and pretend he'd been drowned.

"It's very kind of you to take all this trouble for nothing," ses Mrs. Burtenshaw as Silas got up to go.

"Don't mention it," ses Silas. "It ain't the fust time, and I don't suppose it'll be the last, that I've put myself out to help my feller-creeturs. We all ought to do wot we can for each other."

"Mind, if he finds it out," ses Mrs. Burtenshaw, all of a tremble, "I don't know nothing about it. P'r'aps to make it more life-like I'd better pretend not to see you."

"P'r'aps it would be better," ses Silas, stopping at the street door. "All I ask is that you'll 'ide the poker and anything else that might be laying about handy. And you 'ad better oil the lock so as the key won't make a noise."

Mrs. Burtenshaw shut the door arter 'im, and then she went in and 'ad a quiet sit-down all by 'erself to think it over. The only thing that comforted 'er was that Bill would be in licker, and also that 'e would believe anything in the ghost line.

It was past twelve when a couple o' pals brought him 'ome, and, arter offering to fight all six of 'em, one arter the other, Bill hit the wall for getting in 'is way, and tumbled upstairs to bed. In less than ten minutes 'e was fast asleep, and pore Mrs. Burtenshaw, arter trying her best to keep awake, fell asleep too.

She was woke up suddenly by a noise that froze the marrer
in 'er bones — the most 'art-rending groan she 'ad ever heard
in 'er life; and, raising her 'ead, she saw Silas Winch standing
at the foot of the bed. He 'ad done his face and hands over
with wot is called loominous paint, his cap was pushed at the
back of his 'ead, and wet wisps of 'air was hanging over his
eyes. For a moment Mrs. Burtenshaw's 'art stood still and
then Silas let off another groan that put her on edge all over.
It was a groan that seemed to come from nothing a'most
until it spread into a roar that made the room tremble and
rattled the jug in the wash-stand basin. It shook everything
in the room but Bill, and he went on sleeping like an infant.
Silas did two more groans, and then 'e leaned over the foot
o' the bed, and stared at Bill, as though 'e couldn't believe
his eyesight.

"Try a squeaky one," ses Mrs. Burtenshaw.

Silas tried five squeaky ones, and then he 'ad a fit o' coughing that would ha' woke the dead, as they say, but it didn't
wake Bill.

"Now some more deep ones," ses Mrs. Burtenshaw, in a
w'isper.

Silas licked his lips — forgetting the paint — and tried the
deep ones agin.

"Now mix 'em a bit," ses Mrs. Burtenshaw.

Silas stared at her. "Look 'ere," he ses, very short, "do
you think I'm a fog-horn, or wot?"

He stood there sulky for a moment, and then 'e invented
a noise that nothing living could miss hearing; even Bill
couldn't. He moved in 'is sleep, and arter Silas 'ad done it
twice more he turned and spoke to 'is missus about it. "D'ye
hear?" he ses; "stop it. Stop it at once."

Mrs. Burtenshaw pretended to be asleep, and Bill was just
going to turn over agin when Silas let off another groan. It
was on'y a little one this time, but Bill sat up as though he
'ad been shot, and he no sooner caught sight of Silas standing
there than 'e gave a dreadful 'owl and, rolling over, wropped
'imself up in all the bedclothes 'e could lay his 'ands on. Then

Mrs. Burtenshaw gave a 'owl and tried to get some of 'em back; but Bill, thinking it was the ghost, only held on tighter than ever.

"Bill!" ses Silas Winch, in an awful voice.

Bill gave a kick, and tried to bore a hole through the bed.

"Bill," ses Silas agin, "why don't you answer me? I've come all the way from the bottom of the Pacific Ocean to see you, and this is all I get for it. Haven't you got anything to say to me?"

"Good-by," ses Bill, in a voice all smothered with the bed-clothes.

Silas Winch groaned agin, and Bill, as the shock 'ad made a'most sober, trembled all over.

"The moment I died," ses Silas, "I thought of my promise towards you. 'Bill's expecting me,' I ses, and, instead of staying in comfort at the bottom of the sea, I kicked off the body of the cabin-boy wot was clinging round my leg, and 'ere I am."

"It was very — t-t-thoughtful — of you — Silas," ses Bill; "but you always — w-w-was — thoughtful. Good-by."

Afore Silas could answer, Mrs. Burtenshaw, who felt more comfortable, 'aving got a bit o' the clothes back, thought it was time to put 'er spoke in.

"Lor' bless me, Bill," she ses. "Wotever are you a-talking to yourself like this for? 'Ave you been dreaming?"

"Dreaming!" ses pore Bill, catching hold of her 'and and gripping it till she nearly screamed. "I wish I was. Can't you see it?"

"See it?" ses his wife. "See wot?"

"The ghost," ses Bill, in a 'orrible whisper; "the ghost of my dear, kind old pal, Silas Winch. The best and noblest pal a man ever 'ad. The kindest-'arted ——"

"Rubbish," ses Mrs. Burtenshaw. "You've been dreaming. And as for the kindest-'arted pal, why I've often heard you say ——"

"H'sh!" ses Bill. "I didn't. I'll swear I didn't. I never thought of such a thing."

"You turn over and go to sleep," ses his wife, "hiding your 'ead under the clothes like a child that's afraid o' the dark! There's nothing there, I tell you. Wot next will you see, I wonder? Last time it was a pink rat."

"This is fifty million times worse than pink rats," ses Bill. "I on'y wish it was a pink rat."

"I tell you there is nothing there," ses his wife. "Look!"

Bill put his 'ead up and looked, and then 'e gave a dreadful scream and dived under the bed-clothes agin.

"Oh, well, 'ave it your own way, then," ses his wife. "If it pleases you to think there is a ghost there, and to go on talking to it, do so, and welcome."

She turned over and pretended to go to sleep agin, and arter a minute or two Silas spoke agin in the same hollow voice.

"Bill!" he ses.

"Yes," ses Bill, with a groan of his own.

"She can't see me," ses Silas, "and she can't 'ear me; but I'm 'ere all right. Look!"

"I 'ave looked," ses Bill, with his 'ead still under the clothes.

"We was always pals, Bill, you and me," ses Silas; "many a v'y'age 'ave we had together, mate, and now I'm a-laying at the bottom of the Pacific Ocean, and you are snug and 'appy in your own warm bed. I 'ad to come to see you, according to promise, and over and above that, since I was drowned my eyes 'ave been opened. Bill, you're drinking yourself to death!"

"I — I — didn't know it," ses Bill, shaking all over. "I'll knock it — off a bit, and — thank you — for — w-w-warning me. G-G-Good-bye."

"You'll knock it off altogether," ses Silas Winch, in a awful voice. "You're not to touch another drop of beer, wine, or spirits as long as you live. D'ye hear me?"

"Not — not as medicine?" ses Bill, holding the clothes up a bit so as to be more distinct.

"Not as anything," ses Silas; "not even over Christmas pudding. Raise your right arm above your 'ead and swear by the ghost of pore Silas Winch, as is laying at the bottom of the Pacific Ocean, that you won't touch another drop."

Bill Burtenshaw put 'is arm up and swore it. Then 'e took 'is arm in agin and lay there wondering wot was going to 'appen next.

"If you ever break your oath by on'y so much as a tea-spoonful," ses Silas, "you'll see me agin, and the second time you see me you'll die as if struck by lightning. No man can see me twice and live."

Bill broke out in a cold perspiration all over. "You'll be careful, won't you, Silas?" he ses. "You'll remember you 'ave seen me once, I mean?"

"And there's another thing afore I go," ses Silas. "I've left a widder, and if she don't get 'elp from someone she'll starve."

"Pore thing," ses Bill. "Pore thing."

"If you 'ad died afore me," ses Silas, "I should 'ave looked arter your good wife — wot I've now put in a sound sleep — as long as I lived."

Bill didn't say anything.

"I should 'ave given 'er fifteen shillings a week," ses Silas.

"'Ow much?" ses Bill, nearly putting his 'ead up over the clothes, while 'is wife almost woke up with surprise and anger.

"Fifteen shillings," ses Silas, in 'is most awful voice. "You'll save that over the drink."

"I — I'll go round and see her," ses Bill. "She might be one o' these 'ere independent ——"

"I forbid you to go near the place," ses Silas. "Send it by post every week; 15 Shap Street will find her. Put your arm up and swear it; same as you did afore."

Bill did as 'e was told, and then 'e lay and trembled, as Silas gave three more awful groans.

"Farewell, Bill," he ses. "Farewell. I am going back to my bed at the bottom o' the sea. So long as you keep your oaths I shall stay there. If you break one of 'em or go to see my pore wife I shall appear agin. Farewell! Farewell! Farewell!"

Bill said "Good-bye," and arter a long silence he ventured to put an eye over the edge of the clothes and discovered that the ghost 'ad gone. He lay awake for a couple o' hours, wondering and saying over the address to himself so that he shouldn't forget it, and just afore it was time to get up he fell into a peaceful slumber. His wife didn't get a wink, and she lay there trembling with passion to think 'ow she'd been done, and wondering 'ow she was to alter it.

Bill told 'er all about it in the morning; and then with tears in his eyes 'e went downstairs and emptied a little barrel o' beer down the sink. For the fust two or three days 'e went about with a thirst that he'd ha' given pounds for if 'e'd been allowed to satisfy it, but arter a time it went off, and then, like all teetotallers, 'e began to run down drink and call it pison.

The fust thing 'e did when 'e got his money on Friday was to send off a post-office order to Shap Street, and Mrs. Burtenshaw cried with rage an 'ad to put it down to the headache. She 'ad the headache every Friday for a month, and Bill, wot was feeling stronger and better than he 'ad done for years, felt quite sorry for her.

By the time Bill 'ad sent off six orders she was worn to skin and bone a'most a-worrying over the way Silas Winch was spending her money. She dursn't undeceive Bill for two reasons: fust of all, because she didn't want 'im to take to drink agin; and secondly, for fear of wot he might do to 'er if 'e found out 'ow she'd been deceiving 'im.

She was laying awake thinking it over one night while Bill was sleeping peaceful by her side, when all of a sudden she 'ad an idea. The more she thought of it the better it seemed; but she laid awake for ever so long afore she dared to do more than think. Three or four times she turned and looked at Bill and listened to 'im breathing, and then, trembling all over with fear and excitement, she began 'er little game.

"He did send it," she ses, with a piercing scream. "He did send it."

"W-w-wot's the matter?" ses Bill, beginning to wake up.

Mrs. Burtenshaw didn't take any notice of 'im.

"He did send it," she ses, screaming agin. "Every Friday night reg'lar. Oh, *don't let 'im see you agin.*"

Bill, wot was just going to ask 'er whether she 'ad gone mad, gave a awful 'owl and disappeared right down in the middle o' the bed.

"There's some mistake," ses Mrs. Burtenshaw, in a voice that could ha' been 'eard through arf-a-dozen beds easy. "It must ha' been lost in the post. It must ha' been."

She was silent for a few seconds, then she ses, "All right," she ses, "I'll bring it myself, then, by hand every week. No, Bill shan't come; I'll promise that for 'im. Do go away; he might put his 'ead up at any moment."

She began to gasp and sob, and Bill began to think wot a good wife he 'ad got, when he felt 'er put a couple of pillers over where she judged his 'ead to be, and hold 'em down with her arm.

"Thank you, Mr. Winch," she ses, very loud. "Thank you. Good-bye. Good-bye."

She began to quieten down a bit, although little sobs, like wimmen use when they pretend that they want to leave off crying but can't, kept breaking out of 'er. Then, by and by, she quieted down altogether and a husky voice from near the foot of the bed ses: "Has it gorn?"

"Oh, Bill," she ses, with another sob, "I've seen the ghost!"

"Has it gorn?" ses Bill, agin.

"Yes, it's gorn," ses his wife, shivering. "Oh, Bill, it stood at the foot of the bed looking at me, with its face and 'ands all shiny white, and damp curls on its forehead. Oh!"

Bill came up very slow and careful, but with 'is eyes still shut.

"His wife didn't get the money this week," ses Mrs. Burtenshaw; "but as he thought there might be a mistake somewhere he appeared to me instead of to you. I've got to take the money by hand."

"Yes, I heard," ses Bill; "and mind, if you should lose it or be robbed of it, let me know at once. D'ye hear? *At once!*"

"Yes, Bill," ses 'is wife.

They lay quiet for some time, although Mrs. Burtenshaw still kept trembling and shaking; and then Bill ses: "Next time a man tells you he 'as seen a ghost, p'r'aps you'll believe in 'im."

Mrs. Burtenshaw took out the end of the sheet wot she 'ad stuffed in 'er mouth when 'e began to speak.

"Yes, Bill," she ses.

Bill Burtenshaw gave 'er the fifteen shillings next morning and every Friday night arterwards; and that's 'ow it is that, while other wimmen 'as to be satisfied looking at new hats and clothes in the shop-winders, Mrs. Burtenshaw is able to wear 'em.

QUESTIONS

1. Does the title fit the story? Explain.
2. Who was cleverer, Silas Winch or Mrs. Burtenshaw?
3. This story seems to begin in the same general manner as does "The Pack." Each of these stories opens with a conversation in which a general statement is made. The narrator then announces his intention of proving the statement. What is the important difference between the two beginnings? What other differences can you find?
4. Was Silas Winch a superstitious man?
5. Where in the story did you first suspect that Silas intended to profit by Bill's superstition?
6. Was it necessary to the humor of the story that Mrs. Burtenshaw win out in the end?
7. *Word Study.* — What do the following words mean as they are used in the story: *endearment, serviette?*

Problem: HUMOR
(See page 28.)

1. Why does the author have this story told by the nightwatchman? What reason can you see for the introduction of the black cat?
2. Which do you think is funnier, "Keeping Up Appearances" or "Pigs Is Pigs?" Which has the better title? Which has funnier situations, conversation, characters?
3. Compare what you know of Bill Burtenshaw with what you know of Mike Flannery. Why is there more character development in one story than in the other?
4. W. W. Jacobs is known especially for his amusing situations and humorous conversation. Find examples of each.

The Whirligig of Life *

O. Henry (see page 47)

Those who know only the most popular of O. Henry's stories — such as "The Gift of the Magi," "The Third Ingredient," and "A Service of Love" — have come to think of him as a writer of urban sketches, completely engrossed in the many complications of life in Manhattan. A real student of the short story will tell you that some of his finest stories are set elsewhere — in the Southwest, in southern cities, and in the mountains of the South.

"The Whirligig of Life" is a story of the Cumberland Mountains. It is a more straightforward story than "A Service of Love," and it is told with less comment by the author. It contains, however, many of the special features of O. Henry's best work — the technical skill, the clever turn of phrase, the acute characterization, the humorous sentimentality. All these features make this story an interesting study to the student of short fiction, and all of them go to prove O. Henry a more versatile writer than many of his readers believe.

JUSTICE–OF–THE–PEACE Benaja Widdup sat in the door of his office smoking his elder-stem pipe. Halfway to the Zenith the Cumberland range rose blue-gray in the afternoon haze. A speckled hen swaggered down the main street of the "settlement," cackling foolishly.

Up the road came a sound of creaking axles, and then a slow cloud of dust, and then a bull-cart bearing Ransie Bilbro and his wife. The cart stopped at the Justice's door, and the two climbed down. Ransie was a narrow six feet of sallow brown skin and yellow hair. The imperturbability of the mountains hung upon him like a suit of armor. The woman was calicoed, angled, snuff-brushed, and weary with unknown desires. Through it all gleamed a faint protest of cheated youth unconscious of its loss.

The Justice of the Peace slipped his feet into his shoes, for the sake of dignity, and moved to let them enter.

"We-all," said the woman, in a voice like the wind blowing through pine boughs, "wants a divo'ce." She looked at Ransie to see if he noted any flaw or ambiguity or evasion or partiality or self-partisanship in her statement of their business.

"A divo'ce," repeated Ransie, with a solemn nod. "We-all can't git along together nohow. It's lonesome enough fur to live in the mount'ins when a man and a woman keers fur one another. But when she's a-spittin' like a wildcat or a-sullenin' like a hoot-owl in the cabin, a man ain't got no call to live with her."

"When he's a no-'count varmint," said the woman, without any especial warmth, "a-traipsin' along of scalawags and moonshiners and a-layin' on his back pizen'd 'ith co'n whiskey and a-pesterin' folks with a pack 'o hungry, triflin' houn's to feed!"

"When she keeps a-throwin' skillet lids," came Ransie's antiphony, "and slings b'ilin' water on the best coon-dog in the Cumberlands, and sets herself agin' cookin' a man's victuals, and keeps him awake o' nights accusin' him of a sight of doin's!"

"When he's al'ays a-fightin' the revenues, and gits a hard name in the mount'ins fur a mean man, who's gwine to be able fur to sleep o' nights?"

The Justice of the Peace stirred deliberately to his duties. He placed his one chair and a wooden stool for his petitioners. He opened his book of statutes on the table and scanned the index. Presently he wiped his spectacles and shifted his inkstand.

"The law and the statutes," said he, "air silent on the subjeck of divo'ce as fur as the jurisdiction of this co't air

concerned. But, accordin' to equity and the Constitution and
the golden rule, it's a bad barg'in that can't run both ways.
If a justice of the peace can marry a couple, it's plain that
he is bound to be able to divo'ce 'em. This here office will
issue a decree of divo'ce and abide by the decision of the
Supreme Co't to hold it good."

Ransie Bilbro drew a small tobacco-bag from his trousers
pocket. Out of this he shook upon the table a five-dollar note.
"Sold a b'arskin and two foxes fur that," he remarked. "It's
all the money we got."

"The regular price of a divo'ce in this co't," said the Justice,
"air five dollars." He stuffed the bill into the pocket of his
homespun vest with a deceptive air of indifference. With much
bodily toil and mental travail he wrote the decree upon half
a sheet of foolscap, and then copied it upon the other. Ransie
Bilbro and his wife listened to his reading of the document
that was to give them freedom:

Know all men by these presents that Ransie Bilbro and his wife,
Ariela Bilbro, this day personally appeared before me and promises
that hereinafter they will neither love, honor, nor obey each other,
neither for better nor worse, being of sound mind and body, and accept
summons for divorce according to the peace and dignity of the State.
Herein fail not, so help you God. Benaja Widdup, justice of the peace
in and for the county of Piedmont, State of Tennessee.

The Justice was about to hand one of the documents to
Ransie. The voice of Ariela delayed the transfer. Both men
looked at her. Their dull masculinity was confronted by something sudden and unexpected in the woman.

"Judge, don't you give him that air paper yit. 'Tain't all
settled, nohow. I got to have my rights first. I got to have my
ali-money. 'Tain't no kind of a way to do fur a man to divo'ce
his wife 'thout her havin' a cent fur to do with. I'm a-layin'
off to be a goin' up to brother Ed's up on Hogback Mount'in.
I'm bound fur to have a pa'r of shoes and some snuff and
things besides. Ef Ranse kin affo'd a divo'ce, let him pay me
ali-money."

Ransie Bilbro was stricken to dumb perplexity. There had

been no previous hint of alimony. Women were always bringing up startling and unlooked-for issues.

Justice Benaja Widdup felt that the point demanded judicial decision. The authorities were also silent on the subject of alimony. But the woman's feet were bare. The trail to Hogback Mountain was steep and flinty.

"Ariela Bilbro," he asked, in official tones, "how much did you 'low would be good and sufficient ali-money in the case befo' the co't?"

"I 'lowed," she answered, "fur the shoes and all, to say five dollars. That ain't much fur ali-money, but I reckon that'll git me up to brother Ed's."

"The amount," said the Justice, "air not onreasonable. Ransie Bilbro, you air ordered by the co't to pay the plaintiff the sum of five dollars befo' the decree of divo'ce air issued."

"I hain't no mo' money," breathed Ransie, heavily. "I done paid you all I had."

"Otherwise," said the Justice, looking severely over his spectacles, "you air in contempt of co't."

"I reckon if you gimme till tomorrow," pleaded the husband, "I mout be able to rake or scrape it up somewhars. I never looked for to be a-payin' no ali-money."

"The case air adjourned," said Benaja Widdup, "till tomorrow, when you-all will present yo'selves and obey the order of the co't. Followin' of which the decrees of divo'ce will be delivered." He sat down in the door and began to loosen a shoestring.

"We mout as well go down to Uncle Ziah's," decided Ransie, "and spend the night." He climbed into the cart on one side, and Ariela climbed in on the other. Obeying the flap of his rope, the little red bull slowly came around on a tack, and the cart crawled away in the nimbus arising from its wheels.

Justice-of-the-peace Benaja Widdup smoked his elder-stem pipe. Late in the afternoon he got his weekly paper, and read it until the twilight dimmed its lines. Then he lit the tallow candle on his table, and read until the moon rose, marking the time for supper. He lived in the double log cabin on the slope near the girdled poplar. Going home to supper he crossed a little branch darkened by a laurel thicket. The dark figure of a man stepped from the laurels and pointed a rifle at his breast. His hat was pulled down low, and something covered most of his face.

"I want yo' money," said the figure, "'thout any talk. I'm gettin' nervous, and my finger's a-wabblin' on this here trigger."

"I've only got f-f-five dollars," said the Justice, producing it from his vest pocket.

"Roll it up," came the order, "and stick it in the end of this here gun-bar'l."

The bill was crisp and new. Even fingers that were clumsy and trembling found little difficulty in making a spill of it and inserting it (this with less ease) into the muzzle of the rifle.

"Now I reckon you kin be goin' along," said the robber.

The Justice lingered not on his way.

The next day came the little red bull, drawing the cart to the office door. Justice Benaja Widdup had his shoes on, for he was expecting a visit. In his presence Ransie Bilbro handed to his wife a five-dollar bill. The official's eye sharply viewed it. It seemed to curl up as though it had been rolled and inserted into the end of a gun-barrel. But the Justice refrained from comment. It is true that other bills might be inclined to curl. He handed each one a decree of divorce. Each stood awkwardly silent, slowly folding the guarantee of freedom. The woman cast a shy glance full of constraint at Ransie.

"I reckon you'll be goin' back up to the cabin," she said, "along 'ith the bull-cart. There's bread in the tin box settin' on the shelf. I put the bacon in the b'ilin'-pot to keep the hounds from gittin' it. Don't forget to wind the clock tonight."

"You air a-goin' to your brother Ed's?" asked Ransie, with fine unconcern.

"I was 'lowin' to get along up thar afore night. I ain't sayin' as they'll pester theyselves any to make me welcome, but I hain't nowhar else fur to go. It's a right smart ways, and I reckon I better be goin'. I'll be a-sayin' good-bye, Ranse — that is, if you keer fur to say so."

"I don't know as anybody's a hound dog," said Ransie, in a martyr's voice, "fur to not want to say good-bye — 'less you air so anxious to git away that you don't want me to say it."

Ariela was silent. She folded the five-dollar bill and her decree carefully, and placed them in the bosom of her dress. Benaja Widdup watched the money disappear with mournful eyes behind his spectacles.

And then with his next words he achieved rank (as his thoughts ran) with either the great crowd of the world's sympathizers or the little crowd of its great financiers.

"Be kind o' lonesome in the old cabin to-night, Ranse," he said.

Ransie Bilbro stared out at the Cumberlands, clear blue now in the sunlight. He did not look at Ariela.

"I 'low it might be lonesome," he said; "but when folks gits mad and wants a divo'ce you can't make folks stay."

"There's others wanted a divo'ce," said Ariela, speaking to the wooden stool. "Besides, nobody don't want nobody to stay."

"Nobody never said they didn't."

"Nobody never said they did. I reckon I better start on now to brother Ed's."

"Nobody can't wind that old clock."

"Want me to go back along 'ith you in the cart and wind it fur you, Ranse?"

The mountaineer's countenance was proof against emotion. But he reached out a big hand and enclosed Ariela's thin brown one. Her soul peeped out once through her impassive face, hallowing it.

"Them hounds sha'n't pester you no more," said Ransie. "I reckon I been mean and low down. You wind that clock. Ariela."

"My heart hit's in that cabin, Ranse," she whispered,

"along 'ith you. I ain't a-goin' to git mad no more. Le's be startin', Ranse, so's we kin git home by sundown."

Justice-of-the-peace Benaja Widdup interposed as they started for the door, forgetting his presence.

"In the name of the State of Tennessee," he said, "I forbid you-all to be a-defyin' of its laws and statutes. This co't is mo' than willin' and full of joy to see the clouds of discord and misunderstandin' rollin' away from two lovin' hearts, but it air the duty of the co't to p'eserve the morals and integrity of the State. The co't reminds you that you air no longer man and wife, but air divo'ced by regular decree, and as such air not entitled to the benefits and 'purtenances of the mattermonal estate."

Ariela caught Ransie's arm. Did those words mean that she must lose him now when they had just learned the lesson of life?

"But the co't air prepared," went on the Justice, "fur to remove the disabilities set up by the decree of divo'ce. The co't air on hand to perform the solemn ceremony of marri'ge, thus fixin' things up and enablin' the parties in the case to resume the honor'ble and elevatin' state of mattermony which they desires. The fee fur performin' said ceremony will be, in this case, to wit, five dollars."

Ariela caught the gleam of promise in his words. Swiftly her hand went to her bosom. Freely as an alighting dove the bill fluttered to the Justice's table. Her sallow cheek colored as she stood hand in hand with Ransie and listened to the reuniting words.

Ransie helped her into the cart, and climbed in beside her. The little red bull turned once more, and they set out, hand-clasped, for the mountains.

Justice-of-the-peace Benaja Widdup sat in his door and took off his shoes. Once again he fingered the bill tucked down in his vest pocket. Once again he smoked his elder-stem pipe. Once again the speckled hen swaggered down the main street of the "settlement," cackling foolishly.

QUESTIONS

1. Compare the author's style in this story with that in "A Service o Love." What differences do you see? What similarities? Which style do you like better? Why?

2. Why did the Justice decide that he had the authority to issue a divorce? Was he right?

3. Is Ariela's demand for alimony important to the plot? Explain.

4. Is the conclusion swift, gradual, or slow?

5. How much time does the action of the story cover?

6. *Word Study.* — What do the following words mean as they are used in the story: *ambiguity, imperturbability, partiality, jurisdiction, masculinity, alimony?*

Problem: REVIEW

1. What part does the five-dollar bill play in the plot of the story?

2. Why is the setting important to the story? Point out some instances of local color.

3. What means does O. Henry use to explain the grounds for divorce? Why did he choose this means? Does it save space? Does it shorten the time covered by the story? Does it help him to present his main characters? How?

4. Is this a surprise-ending story? Explain. Does the ending satisfy you? Would you have been satisfied with the ending if there had been real grounds for divorce? Would you have been satisfied with the ending if Ransie and Ariela had remained separate?

5. Is this story romance or realism?

The Three Strangers

Thomas Hardy (1840–1928)

The last of the great Victorians, and one of the greatest novelists of all times, Thomas Hardy was born in Dorsetshire on June 2, 1840. He was educated in King's College, London, and for about five years after receiving his degree studied architecture under John Hicks, a famous ecclesiastical architect. Later he read Greek and Latin with a fellow-student, and spent much of his spare time wandering about old country churches which he sketched and measured. Between 1862 and 1867 he lived in London where he worked at Gothic architecture under Sir A. Blomfield. In 1863, Hardy, just twenty-three years old, was a prizeman of the Royal Institute of British Architects.

Hardy described himself as ". . . an author of prose for twenty-five years and of verse for twenty-eight years." As a matter of fact, he wrote some early verse between 1860 and 1868, but about the latter date he abandoned verse temporarily for prose. After the publication of his first novel in 1871 he wrote a few short stories and many famous novels, some of the best known of which are "Far from the Madding Crowd," "The Mayor of Casterbridge," "Tess of the D'Urbervilles," and "The Return of the Native." Hardy died in the early part of 1928 and was buried in Westminster Abbey.

In all his writing, Hardy was an uncompromising realist; that is, he wrote of simple men and women, of their lives and their trials, and he set his scenes in a simple and familiar landscape, his own county of Dorset, which, in his novels, he calls by its old name of Wessex. He wrote of them simply, too; yet the shadow of an overwhelming fate looms huge and threatening in all his work. The struggles of his simple countrymen become symbolic as we read of them, and, without one word of comparison from the author, readers become aware that a like struggle against impending events goes on, not only in Wessex, but in all the world about them.

348

Hardy is not a terrorist; he seeks neither the grotesquely horrible nor the sordidly brutal in life. When crime and death occur in his novels, he treats them as simply as he does every other part of human life. Many of his novels are tragedies, but they are not imaginary tragedies or theatrical tragedies; they are tragedies of the kind that exist in life, the kind that we all can see if we only stop to look.

"The Three Strangers," an interesting story by this great master of English fiction, is more genial in tone and atmosphere than many of his tales. Yet even with the humor, found in the rustic gathering and simple conversation of the characters, there is a certain somberness of atmosphere; the reader feels that the thought of life as a thing to be endured is ever in the background. The characters, largely rustics, are developed with consummate skill; the setting is rich in local color; and the story employs the now familiar device of the surprise ending. "The Three Strangers" was first published in 1883, and was later included in the author's volume, "Wessex Tales." It is one of two stories which present the rural hangman, a county official much in evidence in the early part of the nineteenth century, when death by hanging was the penalty for dozens of rather trivial offences. This explains why the sympathy of the characters is strongly in favor of the fugitive stranger.

AMONG the few features of agricultural England which retain an appearance but little modified by the lapse of centuries may be reckoned the high, grassy, and furzy downs, coombs, or ewe-leases, as they are indifferently called, that fill a large area of certain counties in the south and southwest. If any mark of human occupation is met with hereon, it usually takes the form of the solitary cottage of some shepherd.

Fifty years ago such a lonely cottage stood on such a down, and may possibly be standing there now. In spite of its loneliness, however, the spot, by actual measurement, was not more than five miles from a county-town. Yet that affected it little. Five miles of irregular upland, during the long inimical seasons, with their sleets, snows, rains, and mists, afford withdrawing space enough to isolate a Timon or a Nebuchadnezzar; much less, in fair weather, to please that less repellent tribe, the poets, philosophers, artists, and others who "conceive and meditate of pleasant things."

Some old earthern camp or barrow, some clump of trees, at least some starved fragment of ancient hedge is usually taken advantage of in the erection of these forlorn dwellings. But, in the present case, such a kind of shelter had been disregarded. Higher Crowstairs, as the house was called, stood quite detached and undefended. The only reason for its precise situation seemed to be the crossing of two footpaths at right angles hard by, which may have crossed here and thus for a good five hundred years. Hence the house was exposed to the elements on all sides. But, though the wind up here blew unmistakably when it did blow, and the rain hit hard whenever it fell, the various weathers of the winter season were not quite so formidable on the coomb as they were imagined to be by dwellers on low ground. The raw rimes were not so pernicious as in the hollows, and the frosts were scarcely so severe. When the shepherd and his family who tenanted the house were pitied for their sufferings from the exposure, they said that upon the whole they were less inconvenienced by "wuzzes and flames" (hoarses and phlegms) than when they had lived by the stream of a snug neighboring valley.

The night of March 28, 182–, was precisely one of the nights that were wont to call forth these expressions of commiseration. The level rainstorm smote walls, slopes, and hedges like the clothyard shafts of Senlac and Crecy. Such sheep and outdoor animals as had no shelter stood with their buttocks to the winds; while the tails of little birds trying to roost on some scraggy thorn were blown inside-out like umbrellas. The gable-end of the cottage was stained with wet, and the eaves-droppings flapped against the wall. Yet never was commiseration for the shepherd more misplaced. For that cheerful rustic was entertaining a large party in glorification of the christening of his second girl.

The guests had arrived before the rain began to fall, and

they were all now assembled in the chief or living room of the dwelling. A glance into the apartment at eight o'clock on this eventful evening would have resulted in the opinion that it was as cosy and comfortable a nook as could be wished for in boisterous weather. The calling of its inhabitant was proclaimed by a number of highly-polished sheep-crooks without stems that were hung ornamentally over the fireplace, the curl of each shining crook varying from the antiquated type engraved in the patriarchal pictures of old family Bibles to the most approved fashion of the last local sheep-fair. The room was lighted by half-a-dozen candles, having wicks only a trifle smaller than the grease which enveloped them, in candlesticks that were never used but at high-days, holydays, and family feasts. The lights were scattered about the room, two of them standing on the chimney-piece. This position of candles was in itself significant. Candles on the chimney-piece always meant a party.

On the hearth, in front of a back-brand to give substance, blazed a fire of thorns, that crackled "like the laughter of the fool."

Nineteen persons were gathered here. Of these, five women, wearing gowns of various bright hues, sat in chairs along the wall; girls shy and not shy filled the window-bench; four men, including Charley Jake the hedge-carpenter, Elijah New the parish-clerk, and John Pitcher, a neighboring dairyman, the shepherd's father-in-law, lolled in the settle; a young man and maid, who were blushing over tentative *pourparlers* on a life-companionship, sat beneath the corner-cupboard; and an elderly engaged man of fifty or upward moved restlessly about from spots where his betrothed was not to the spot where she was. Enjoyment was pretty general, and so much the more prevailed in being unhampered by conventional restrictions. Absolute confidence in each other's good opinion begat perfect ease, while the finishing stroke of manner, amounting to a truly princely serenity, was lent to the majority by the absence of any expression or trait denoting that they wished to get on in the world, enlarge their minds, or do any eclipsing thing whatever — which nowadays so generally nips the bloom and *bonhomie* of all except the two extremes of the social scale.

Shepherd Fennel had married well, his wife being a dairyman's daughter from a vale at a distance, who brought fifty guineas in her pocket — and kept them there, till they should be required for ministering to the needs of a coming family. This frugal woman had been somewhat exercised as to the character that should be given to the gathering. A sit-still party had its advantages; but an undisturbed position of ease in chairs and settles was apt to lead on the men to such an unconscionable deal of toping that they would sometimes fairly drink the house dry. A dancing-party was the alternative; but this, while avoiding the foregoing objection on the score of good drink, had a counter-balancing disadvantage in the matter of good victuals, the ravenous appetites engendered by the exercise causing immense havoc in the buttery. Shepherdess Fennel fell back upon the intermediate plan of mingling short dances with short periods of talk and singing, so as to hinder any ungovernable rage in either. But this scheme was entirely confined to her own gentle mind: the shepherd himself was in the mood to exhibit the most reckless phases of hospitality.

The fiddler was a boy of those parts, about twelve years of age, who had a wonderful dexterity in jigs and reels, though his fingers were so small and short as to necessitate a constant shifting for the high notes, from which he scrambled back to the first position with sounds not of unmixed purity of tone. At seven the shrill tweedle-dee of this youngster had begun, accompanied by a booming ground-bass from Elijah New, the parish-clerk, who had thoughtfully brought with him his favorite musical instrument, the serpent. Dancing was instantaneous, Mrs. Fennel privately enjoining the players on no account to let the dance exceed the length of a quarter of an hour.

But Elijah and the boy, in the excitement of their position, quite forgot the injunction. Moreover, Oliver Giles, a man of

seventeen, one of the dancers, who was enamored of his partner, a fair girl of thirty-three rolling years, had recklessly
handed a new crown-piece to the musicians, as a bribe to
keep going as long as they had muscle and wind. Mrs. Fennel,
seeing the steam begin to generate on the countenances of
her guests, crossed over and touched the fiddler's elbow and
put her hand on the serpent's mouth. But they took no notice,
and fearing she might lose her character of genial hostess if
she were to interfere too markedly, she retired and sat down
helpless. And so the dance whizzed on with cumulative fury,
the performers moving in their planet-like courses, direct and
retrograde, from apogee to perigee, till the hand of the well-
kicked clock at the bottom of the room had traveled over the
circumference of an hour.

While these cheerful events were in course of enactment
within Fennel's pastoral dwelling, an incident having considerable bearing on the party had occurred in the gloomy
night without. Mrs. Fennel's concern about the growing
fierceness of the dance corresponded in point of time with
the ascent of a human figure to the solitary hill of Higher
Crowstairs from the direction of the distant town. This personage strode on through the rain without a pause, following
the little-worn path which, further on in its course, skirted
the shepherd's cottage.

It was nearly the time of full moon, and on this account,
though the sky was lined with a uniform sheet of dripping
cloud, ordinary objects out of doors were readily visible. The
sad, wan light revealed the lonely pedestrian to be a man of
supple frame; his gait suggested that he had somewhat passed
the period of perfect and instinctive agility, though not so
far as to be otherwise than rapid of motion when occasion
required. At a rough guess, he might have been about forty
years of age. He appeared tall, but a recruiting sergeant, or
other person accustomed to the judging of men's heights by
the eye, would have discerned that this was chiefly owing to
his gauntness, and that he was not more than five-feet-eight
or nine.

Notwithstanding the regularity of his tread, there was caution in it, as in that of one who mentally feels his way; and despite the fact that it was not a black coat nor a dark garment of any sort that he wore, there was something about him which suggested that he naturally belonged to the black-coated tribes of men. His clothes were of fustian, and his boots hobnailed, yet in his progress he showed not the mud-accustomed bearing of hobnailed and fustianed peasantry.

By the time that he had arrived abreast of the shepherd's premises the rain came down, or rather came along, with yet more determined violence. The outskirts of the little settlement partially broke the force of wind and rain, and this induced him to stand still. The most salient of the shepherd's domestic erections was an empty sty at the forward corner of his hedgeless garden, for in these latitudes the principle of masking the homelier features of your establishment by a conventional frontage was unknown. The traveler's eye was attracted to this small building by the pallid shine of the wet slates that covered it. He turned aside, and, finding it empty, stood under the pent-roof for shelter.

While he stood, the boom of the serpent within the adjacent house, and the lesser strains of the fiddler, reached the spot as an accompaniment to the surging hiss of the flying rain on the sod, its louder beating on the cabbage-leaves of the garden, on the eight or ten beehives just discernible by the path, and its dripping from the eaves into a row of buckets and pans that had been placed under the walls of the cottage. For at Higher Crowstairs, as at all such elevated domiciles, the grand difficulty of housekeeping was an insufficiency of water; and a casual rainfall was utilized by turning out, as catchers, every utensil that the house contained. Some queer stories might be told of the contrivances for economy in suds and dish-waters that are absolutely necessitated in upland habitations during the droughts of summer. But at this season there were no such exigencies; a mere acceptance of what the skies bestowed was sufficient for an abundant store.

At last the notes of the serpent ceased and the house was

silent. This cessation of activity aroused the solitary pedestrian from the reverie into which he had lapsed, and, emerging from the shed, with an apparently new intention, he walked up the path to the house-door. Arrived here, his first act was to kneel down on a large stone beside the row of vessels, and to drink a copious draught from one of them. Having quenched his thirst he rose and lifted his hand to knock, but paused with his eye upon the panel. Since the dark surface of the wood revealed absolutely nothing, it was evident that he must be mentally looking through the door, as if he wished to measure thereby all the possibilities that a house of this sort might include, and how they might bear upon the question of his entry.

In his indecision he turned and surveyed the scene around. Not a soul was anywhere visible. The garden path stretched downward from his feet, gleaming like the track of a snail; the roof of the little well (mostly dry), the well-cover, the top rail of the garden-gate, were varnished with the same dull liquid glaze; while, far away in the vale, a faint whiteness of more than usual extent showed that the rivers were high in the meads. Beyond all this winked a few bleared lamplights through the beating drops — lights that denoted the situation of the county-town from which he had appeared to come. The absence of all notes of life in that direction seemed to clinch his intentions, and he knocked at the door.

Within, a desultory chat had taken the place of movement and musical sound. The hedge-carpenter was suggesting a song to the company, which nobody just then was inclined to undertake, so that the knock afforded a not unwelcome diversion.

"Walk in!" said the shepherd promptly.

The latch clicked upward, and out of the night our pedestrian appeared upon the door-mat. The shepherd arose, snuffed two of the nearest candles, and turned to look at him.

Their light disclosed that the stranger was dark in complexion and not unprepossessing as to feature. His hat, which for a moment he did not remove, hung low over his eyes, without concealing that they were large, open, and determined, moving with a flash rather than a glance round the room. He seemed pleased with his survey, and, baring his shaggy head, said, in a rich deep voice, "The rain is so heavy, friends, that I ask leave to come in and rest awhile."

"To be sure, stranger," said the shepherd. "And faith, you've been lucky in choosing your time, for we are having a bit of a fling for a glad cause — though, to be sure, a man could hardly wish that glad cause to happen more than once a year."

"Nor less," spoke up a woman. "For 'tis best to get your family over and done with, as soon as you can, so as to be all the earlier out of the fag o't."

"And what may be this glad cause?" asked the stranger.

"A birth and christening," said the shepherd.

The stranger hoped his host might not be made unhappy either by too many or too few of such episodes, and being invited by a gesture to a pull at the mug, he readily acquiesced. His manner, which, before entering, had been so dubious, was not altogether that of a careless and candid man.

"Late to be traipsing athwart this coomb — hey?" said the engaged man of fifty.

"Late it is, master, as you say. I'll take a seat in the chimney-corner, if you have nothing to urge against it, ma'am; for I am a little moist on the side that was next the rain."

Mrs. Shepherd Fennel assented, and made room for the self-invited comer, who, having got completely inside the chimney-corner, stretched out his legs and his arms with the expansiveness of a person quite at home.

"Yes, I am rather cracked in the vamp," he said freely, seeing that the eyes of the shepherd's wife fell upon his boots, "and I am not well fitted either. I have had some rough times lately, and have been forced to pick up what I can get in the way of wearing, but I must find a suit better fit for working-days when I reach home."

"One of hereabouts?" she inquired.

"Not quite that — further up the country."

"I thought so. And so be I; and by your tongue you come from my neighborhood."

"But you would hardly have heard of me," he said quickly. "My time would be long before yours, ma'am, you see."

This testimony to the youthfulness of his hostess had the effect of stopping her cross-examination.

"There is only one thing more wanted to make me happy," continued the new-comer. "And that is a little baccy, which I am sorry to say I am out of."

"I'll fill your pipe," said the shepherd.

"I must ask you to lend me a pipe likewise."

"A smoker, and no pipe about 'ee?"

"I have dropped it somewhere on the road."

The shepherd filled and handed him a new clay pipe, saying, as he did so, "Hand me your baccy-box — I'll fill that, too, now I am about it."

The man went through the movement of searching his pockets.

"Lost that, too?" said his entertainer, with some surprise.

"I am afraid so," said the man with some confusion. "Give it to me in a screw of paper." Lighting his pipe at the candle with a suction that drew the whole flame into the bowl, he resettled himself in the corner and bent his looks upon the faint steam from his damp legs, as if he wished to say no more.

Meanwhile the general body of guests had been taking little notice of this visitor by reason of an absorbing discussion in which they were engaged with the band about a tune for the next dance. The matter being settled, they were about to stand up when an interruption came in the shape of another knock at the door.

At sound of the same the man in the chimney-corner took up the poker and began stirring the brands as if doing it thoroughly were the one aim of his existence; and a second time the shepherd said, "Walk in!" In a moment another man stood upon the straw-woven door-mat. He, too, was a stranger.

This individual was one of a type radically different from

the first. There was more of the commonplace in his manner, and a certain jovial cosmopolitanism sat upon his features. He was several years older than the first arrival, his hair being slightly frosted, his eyebrows bristly, and his whiskers cut back from his cheeks. His face was rather full and flabby, and yet it was not altogether a face without power. A few grog-blossoms marked the neighborhood of his nose. He flung back his long drab greatcoat, revealing that beneath it he wore a suit of cinder-gray shade throughout, large heavy seals, of some metal or other that would take a polish, dangling from his fob as his only personal ornament. Shaking the water-drops from his low-crowned glazed hat, he said, "I must ask for a few minutes' shelter, comrades, or I shall be wetted to my skin before I get to Casterbridge."

"Make yourself at home, master," said the shepherd, perhaps a trifle less heartily than on the first occasion. Not that Fennel had the least tinge of niggardliness in his composition; but the room was far from large, spare chairs were not numerous, and damp companions were not altogether desirable at close quarters for the women and girls in their bright-colored gowns.

However, the second comer, after taking off his greatcoat, and hanging his hat on a nail in one of the ceiling-beams as if he had been specially invited to put it there, advanced and sat down at the table. This had been pushed so closely into the chimney-corner, to give all available room to the dancers, that its inner edge grazed the elbow of the man who had ensconced himself by the fire; and thus the two strangers were brought into close companionship. They nodded to each other by way of breaking the ice of unacquaintance, and the first stranger handed his neighbor the family mug — a huge vessel of brown ware, having its upper edge worn away like a threshold by the rub of whole generations of thirsty lips that had gone the way of all flesh, and bearing the following inscription burnt upon its rotund side in yellow letters:

THERE IS NO FUN
UNTILL I CUM

The other man, nothing loth, raised the mug to his lips, and drank on, and on, and on — till a curious blueness overspread the countenance of the shepherd's wife, who had regarded with no little surprise the first stranger's free offer to the second of what did not belong to him to dispense.

"I knew it!" said the toper to the shepherd with much satisfaction. "When I walked up your garden before coming in, and saw the hives all of a row, I said to myself, 'Where there's bees there's honey, and where there's honey there's mead.' But mead of such a truly comfortable sort as this I really didn't expect to meet in my older days." He took yet another pull at the mug, till it assumed an ominous elevation.

"Glad you enjoy it!" said the shepherd warmly.

"It is goodish mead," assented Mrs. Fennel, with an absence of enthusiasm which seemed to say that it was possible to buy praise for one's cellar at too heavy a price. "It is trouble enough to make — and really I hardly think we shall make any more. For honey sells well, and we ourselves can make shift with a drop o' small mead and metheglin for common use from the comb-washings."

"Oh, but you'll never have the heart!" reproachfully cried the stranger in cinder-gray, after taking up the mug a third time and setting it down empty. "I love mead, when 'tis old like this, as I love to go to church o' Sundays, or to relieve the needy any day of the week."

"Ha, ha, ha!" said the man in the chimney-corner, who in spite of the taciturnity induced by the pipe of tobacco could not or would not refrain from this slight testimony to his comrade's humor.

Now the old mead of those days, brewed of the purest first year or maiden honey, four pounds to the gallon — with its due complement of white of eggs, cinnamon, ginger, cloves, mace, rosemary, yeast, and processes of working, bottling, and cellaring — tasted remarkably strong; but it did not taste so strong as it actually was. Hence, presently, the stranger in cinder-gray at the table, moved by its creeping influence, unbuttoned his waistcoat, threw himself back in his chair, spread his legs, and made his presence felt in various ways.

"Well, well, as I say," he resumed, "I am going to Casterbridge, and to Casterbridge I must go. I should have been almost there by this time; but the rain drove me into your dwelling, and I'm not sorry for it."

"You don't live in Casterbridge?" said the shepherd.

"Not as yet; though I shortly mean to move there."

"Going to set up in trade, perhaps?"

"No, no," said the shepherd's wife. "It is easy to see that the gentleman is rich, and don't want to work at anything."

The cinder-gray stranger paused, as if to consider whether he would accept that definition of himself. He presently rejected it by answering, "Rich is not quite the word for me, dame. I do work, and I must work. And even if I only get to Casterbridge by midnight I must begin work there at eight to-morrow morning. Yes, het or wet, blow or snow, famine or sword, my day's work tomorrow must be done."

"Poor man! Then, in spite o' seeming, you be worse off than we," replied the shepherd's wife.

"'Tis the nature of my trade, men and maidens. 'Tis the nature of my trade more than my poverty. . . . But really and truly I must up and off, or I shan't get a lodging in the town." However, the speaker did not move, and directly added, "There's time for one more draught of friendship before I go; and I'd perform it at once if the mug were not dry."

"Here's a mug o' small," said Mrs. Fennel. "Small, we call it, though to be sure 'tis only the first wash o' the combs."

"No," said the stranger disdainfully. "I won't spoil your first kindness by partaking o' your second."

"Certainly not," broke in Fennel. "We don't increase and multiply every day, and I'll fill the mug again." He went away to the dark place under the stairs where the barrel stood. The shepherdess followed him.

"Why should you do this?" she said reproachfully, as soon as they were alone. "He's emptied it once, though it held enough for ten people; and now he's not contented wi' the small, but must needs call for more o' the strong! And a stranger unbeknown to any of us. For my part, I don't like the look o' the man at all."

"But he's in the house, my honey; and 'tis a wet night, and a christening. Daze it, what's a cup of mead more or less? There'll be plenty more next bee-burning."

"Very well — this time, then," she answered, looking wistfully at the barrel. "But what is the man's calling, and where is he one of, that he should come in and join us like this?"

"I don't know. I'll ask him again."

The catastrophe of having the mug drained dry at one pull by the stranger in cinder-gray was effectually guarded against this time by Mrs. Fennel. She poured out his allowance in a small cup, keeping the large one at a discreet distance from him. When he had tossed off his portion the shepherd renewed his inquiry about the stranger's occupation.

The latter did not immediately reply, and the man in the chimney-corner, with sudden demonstrativeness, said, "Anybody may know my trade — I'm a wheelwright."

"A very good trade for these parts," said the shepherd.

"And anybody may know mine — if they've the sense to find it out," said the stranger in cinder-gray.

"You may generally tell what a man is by his claws," observed the hedge-carpenter, looking at his own hands. "My fingers be as full of thorns as an old pin-cushion is of pins."

The hands of the man in the chimney-corner instinctively sought the shade, and he gazed into the fire as he resumed his pipe. The man at the table took up the hedge-carpenter's remark, and added smartly, "True; but the oddity of my trade is that, instead of setting a mark upon me, it sets a mark upon my customers."

No observation being offered by anybody in elucidation of this enigma, the shepherd's wife once more called for a song. The same obstacles presented themselves as at the former time — one had no voice, another had forgotten the first verse. The stranger at the table, whose soul had now risen to a good working temperature, relieved the difficulty by exclaiming that, to start the company, he would sing himself. Thrusting one thumb into the armhole of his waistcoat, he waved the other hand in the air, and, with an extemporizing gaze at the shining sheep-crooks above the mantelpiece, began:

> "O my trade it is the rarest one,
>   Simple shepherds all —
> My trade is a sight to see;
> For my customers I tie, and take them up on high,
>   And waft 'em to a far countree!"

The room was silent when he had finished the verse — with one exception, that of the man in the chimney-corner, who, at the singer's word, "Chorus!" joined him in a deep bass voice of musical relish —

> "And waft 'em to a far countree!"

Oliver Giles, John Pitcher the dairyman, the parish-clerk, the engaged man of fifty, the row of young women against the wall, seemed lost in thought not of the gayest kind. The shepherd looked meditatively on the ground, the shepherdess gazed keenly at the singer, and with some suspicion; she was doubting whether this stranger were merely singing an old song from recollection, or was composing one there and then for the occasion. All were as perplexed at the obscure revelation as the guests at Belshazzar's Feast, except the man in the chimney-corner, who quietly said, "Second verse, stranger," and smoked on.

The singer thoroughly moistened himself from his lips inwards, and went on with the next stanza as requested:

> "My tools are but common ones,
>   Simple shepherds all —
> My tools are no sight to see:
> A little hempen string, and a post whereon to swing,
>   Are implements enough for me!"

Shepherd Fennel glanced round. There was no longer any doubt that the stranger was answering his question rhythmically. The guests one and all started back with suppressed exclamations. The young woman engaged to the man of fifty

fainted halfway, and would have proceeded, but finding him
wanting in alacrity for catching her she sat down trembling.

"Oh, he's the ——!" whispered the people in the background, mentioning the name of an ominous public officer.
"He's come to do it! 'Tis to be at Casterbridge jail tomorrow
— the man for sheep-stealing — the poor clock-maker we
heard of, who used to live away at Shottsford and had no
work to do — Timothy Summers, whose family were a-starv-
ing, and so he went out of Shottsford by the highroad, and
took a sheep in open daylight defying the farmer and the
farmer's wife and the farmer's lad, and every man jack among
'em. He" (and they nodded toward the stranger of the deadly
trade) "is come from up the country to do it because there's
not enough to do in his own county-town, and he's got the
place here now our own county man's dead; he's going to live
in the same cottage under the prison wall."

The stranger in cinder-gray took no notice of this whispered string of observations, but again wetted his lips. Seeing
that his friend in the chimney-corner was the only one who
reciprocated his joviality in any way, he held out his cup
toward that appreciative comrade, who also held out his own.
They clinked together, the eyes of the rest of the room hanging upon the singer's actions. He parted his lips for the third
verse; but at that moment another knock was audible upon
the door. This time the knock was faint and hesitating.

The company seemed scared; the shepherd looked with
consternation toward the entrance, and it was with some
effort that he resisted his alarmed wife's deprecatory glance,
and uttered for the third time the welcoming words "Walk
in!"

The door was gently opened, and another man stood upon
the mat. He, like those who had preceded him, was a stranger.
This time it was a short, small personage, of fair complexion,
and dressed in a decent suit of dark clothes.

"Can you tell me the way to ——?" he began: when,
gazing round the room to observe the nature of the company
amongst whom he had fallen, his eyes lighted on the stranger

in cinder-gray. It was just at the instant when the latter, who had thrown his mind into his song with such a will that he scarcely heeded the interruption, silenced all whispers and inquiries by bursting into his third verse —

> "Tomorrow is my working day,
>   Simple shepherds all —
> Tomorrow is a working day for me:
> For the farmer's sheep is slain, and the lad who did it ta'en,
>   And on his soul may God ha' merc-y!"

The stranger in the chimney-corner, waving cups with the singer so heartily that his mead splashed over on the hearth, repeated in his bass voice as before —

> "And on his soul may God ha' merc-y!"

All this time the third stranger had been standing in the doorway. Finding now that he did not come forward or go on speaking, the guests particularly regarded him. They noticed to their surprise that he stood before them the picture of abject terror — his knees trembling, his hand shaking so violently that the door-latch by which he supported himself rattled audibly: his white lips were parted, and his eyes fixed on the merry officer of justice in the middle of the room. A moment more and he had turned, closed the door, and fled.

"What a man can it be?" said the shepherd.

The rest, between the awfulness of their late discovery and the odd conduct of this third visitor, looked as if they knew not what to think, and said nothing. Instinctively they withdrew further and further from the grim gentleman in their midst, whom some of them seemed to take for the Prince of Darkness himself, till they formed a remote circle, an empty space of floor being left between them and him —

> "... circulus, cujus centrum diabolus."

The room was so silent — though there were more than twenty people in it — that nothing could be heard but the patter of the rain against the window-shutters, accompanied by the occasional hiss of a stray drop that fell down the chimney into the fire, and the steady puffing of the man in the corner, who had now resumed his long pipe of clay.

The stillness was unexpectedly broken. The distant sound of a gun reverberated through the air — apparently from the direction of the county-town.

"Be jiggered!" cried the stranger who had sung the song, jumping up.

"What does that mean?" asked several.

"A prisoner escaped from the jail — that's what it means."

All listened. The sound was repeated, and none of them spoke but the man in the chimney-corner, who said quietly, "I've often been told that in this county they fire a gun at such times; but I never heard it till now."

"I wonder if it is *my* man?" murmured the personage in cinder-gray.

"Surely it is!" said the shepherd involuntarily. "And surely we've zeed him! That little man who looked in at the door by now, and quivered like a leaf when he zeed ye and heard your song!"

"His teeth chattered, and the breath went out of his body," said the dairyman.

"And his heart seemed to sink within him like a stone," said Oliver Giles.

"And he bolted as if he'd been shot at," said the hedge-carpenter.

"True — his teeth chattered, and his heart seemed to sink; and he bolted as if he'd been shot at," slowly summed up the man in the chimney-corner.

"I didn't notice it," remarked the hangman.

"We were all a-wondering what made him run off in such a fright," faltered one of the women against the wall, "and now 'tis explained!"

The firing of the alarm-gun went on at intervals, low and sullenly, and their suspicions became a certainty. The sinister gentleman in cinder-gray roused himself. "Is there a constable here?" he asked, in thick tones. "If so, let him step forward."

The engaged man of fifty stepped quavering out from the wall, his betrothed beginning to sob on the back of the chair.

"You are a sworn constable?"

"I be, sir."

"Then pursue the criminal at once, with assistance, and bring him back here. He can't have gone far."

"I will, sir, I will — when I've got my staff. I'll go home and get it, and come sharp here, and start in a body."

"Staff! — never mind your staff; the man'll be gone!"

"But I can't do nothing without my staff — can I, William, and John, and Charles Jake? No; for there's the king's royal crown a painted on en in yaller and gold, and the lion and the unicorn, so as when I raise en up and hit my prisoner, 'tis made a lawful blow thereby. I wouldn't 'tempt to take up a man without my staff — no, not I. If I hadn't the law to gie me courage, why, instead o' my taking up him he might take up me!"

"Now, I'm a king's man myself, and can give you authority enough for this," said the formidable officer in gray. "Now then, all of ye, be ready. Have ye any lanterns?"

"Yes — have ye any lanterns? — I demand it!" said the constable.

"And the rest of you able-bodied ——"

"Able-bodied men — yes — the rest of ye!" said the constable.

"Have you some good stout staves and pitchforks ——"

"Staves and pitchforks — in the name o' the law! And take 'em in yer hands and go in quest, and do as we in authority tell ye!"

Thus aroused, the men prepared to give chase. The evidence was, indeed, though circumstantial, so convincing that but little argument was needed to show the shepherd's guests that after what they had seen it would look very much like connivance if they did not instantly pursue the unhappy third stranger, who could not as yet have gone more than a few hundred yards over such uneven country.

A shepherd is always well provided with lanterns; and,

lighting these hastily, and with hurdle-staves in their hands, they poured out of the door, taking a direction along the crest of the hill, away from the town, the rain having fortunately a little abated.

Disturbed by the noise, or possibly by unpleasant dreams of her baptism, the child who had been christened began to cry heart-brokenly in the room overhead. These notes of grief came down through the chinks of the floor to the ears of the women below, who jumped up one by one, and seemed glad of the excuse to ascend and comfort the baby, for the incidents of the last half-hour greatly oppressed them. Thus in the space of two or three minutes the room on the ground-floor was deserted quite.

But it was not for long. Hardly had the sound of footsteps died away when a man returned round the corner of the house from the direction the pursuers had taken. Peeping in at the door, and seeing nobody there, he entered leisurely. It was the stranger of the chimney-corner, who had gone out with the rest. The motive of his return was shown by his helping himself to a cut piece of skimmer-cake that lay on a ledge beside where he had sat, and which he had apparently forgotten to take with him. He also poured out half a cup more mead from the quantity that remained, ravenously eating and drinking these as he stood. He had not finished when another figure came in just as quietly — his friend in cinder-gray.

"Oh — you here?" said the latter, smiling. "I thought you had gone to help in the capture." And this speaker also revealed the object of his return by looking solicitously round for the fascinating mug of old mead.

"And I thought you had gone," said the other, continuing his skimmer-cake with some effort.

"Well, on second thoughts, I felt there were enough without me," said the first confidentially, "and such a night as it is, too. Besides, 'tis the business o' the Government to take care of its criminals — not mine."

"True; so it is. And I felt as you did, that there were enough without me."

"I don't want to break my limbs running over the humps and hollows of this wild country."

"Nor I neither, between you and me."

"These shepherd-people are used to it — simple-minded souls, you know, stirred up to anything in a moment. They'll have him ready for me before the morning, and no trouble to me at all."

"They'll have him, and we shall have saved ourselves all labor in the matter."

"True, true. Well, my way is to Casterbridge; and 'tis as much as my legs will do to take me that far. Going the same way?"

"No, I am sorry to say! I have to get home over there" (he nodded indefinitely to the right), "and I feel as you do, that it is quite enough for my legs to do before bedtime."

The other had by this time finished the mead in the mug, after which, shaking hands heartily at the door, and wishing each other well, they went their several ways.

In the meantime the company of pursuers had reached the end of the hog's-back elevation which dominated this part of the down. They had decided on no particular plan of action; and, finding that the man of the baleful trade was no longer in their company, they seemed quite unable to form any such plan now. They descended in all directions down the hill, and straightway several of the party fell into the snare set by Nature for all misguided midnight ramblers over this part of the cretaceous formation. The "lanchets," or flint slopes, which belted the escarpment at intervals of a dozen yards, took the less cautious ones unawares, and losing their footing on the rubbly steep they slid sharply downwards, the lanterns rolling from their hands to the bottom, and there lying on their sides till the horn was scorched through.

When they had again gathered themselves together, the shepherd, as the man who knew the country best, took the lead, and guided them round these treacherous inclines. The lanterns, which seemed rather to dazzle their eyes and warn the fugitive than to assist them in the exploration, were extinguished, due silence was observed; and in this more rational order they plunged into the vale. It was a grassy, briery, moist defile, affording some shelter to any person who had sought it; but the party perambulated it in vain, and ascended on the other side. Here they wandered apart, and after an interval closed together again to report progress. At the second time of closing in they found themselves near a lonely ash, the single tree on this part of the coomb, probably sown there by a passing bird some fifty years before. And here, standing a little to one side of the trunk, as motionless as the trunk itself, appeared the man they were in quest of, his outline being well defined against the sky beyond. The band noiselessly drew up and faced him.

"Your money or your life!" said the constable sternly to the still figure.

"No, no," whispered John Pitcher. "'Tisn't our side ought to say that. That's the doctrine of vagabonds like him, and we be on the side of the law."

"Well, well," replied the constable impatiently; "I must say something, mustn't I? and if you had all the weight o' this undertaking upon your mind, perhaps you'd say the wrong thing too! — Prisoner at the bar, surrender, in the name of the Father — the Crown, I mane!"

The man under the tree seemed now to notice them for the first time, and, giving them no opportunity whatever for exhibiting their courage, he strolled slowly toward them. He was, indeed, the little man, the third stranger; but his trepidation had in a great measure gone.

"Well, travelers," he said, "did I hear ye speak to me?"

"You did: you've got to come and be our prisoner at once!" said the constable. "We arrest 'ee on the charge of not biding in Casterbridge jail in a decent proper manner to be hung tomorrow morning. Neighbors, do your duty, and seize the culpet!"

On hearing the charge, the man seemed enlightened, and, saying not another word, resigned himself with preternatural civility to the search-party, who, with their staves in their hands, surrounded him on all sides, and marched him back toward the shepherd's cottage.

It was eleven o'clock by the time they arrived. The light shining from the open door, a sound of men's voices within, proclaimed to them as they approached the house that some new events had arisen in their absence. On entering they discovered the shepherd's living room to be invaded by two officers from Casterbridge jail, and a well-known magistrate who lived at the nearest country-seat, intelligence of the escape having become generally circulated.

"Gentlemen," said the constable, "I have brought back your man — not without risk and danger; but everyone must do his duty! He is inside this circle of able-bodied persons, who have lent me useful aid, considering their ignorance of Crown work. Men, bring forward your prisoner!" And the third stranger was led to the light.

"Who is this?" said one of the officials.

"The man," said the constable.

"Certainly not," said the turnkey; and the first corroborated his statement.

"But how can it be otherwise?" asked the constable. "Or why was he so terrified at sight o' the singing instrument of the law who sat there?" Here he related the strange behavior of the third stranger on entering the house during the hangman's song.

"Can't understand it," said the officer coolly. "All I know is that it is not the condemned man. He's quite a different character from this one; a gauntish fellow, with dark hair and eyes, rather good-looking, and with a musical bass voice that if you heard it once you'd never mistake as long as you lived."

"Why, souls — 'twas the man in the chimney-corner!"

"Hey — what?" said the magistrate, coming forward after inquiring particulars from the shepherd in the background. "Haven't you got the man after all?"

"Well, sir," said the constable, "he's the man we were in search of, that's true; and yet he's not the man we were in search of. For the man we were in search of was not the man we wanted, sir, if you understand my every-day way; for 'twas the man in the chimney-corner!"

"A pretty kettle of fish altogether!" said the magistrate. "You had better start for the other man at once."

The prisoner now spoke for the first time. The mention of the man in the chimney-corner seemed to have moved him as nothing else could do. "Sir," he said, stepping forward to the magistrate, "take no more trouble about me. The time is come when I may as well speak. I have done nothing; my crime is that the condemned man is my brother. Early this afternoon I left home at Shottsford to tramp it all the way to Casterbridge jail to bid him farewell. I was benighted, and called here to rest and ask the way. When I opened the door I saw before me the very man, my brother, that I thought to see in the condemned cell at Casterbridge. He was in this chimney-corner; and jammed close to him, so that he could not have got out if he had tried, was the executioner who'd come to take his life, singing a song about it and not knowing that it was his victim who was close by, joining in to save appearances. My brother looked a glance of agony at me, and I knew he meant, 'Don't reveal what you see; my life depends on it.' I was so terror-struck that I could hardly stand, and, not knowing what I did, I turned and hurried away."

The narrator's manner and tone had the stamp of truth, and his story made a great impression on all around. "And do you know where your brother is at the present time?" asked the magistrate.

"I do not. I have never seen him since I closed this door."

"I can testify to that, for we've been between ye ever since," said the constable.

"Where does he think to fly to? — what is his occupation?"

"He's a watch-and-clock-maker, sir."

"'A said 'a was a wheelwright — a wicked rogue," said the constable.

"'The wheels of clocks and watches he meant, no doubt," said Shepherd Fennel. "I thought his hands were palish for's trade."

"Well, it appears to me that nothing can be gained by re-taining this poor man in custody," said the magistrate; "your business lies with the other, unquestionably."

And so the little man was released off-hand; but he looked nothing the less sad on that account, it being beyond the power of magistrate or constable to raze out the written troubles in his brain, for they concerned another whom he regarded with more solicitude than himself. When this was done, and the man had gone his way, the night was found to be so far advanced that it was deemed useless to renew the search before the next morning.

Next day, accordingly, the quest for the clever sheep-stealer became general and keen, to all appearance at least. But the intended punishment was cruelly disproportioned to the trans-gression, and the sympathy of a great many country-folk in that district was strongly on the side of the fugitive. More-over, his marvelous coolness and daring in hob-and-nobbing with the hangman, under the unprecedented circumstances of the shepherd's party, won their admiration. So that it may be questioned if all those who ostensibly made themselves so busy in exploring woods and fields and lanes were quite so thorough when it came to the private examination of their own lofts and outhouses. Stories were afloat of a mysterious figure being occasionally seen in some old overgrown track-way or other, remote from turnpike roads; but when a search was instituted in any of these suspected quarters nobody was found. Thus the days and weeks passed without tidings.

In brief, the bass-voiced man of the chimney-corner was never recaptured. Some said that he went across the sea, others that he did not, but buried himself in the depths of a populous city. At any rate, the gentleman in cinder-gray never did his morning's work at Casterbridge, nor met any-where at all, for business purposes, the genial comrade with whom he had passed an hour of relaxation in the lonely house on the coomb.

The grass has long been green on the graves of Shepherd Fennel and his frugal wife; the guests who made up the christening party have mainly followed their entertainers to the tomb; the baby in whose honor they all had met is a matron in the sere and yellow leaf. But the arrival of the three strangers at the shepherd's that night, and the details connected therewith, is a story as well known as ever in the country about Higher Crowstairs.

QUESTIONS

1. Describe the important characters in "The Three Strangers."
2. On what occasion was the shepherd's party held? Can you see any reason for the author's choice of this particular occasion?
3. Find passages of particularly good description.
4. Did you expect the story to end as it does? What hints has the author given to prepare for the ending?
5. Of what crime was the escaped prisoner accused? Find evidence in the story that the farmers' sympathy was with the fugitive.
6. Do you think a very modern writer would have added the last paragraph to the story? Explain.
7. *Word Study.* — What do the following words mean as they are used in the story: *inimical, pernicious, generate, cumulative, salient, exigency, taciturnity, complement?*

Problem: REVIEW

1. What elements of realism do you find in "The Three Strangers"? Do you find anything of romance in it?
2. What is the setting of the story? Is it suited to the plot? What effect do the time and the conditions under which the story opens have on the atmosphere of the story? What helps to counterbalance this effect?
3. Find illustrations of local color in the story. Find illustrations of dialect.
4. Is there much conversation in the story? What purposes does the conversation serve?
5. Which of the three strangers talks the most? Which tells most about himself by his actions? Which stands out most clearly in your mind? Why?
6. Can you see why the author tells the story himself? Would any one of the characters in the story have noticed all the things that the author tells us about the country, the house, the weather, and the other characters?

The Little Cask *

Guy de Maupassant (1850–1893)

Guy de Maupassant was born of a Norman family at Château Miromesnil on August 5, 1850. As a child, young Guy made friends with many of the Norman fishermen and peasants and very probably acquired from them something of their hard, bitter, uncompromising view of life. De Maupassant was educated in Normandy and served there in the French army during the Franco-Prussian War. Later, he went to Paris and worked for ten years as a clerk in the Civil Service, relaxing from this dull routine by meeting with friends and boating on the river.

Gustave Flaubert, a friend of the family and himself a writer of note, helped De Maupassant to perfect his style. The advice he gave his young student is sound today. "Whatever the thing we wish to say, there is but one word to express it, but one verb to give it motion, but one adjective to qualify it. We must seek till we find this noun, this verb, and this adjective, and never be content with getting very near it, never allow ourselves to play tricks, even happy ones, or have recourse to sleights of language to avoid a difficulty."

De Maupassant profited by the advice. For years he practised writing, striving always for clarity of style — for the one word. In 1880, he published his famous story "Boule de Suif" (Ball of Fat), which definitely proved that he had learned the lessons he had been so carefully taught.

Although De Maupassant wrote some poetry, a few dramas, and several novels, his reputation rests largely upon his short stories. In these stories he proved himself a master of technique and of characterization. He possessed a rather cynical view of life, unpleasant, but none the less sincere. For the weak, the erring, the poor, and the oppressed he exhibited an ironic sympathy. As a writer, he was totally lacking in humor although

* Translated by Ruth Young Eaton.

*there is possibly a certain grim humor in some of the situations
he has created for his characters.*

*In "The Little Cask," the reader catches a glimpse of the
peculiar, unlovely psychology of the peasant whose worship of
property has brutalized all of his finer feelings and sensibilities.
Greed is always unattractive, and in "The Little Cask" De Maupassant has depicted for us some of the tragic results of avarice.
The story is swift in action and flawless in technique, every incident of the plot being the logical outcome of the one preceding;
the characters are individual and superbly drawn, and the setting
is authentic.*

M. CHICOT, the innkeeper of Epreville, stopped
his cart in front of the farmhouse of Mother Magloire. He
was a jovial fellow, about forty years old, ruddy and corpulent, and he gave the impression of being crafty. He hitched
his horse to the gatepost and entered the court.

M. Chicot owned property adjoining the old woman's land,
and, for a long time, he had coveted hers. Many times he had
tried to buy it, but Mother Magloire obstinately refused to
sell.

"I was born here, and here I shall die,'' she always said.

He found her outside her door paring potatoes. She was
seventy-two years old, dried up, lined and bent, but untiring
as a young girl. Chicot gave her a friendly clap on the back
and then sat down on a stool beside her.

"Well! Mother, and how's your health, still fine?"

"Not so bad, and yours, Master Prosper?"

"Oh, a few aches; outside of that, pretty fair."

"Well, that's good!"

And she said nothing more. Chicot watched her doing her
task. Her fingers, bent, knotted, hard as crabs' claws, seized
the grayish tubercles in one hand like pincers, and quickly
turned them around, paring off long strips of peel with the
blade of an old knife which she held in the other hand. When
the potato had become entirely yellow, she would throw it in
a pail of water. Three daring chickens crept one after the other

as far as the hem of her skirts to pick up the parings, and then scuttled off, carrying their booty in their beaks.

Chicot seemed troubled, hesitating, anxious, as if he had something on his mind that he did not wish to say. Finally he remarked,

"Tell me, now, Mother Magloire, this farm of yours — don't you ever want to sell it to me?"

"Certainly not. You can make up your mind in that score. What I have said, I mean, so let's not refer to the matter again."

"All right, only I think I have devised a scheme which we shall both like."

"What is it?"

"Just this: you can sell me the farm and retain it just the same. You don't understand? Just listen to this."

The old woman stopped paring her vegetables and looked at the innkeeper attentively from under her shaggy eyebrows. He continued:

"Let me explain. I shall give you a hundred and fifty francs every month. Do you understand? Every month! I shall bring here in my wagon thirty crowns. And it won't make the least bit of difference to you, not the least! You will stay in your home; you won't trouble yourself with me; you won't do anything for me: you will only take my money. How does that appeal to you?"

He looked at her with a happy, good-natured expression but the old woman glanced back at him with distrust, as if she were searching for some trap.

"It is all right as far as I can see, but," she asked, "you don't think it is going to get the farm for you, do you?"

"Don't you worry about that. You will stay here just as long as God Almighty is willing that you should live. You will stay in your own home, only you will sign a paper before a notary, that, after you are finished with the farm, it will come to me. You have no children — only a few nephews who have scarcely any hold on you. Is that all right for you?

You keep your property during your life, and I give you thirty crowns a month. It is all gain for you."

The old woman was still surprised and puzzled, but inclined to accept. She replied:

"I don't say 'no,' but I want to think it over. Come back sometime next week and we will talk it over. I will give you my answer then."

Master Chicot went away as happy as a king who had just conquered an empire.

Mother Magloire kept thinking about it. She did not sleep that night, and for four days she was in a fever of hesitation. She detected something in the offer which was not to her advantage, but the thought of thirty crowns a month, of all that beautiful jingling money that would come to roll around in her apron pocket, which would fall as if from Heaven, without any effort on her part, filled her with covetousness. Then she went to hunt for a notary and tell him her case. He advised her to accept Chicot's proposition, but to ask for fifty crowns instead of thirty because her farm was worth sixty thousand francs at the lowest estimate.

"If you live fifteen years," the notary said, "in that way he will pay even then only forty-five thousand."

The old woman trembled at the thought of fifty crowns a month, but she was still suspicious, fearing a thousand unforeseen tricks and she stayed till evening asking questions, unable to make up her mind to leave. Finally she gave the notary instructions to draw up the deed, and went home with her head in a whirl, just as if she had drunk four jugs of new cider.

When Chicot came to get her answer, she took a lot of persuading and declared she could not make up her mind what to do, but all the time she was distracted by the idea that he might not consent to give the fifty crowns a month. Finally, when he became insistent, she told him what she wanted for her farm.

He looked surprised and disappointed, and refused. Then, in order to win him over, the old woman began to argue on the probable duration of her life.

"I can't have but five or six years more to live. Here I am nearly seventy-three and none too hearty at that. The other evening I thought I was going to die. It seemed to me that my soul was being dragged out of my body and I could scarcely crawl to my bed." But Chicot didn't let himself be taken in.

"Come, now," he said, "old woman, you are as solid as a church bell. You will live to be a hundred at least. You will see me buried, I'm sure."

They spent the whole day in discussion, but as the old woman would not give in, the innkeeper finally consented to give her the fifty crowns a month. They signed the deed the next day, and Mother Magloire drew out ten crowns from her wine jug.

Three years rolled by. The old woman lived as if protected by a charm. She seemed not to have aged a day, and Chicot was in despair. It seemed to him that he had been paying this rent for fifty years, and that he had been tricked, cheated, ruined. From time to time he paid a visit to the old farmer woman, as in July we go into the fields to see if the wheat is ripe enough to harvest. She received him with a malicious gleam in her eye. One would say that she was congratulating herself on the good trick she had played on him, and he would quickly get back into his wagon murmuring, "You won't die then, you old brute!"

He didn't know what to do. When he saw her, he wanted to strangle her. He hated her with a ferocious, crafty hatred, with the hatred of a peasant who has been robbed, and he began to think of ways to get rid of her.

Finally, one day, he came to see her, rubbing his hands as he did the first time when he had proposed the bargain. After he had talked for some time, he said,

"Tell me, now, Mother, why haven't you stopped for dinner at my inn when you have been at Epreville? People have been talking about it; they say that we are not good friends, and that grieves me. You know at my place you

don't pay anything. Just stop in whenever you feel like it.
It will give me a great deal of pleasure."

Mother Magloire didn't make him repeat his offer, but the
next day, as she was going to market in her carriage driven
by her servant Celestin, without any hesitancy she had her
horse put in Chicot's stable, and went into the inn to claim
the promised dinner.

The delighted innkeeper treated her like a great lady. He
served her with chicken, black pudding, chitterlings, leg of
mutton, and bacon and cabbage. But, as she had always been
a very moderate eater since childhood, she ate almost nothing.
Her usual fare had always been a little soup and a crust of
bread and butter. Chicot was disappointed, but he kept insisting that she eat. Neither could he prevail upon her to drink
anything; she refused even coffee.

Finally he said, "Surely you always accept a small glass of
wine."

"Oh, yes! I won't say 'no'!"

And he shouted as loudly as he could across the room,
"Rosalie, bring the extra-fine brandy — you know, the
special."

The servant appeared, bringing a long bottle decorated
with a paper wine leaf. He filled two liqueur glasses.

"Taste that, Mother; it is some of the famous brand."

The good woman began to drink very slowly, in little swal-
lows to make the pleasure last. When she had emptied her
glass, she held it up again to get the last drop; then she exclaimed,

"Yes, that is very excellent."

She had not finished speaking before Chicot had poured
out a second glass for her. She wanted to refuse, but it was
too late, and she drank it slowly, as she had the first. Then
he wanted her to accept a third glass, but she declined. He
insisted, adding,

"Why, that is just as weak as milk. See *I* drink ten or
twelve glasses without any embarrassment. It goes down
like sugar and leaves no unpleasant effects in the stomach

or the head. One would say that it evaporates on the tongue.
There is nothing better for one's health!"

As she was very anxious to have it, she gave in, but she
took only half of the glassful.

Then acting from an impulse of generosity, Chicot exclaimed,

"Look here, since you like it so well, I am going to give you
a little cask of it, a little token to show that we are good
friends."

The good woman did not say "no," and she went away a
little unsteadily.

The next day the innkeeper drove into the courtyard of
Mother Magloire and took from the bottom of his wagon a
small barrel with iron hoops. Then he wanted her to taste
the contents to be sure that it was some of the same fine
brandy. When they had both had three glasses, he reminded
her as he was going away,

"Now, you know, when that is gone, there is still more
where that came from. Don't be bashful. The sooner it is
finished, the better pleased I shall be."

And he got up into his wagon.

He came back four days later. The old woman was near her
door cutting bread for supper. He went up to where she was
and greeted her, getting close enough to be able to smell her
breath. When he caught a whiff of alcohol, he was pleased.

"Aren't you going to offer me a glass of brandy?" he asked.
Then they clinked glasses two or three times.

Soon there was a report going about that occasionally
Mother Magloire was getting drunk all by herself. She was
picked up first in her kitchen, later in the courtyard, then in
the country roads, and she had to be carried home lifeless as
a log.

Chicot never went to her house now, and when anyone
spoke to him about the peasant woman, with a sad expression
in his face he murmured,

"It is too bad, at her age, to have become addicted to a
habit like that! You know, when one is old, there isn't any
remedy. It will end up by playing a bad trick on her!"

And it did play a bad trick on her. She died the following winter, about Christmas time. She fell intoxicated in the snow.

When Master Chicot took possession of the farm, he remarked, "You know, it wasn't at all necessary. She could easily have lived ten years more."

QUESTIONS

1. What scheme did Chicot propose to Mother Magloire?
2. Why did it appeal to her more than outright sale?
3. What advice did the notary give to the old woman? Was it good advice?
4. How do you know that Chicot tired of his bargain? Was he really losing by it?
5. Why is the little cask the important object in the story?
6. *Word Study.* — What do the following words mean as they are used in the story: *notary, covetousness?*

Problem: REVIEW

1. Where does the introduction to "The Little Cask" begin and end? Is there enough introduction? Pick out the sentences of actual introductory material.
2. What is the climax of the story? Pick out the incidents leading up to the climax. Does your interest rise steadily up to the climax? Does it fall off immediately after the climax? Explain.
3. What traits of character can you point out as belonging definitely to Chicot? To Mother Magloire? How do you know they have these traits? Are they brought out by actions, by conversation, by author's comment, or by comments of other characters?
4. What is the setting of this story? What is its atmosphere; its tone? What examples of local color can you find in the story?
5. What is the underlying idea of "The Little Cask"? Is it stated anywhere? Is it as easy to find as in the theme stories?
6. What is the chief element in the story — plot, setting, character, or theme?

By the Waters of Babylon *

Stephen Vincent Benét (1898–1943)

*Since great-grandfather, grandfather, and father —
Colonel J. Walker Benét — had all been United States Army
officers, Stephen Vincent was born into a home with a strong
military tradition, although the Benét children (William Rose,
Stephen Vincent, and Laura) all became writers. As Colonel
Benét was a lover of good literature and enjoyed reading poetry
to his family, it is not surprising that the children came to love
poetry and wrote it when they grew older. As a young man, however, Stephen did attempt an army career, but poor eyesight kept
him from following in his father's footsteps. Quite naturally, the
Benét children grew up in various army posts. Stephen received
his early schooling in California and Georgia and his college
education at Yale, in New Haven, Connecticut. Indeed, young
Benét had two volumes of poetry published while he was still a
student at Yale, where he was graduated in 1919, just twelve
years after his older brother, William Rose Benét. A little later,
while Stephen Vincent was studying at the University of Paris,
he met and married Rosemary Carr, herself a writer and journalist. When he was barely in his early thirties, the young poet
wrote his famous work, "John Brown's Body," which quickly
became a best-seller (an unheard of thing for a book of poetry)
and which won the Pulitzer Prize for poetry in 1929. Some
years later, "Western Star," another poem by Benét also won a
Pulitzer award.*

*Although he wrote four novels, Stephen Vincent Benét won
the greatest amount of fame as a poet and a writer of particularly
distinguished short stories. The well-known "The Devil and
Daniel Webster" was made into an unusual motion picture
and also an opera. Other excellent stories by Benét are "Johnny
Pye and the Fool Killer," "A Tooth for Paul Revere," "Free-*

dom's a Hard-Bought Thing," "The Bishop's Beggar," and of course the following selection, "By the Waters of Babylon."

During his last years, the author spent part of his time at his summer home in Stonington, Connecticut. For years, he served on the editorial staff of "The Saturday Review of Literature." He died rather suddenly from a heart attack in New York City in 1943 in his forty-fifth year.

Someone once stated that Stephen Vincent Benét always showed a highly emotional approach to matters of great national import. He loved his country deeply and was tremendously concerned about the dangers which threatened it. In a prayer written for and read by the late President Franklin D. Roosevelt on Flag Day, June 14, 1942, about a year before the poet's sudden death, he had written:

"Grant us a common faith that man shall know bread and peace — that he shall know justice and righteousness, freedom and security . . ." In "The Burning of the Books," he had already written: "Our earth is but a small star in the great universe. Yet of it we can make, if we choose, a planet unvexed by war, untroubled by hunger or fear, undivided by senseless distinctions of race, color, or theory."

"By the Waters of Babylon" shows clearly the author's great concern for the safety and welfare of our United States. It is a story which must be read slowly and thoughtfully and pondered over more than once, for it was written to make people think rather than to entertain or amuse them, and it is another excellent example of the story of theme, sometimes called the "apologue." The author is speaking not only to the people of America but also to all the people of the entire world. Written years before atomic weapons were actualities and long before the author could possibly have known anything about atomic energy, the story furnishes proof of the theory that the keenest minds are possessed by two types of people — great poets and great scientists — both of whom have much in common. If "By the Waters of Babylon" were compulsory reading for every pupil in every school in every nation of our world — and if the story were discussed fully and thoughtfully, there would undoubtedly be more chance for the eventual coming of genuine World Peace.

THE north and the west and the south are good hunting ground, but it is forbidden to go east. It is forbidden to go to any of the Dead Places except to search for metal and then he who touches the metal must be a priest or the son of a priest. Afterwards, both the man and the metal must be purified. These are the rules and the laws; they are well made. It is forbidden to cross the great river and look upon the place that was the Place of the Gods — this is most strictly forbidden. We do not even say its name though we know its name. It is there that spirits live, and demons — it is there that there are the ashes of the Great Burning. These things are forbidden — they have been forbidden since the beginning of time.

My father is a priest; I am the son of a priest. I have been in the Dead Places near us with my father — at first, I was afraid. When my father went into the house to search for the metal, I stood by the door and my heart felt small and weak. It was a dead man's house, a spirit house. It did not have the smell of man, though there were old bones in a corner. But it is not fitting that a priest's son should show fear. I looked at the bones in the shadow and kept my voice still.

Then my father came out with the metal — a good, strong piece. He looked at me with both eyes but I had not run away. He gave me the metal to hold — I took it and did not die, so he knew that I was truly his son and would be a priest in my time. That was when I was very young — nevertheless, my brothers would not have done it, though they are good hunters. After that, they gave me the good piece of meat and the warm corner by the fire. My father watched over me — he was glad that I should be a priest. But when I boasted or wept without a reason, he punished me more strictly than my brothers. That was right.

After a time, I myself was allowed to go into the dead houses and search for metal. So I learned the ways of those houses — and if I saw bones, I was no longer afraid. The bones are light and old — sometimes they will fall into dust if you touch them. But that is a great sin.

I was taught the chants and the spells — I was taught how to stop the running of blood from a wound and many secrets. A priest must know many secrets — that was what my father said.

If the hunters think we do all things by chants and spells, they may believe so — it does not hurt them. I was taught how to read in the old books and how to make the old writings — that was hard and took a long time. My knowledge made me happy — it was like a fire in my heart. Most of all, I liked to hear of the Old Days and the stories of the gods. I asked myself many questions that I could not answer, but it was good to ask them. At night, I would lie awake and listen to the wind — it seemed to me that it was the voice of the gods as they flew through the air.

We are not ignorant like the Forest People — our women spin wool on the wheel; our priests wear a white robe. We do not eat grubs from the tree; we have not forgotten the old writings, although they are hard to understand. Nevertheless, my knowledge and my lack of knowledge burned in me — I wished to know more. When I was a man at last, I came to my father and said, "It is time for me to go on my journey. Give me your leave."

He looked at me for a long time, stroking his beard; then he said at last, "Yes. It is time." That night, in the house of the priesthood, I asked for and received purification. My body hurt but my spirit was a cool stone. It was my father himself who questioned me about my dreams.

He bade me look into the smoke of the fire and see — I saw and told what I saw. It was what I have always seen — a river, and, beyond it, a great Dead Place and in it the gods walking. I have always thought about that. His eyes were stern when I told him — he was no longer my father but a priest. He said, "This is a strong dream."

"It is mine," I said, while the smoke waved and my head felt light. They were singing the Star song in the outer chamber and it was like the buzzing of bees in my head.

He asked me how the gods were dressed and I told him

how they were dressed. We know how they were dressed from the book, but I saw them as if they were before me. When I had finished, he threw the sticks three times and studied them as they fell.

"This is a very strong dream," he said. "It may eat you up."

"I am not afraid," I said and looked at him with both eyes. My voice sounded thin in my ears but that was because of the smoke.

He touched me on the breast and the forehead. He gave me the bow and the three arrows.

"Take them," he said. "It is forbidden to travel east. It is forbidden to cross the river. It is forbidden to go to the Place of the Gods. All these things are forbidden."

"All these things are forbidden," I said, but it was my voice that spoke and not my spirit. He looked at me again.

"My son," he said. "Once I had young dreams. If your dreams do not eat you up, you may be a great priest. If they eat you, you are still my son. Now go on your journey."

I went fasting, as is the law. My body hurt but not my heart. When the dawn came, I was out of sight of the village. I prayed and purified myself, waiting for a sign. The sign was an eagle. It flew east.

Sometimes signs are sent by bad spirits. I waited again on the flat rock, fasting, taking no food. I was very still — I could feel the sky above me and the earth beneath. I waited till the sun was beginning to sink. Then three deer passed in the valley going east — they did not mind me or see me. There was a white fawn with them — a very great sign.

I followed them, at a distance, waiting for what would happen. My heart was troubled about going east, yet I knew that I must go. My head hummed with my fasting — I did not even see the panther spring upon the white fawn. But, before I knew it, the bow was in my hand. I shouted and the panther lifted his head from the fawn. It is not easy to kill a panther with one arrow but the arrow went through his eye and into his brain. He died as he tried to spring — he rolled

over, tearing at the ground. Then I knew that I was meant
to go east — I knew that was my journey. When the night
came, I made my fire and roasted meat.

It is eight suns' journey to the east and a man passes by
many Dead Places. The Forest People are afraid of them
but I am not. Once I made my fire on the edge of a Dead
Place at night and, next morning, in the dead house, I found
a good knife, little rusted. That was small to what came afterward but it made my heart feel big. Always when I looked
for game, it was in front of my arrow, and twice I passed
hunting parties of the Forest People without their knowing.
So I knew my magic was strong and my journey clean, in
spite of the law.

Toward the setting of the eighth sun, I came to the banks
of the great river. It was half-a-day's journey after I had left
the god road — we do not use the god roads now, for they
are falling apart into great blocks of stone, and the forest is
safer going. A long way off, I had seen the water through trees
but the trees were thick. At last, I came out upon an open
place at the top of a cliff. There was the great river below,
like a giant in the sun. It is very long, very wide. It could eat
all the streams we know and still be thirsty. It's name is
Ou-dis-sun, the Sacred, the Long. No man of my tribe had
seen it, not even my father, the priest. It was magic and I
prayed.

Then I raised my eyes and looked south. It was there, the
Place of the Gods.

How can I tell what it was like — you do not know? It
was there, in the red light, and they were too big to be houses.
It was there with the red light upon it, mighty and ruined.
I knew that in another moment the gods would see me. I
covered my eyes with my hands and crept back into the forest.

Surely, that was enough to do, and live. Surely, it was
enough to spend the night upon the cliff. The Forest People
themselves do not come near. Yet, all through the night, I
knew that I should have to cross the river and walk in the
places of the gods, although the gods ate me up. My magic

did not help me at all and yet there was a fire in my bowels, a fire in my mind. When the sun rose, I thought, "My journey has been clean. Now I will go home from my journey." But even as I thought so, I knew I could not. If I went to the Place of the Gods, I would surely die, but if I did not go, I could never be at peace with my spirit again. It is better to lose one's life than one's spirit, if one is a priest and the son of a priest.

Nevertheless, as I made the raft, the tears ran out of my eyes. The Forest People could have killed me without fight, if they had come upon me then, but they did not come. When the raft was made, I said the sayings for the dead and painted myself for death. My heart was cold as a frog and my knees like water, but the burning in my mind would not let me have peace. As I pushed the raft from the shore, I began my death song — I had the right. It was a fine song.

"I am John, son of John," I sang. "My people are the Hill People. They are the men.
I go into the Dead Places but I am not slain.
I take the metal from the Dead Places but I am not blasted.
I travel upon the god-roads and am not afraid. E-yah! I have killed the panther; I have killed the fawn!
E-yah! I have come to the great river. No man has come there before.
It is forbidden to go east, but I have gone, forbidden to go on the great river, but I am there.
Open your hearts, you spirits, and hear my song.
Now I go to the Place of the Gods; I shall not return.
My body is painted for death and my limbs weak, but my heart is big as I go to the Place of the Gods!"

All the same, when I came to the Place of the Gods, I was afraid, afraid. The current of the great river is very strong — it gripped my raft with its hands. That was magic, for the river itself is wide and calm. I could feel evil spirits about me, in the bright morning; I could feel their breath on my neck as I was swept down the stream. Never have I been so much alone — I tried to think of my knowledge, but it was a squirrel's heap of winter nuts. There was no strength in my knowledge any more and I felt small and naked as a new-hatched bird — alone upon the great river, the servant of the gods.

Yet, after a while, my eyes were opened and I saw. I saw both banks of the river — I saw that once there had been god-roads across it, though now they were broken and fallen like broken vines. Very great they were, and wonderful and broken — broken in the time of the Great Burning when the fire fell out of the sky. And always the current took me nearer to the Place of the Gods, and the huge ruins rose before my eyes.

I do not know the customs of rivers — we are the People of the Hills. I tried to guide my raft with the pole, but it spun around. I thought the river meant to take me past the Place of the Gods and out into the Bitter Water of the legends. I grew angry then — my heart felt strong. I said aloud, "I am a priest and the son of a priest!" The gods heard me — they showed me how to paddle with the pole on one side of the raft. The current changed itself — I drew near to the Place of the Gods.

When I was very near, my raft struck and turned over. I can swim in our lakes — I swam to the shore. There was a great spike of rusted metal sticking out into the river — I hauled myself up upon it and sat there, panting. I had saved my bow and two arrows and the knife I had found in the Dead Place but that was all. My raft went whirling downstream toward the Bitter Water. I looked after it, and thought if it had trod me under, at least I would be safely dead. Nevertheless, when I had dried my bowstring and re-strung it, I walked forward to the Place of the Gods.

It felt like ground underfoot; it did not burn me. It is not true what some of the tales say, that the ground there burns forever, for I have been there. Here and there were the marks and stains of the Great Burning, on the ruins; that is true. But they were old marks and old stains. It is not true either, what some of our priests say, that it is an island covered with fogs and enchantments. It is not. It is a great Dead Place — greater than any Dead Place we know. Everywhere in it there are god-roads, though most are cracked and broken. Everywhere there are the ruins of the high towers of the gods.

How shall I tell what I saw? I went carefully, my strung bow in my hand, my skin ready for danger. There should have been the wailings of spirits and the shrieks of demons, but there were not. It was very silent and sunny where I had landed — the wind and the rain and the birds that drop seeds had done their work — the grass grew in the cracks of the broken stone. It is a fair island — no wonder the gods built there. If I had come there, a god, I also would have built.

How shall I tell what I saw? The towers are not all broken — here and there one still stands, like a great tree in a forest, and the birds nest high. But the towers themselves look blind, for the gods are gone. I saw a fish-hawk catching fish in the river. I saw a little dance of white butterflies over a great heap of broken stones and columns. I went there and looked about me — there was a carved stone with cut-letters, broken in half. I can read letters but I could not understand these. They said UBTREAS. There was also a shattered image of a man or a god. It had been made of white stone and he wore his hair tied back like a woman's. His name was ASHING, as I read on the cracked half of a stone. I thought it wise to pray to ASHING, though I do not know that god.

How shall I tell what I saw? There was no smell of man left, on stone or metal. Nor were there many trees in that wilderness of stone. There are many pigeons, nesting and dropping in the towers — the gods must have loved them, or, perhaps, they used them for sacrifices. There are wild cats that roam the god-roads, green-eyed, unafraid of man. At night they wail like demons but they are not demons. The wild dogs are more dangerous, for they hunt in a pack, but them I did not meet till later. Everywhere there are the carved stones, carved with magical numbers or words.

I went north — I did not try to hide myself. When a god or a demon saw me, then I would die, but meanwhile I was no longer afraid. My hunger for knowledge burned in me — there was so much that I could not understand. After a while,

I knew that my belly was hungry. I could have hunted for my meat, but I did not hunt. It is known that the gods did not hunt as we do — they got their food from enchanted boxes and jars. Sometimes, these are still found in the Dead Places — once, when I was a child and foolish, I opened such a jar and tasted it and found the food sweet. But my father found out and punished me for it strictly, for, often, that food is death. Now, though, I had long gone past what was forbidden, and I entered the likeliest towers, looking for the food of the gods.

I found it at last in the ruins of a great temple in the mid-city. A mighty temple it must have been, for the roof was painted like the sky at night with its stars — that much I could see, though the colors were faint and dim. It went down into great caves and tunnels — perhaps they kept their slaves there. But when I started to climb down, I heard the squeaking of rats, so I did not go — rats are unclean, and there must have been many tribes of them, from the squeaking. But near there, I found food, in the heart of a ruin, behind a door that still opened. I ate only the fruits from the jars — they had a very sweet taste. There was drink, too, in bottles of glass — the drink of the gods was strong and made my head swim. After I had eaten and drunk, I slept on the top of a stone, my bow at my side.

When I woke, the sun was low. Looking down from where I lay, I saw a dog sitting on his haunches. His tongue was hanging out of his mouth; he looked as if he were laughing. He was a big dog, with a gray-brown coat, as big as a wolf. I sprang up and shouted at him but he did not move — he just sat there as if he were laughing. I did not like that. When I reached for a stone to throw, he moved swiftly out of the way of the stone. He was not afraid of me; he looked at me as if I were meat. No doubt I could have killed him with an arrow, but I did not know if there were others. Moreover, night was falling.

I looked about me — not far away there was a great broken god road, leading north. The towers were high enough, but

not so high, and while many of the dead-houses were wrecked,
there were some that stood. I went toward this god-road,
keeping to the heights of the ruins, while the dog followed.
When I had reached the god-road, I saw there were others
behind him. If I had slept later, they would have come upon
me asleep and torn out my throat. As it was, they were sure
enough of me; they did not hurry. When I went into the
dead-house, they kept watch at the entrance — doubtless
they thought they would have a fine hunt. But a dog cannot
open a door and I knew, from the books, that the dogs did
not like to live on the ground but on high.

I had just found a door I could open when the dogs decided
to rush. Ha! They were surprised when I shut the door in
their faces — it was a good door, of strong metal. I could hear
their foolish baying beyond it but I did not stop to answer
them. I was in darkness — I found stairs and climbed. There
were many stairs, turning around till my head was dizzy.
At the top was another door — I found the knob and opened
it. I was in a long small chamber — on one side of it was a
bronze door that could not be opened, for it had no handle.
Perhaps there was a magic word to open it but I did not
have the word. I turned to the door in the opposite side of
the wall. The lock of it was broken and I opened it and went
in.

Within, there was a place of great riches. The god who lived
there must have been a powerful god. The first room was a
small ante-room — I waited there for some time, telling the
spirits of the place that I came in peace and not as a robber.
When it seemed to me that they had had time to hear me, I
went on. Ah, what riches! Few, even, of the windows had
been broken — it was all as it had been. The great windows
that looked over the city had not been broken at all though
they were dusty and streaked with many years. There were
coverings on the floors, the colors not greatly faded, and the
chairs were soft and deep. There were pictures upon the walls,
very strange, very wonderful — I remember one of a bunch
of flowers in a jar — if you came close to it, you could see

nothing but bits of color, but if you stood away from it, the flowers might have been picked yesterday. It made my heart feel strange to look at this picture — and to look at the figure of a bird, in some hard clay, on a table and see it so like our birds. Everywhere there were books and writings, many in tongues that I could not read. The god who lived there must have been a wise god and full of knowledge. I felt I had right there, as I sought knowledge also.

Nevertheless, it was strange. There was a washing-place but no water — perhaps the gods washed in air. There was a cooking place but no wood, and though there was a machine to cook food, there was no place to put fire in it. Nor were there candles or lamps — there were things that looked like lamps but they had neither oil nor wick. All these things were magic but I touched them and lived — the magic had gone out of them. Let me tell one thing to show. In the washing-place, a thing said "Hot" but it was not hot to the touch — another thing said "Cold" but it was not cold. This must have been a strong magic but the magic was gone. I do not understand — they had ways — I wish that I knew.

It was close and dry and dusty in their house of the gods. I have said the magic was gone but that is not true — it had gone from the magic things but it had not gone from the place. I felt the spirits about me, weighing upon me. Nor had I ever slept in a Dead Place before — and yet, tonight I must sleep there. When I thought of it, my tongue felt dry in my throat, in spite of my wish for knowledge. Almost I would have gone down again and faced the dogs, but I did not.

I had not gone through all the rooms when the darkness fell. When it fell, I went back to the big room looking over the city and made fire. There was a place to make fire and a box with wood in it, though I do not think they cooked there. I wrapped myself in a floor-covering and slept in front of the fire — I was very tired.

Now I tell what is very strong magic. I woke in the midst of the night. When I woke, the fire had gone out and I was cold. It seemed to me that all around me there were whisper-ings and voices. I closed my eyes to shut them out. Some will say that I slept again, but I do not think that I slept. I could feel the spirits drawing my spirit out of my body as a fish is drawn on a line.

Why should I lie about it? I am a priest and the son of a priest. If there are spirits, as they say, in the small Dead Places near us, what spirits must there not be in that great Place of the Gods? And would not they wish to speak? After such long years? I know that I felt myself drawn as a fish is drawn on a line. I had stepped out of my body — I could see my body asleep in front of the cold fire, but it was not I. I was drawn to look out upon the city of the gods.

It should have been dark, for it was night, but it was not dark. Everywhere there were lights — lines of light — circles and blurs of light — ten thousand torches would not have been the same. The sky itself was alight — you could barely see the stars for the glow in the sky. I thought to myself "This is strong magic" and trembled. There was a roaring in my ears like the rushing of rivers. Then my eyes grew used to the light and my ears to the sound. I knew that I was seeing the city as it had been when the gods were alive.

That was a sight indeed — yes, that was a sight: I could not have seen it in the body — my body would have died. Everywhere went the gods, on foot and in chariots — there were gods beyond number and counting, and their chariots blocked the streets. They had turned night to day for their pleasure — they did not sleep with the sun. The noise of their coming and going was the noise of many waters. It was magic what they could do — it was magic what they did.

I looked out of another window — the great vines of their bridges were mended and the god-roads went east and west. Restless, restless, were the gods and always in motion! They burrowed tunnels under rivers — they flew in the air. With unbelievable tools they did giant works — no part of the earth was safe from them, for, if they wished for a thing, they summoned it from the other side of the world. And always, as they labored and rested, as they feasted and made love, there was a drum in their ears — the pulse of the giant city, beating and beating like a man's heart.

Were they happy? What is happiness to the gods? They were great; they were mighty; they were wonderful and terrible. As I looked upon them and their magic, I felt like a child — but a little more, it seemed to me, and they would pull down the moon from the sky. I saw them with wisdom beyond wisdom and knowledge beyond knowledge. And yet not all they did was well done — even I could see that — and yet their wisdom could not grow until all was peace.

Then I saw their fate come upon them and that was terrible, past speech. It came upon them as they walked the streets of their city. I have been in the fights with the Forest People — I have seen men die. But this was not like that. When gods war with gods, they use weapons we do not know. It was fire falling out of the sky and a mist that poisoned. It was the time of the Great Burning and the Destruction. They ran about like ants in the streets of their city — poor gods, poor gods! Then the towers began to fall. A few escaped — yes, a few. The legends tell it. But even after the city had become a Dead Place, for many years the poison was still in the ground. I saw it happen; I saw the last of them die. It was darkness over the broken city and I wept.

All this, I saw; I saw it as I have told it, though not in the body. When I woke in the morning, I was hungry, but I did not think first of my hunger, for my heart was perplexed and confused. I knew the reason for the Dead Places but I did not see why it had happened. It seemed to me it should not have happened, with all the magic they had. I went through the house looking for an answer. There was so much in the house I could not understand — and yet I am a priest and the son of a priest. It was like being on one side of the great river, at night, with no light to show the way.

Then I saw the dead god. He was sitting in his chair, by the window, in a room I had not entered before and, for the first moment, I thought that he was alive. Then I saw the skin on the back of his hand — it was like dry leather. The room was shut, hot and dry — no doubt that had kept him as he was. At first I was afraid to approach him — then the fear left me. He was sitting looking out over the city — he was dressed in the clothes of the gods. His age was neither young nor old — I could not tell his age. But there was wisdom in his face and great sadness. You could see that he would have not run away. He had sat at his window, watching his city die — then he himself had died. But it is better to lose one's life than one's spirit — and you could see from the face that his spirit had not been lost. I knew that if I touched him, he would fall into dust — and yet there was something unconquered in the face.

That is all of my story, for then I knew he was a man — I knew then that they had been men, neither gods nor demons. It is a great knowledge, hard to tell and believe. They were men — they went a dark road, but they were men. I had no fear after that — I had no fear going home, though twice I fought off the dogs and once I was hunted for two days by the Forest People. When I saw my father again, I prayed and was purified. He touched my lips and my breast; he said, "You went away a boy. You come back a man and a priest."

I said, "Father, they were men! I have been in the Place of the Gods and seen it! Now slay me, if it is the law — but still I know they were men."

He looked at me out of both eyes. He said, "The law is not always the same shape — you have done what you have done. I could not have done it my time, but you come after me. Tell!"

I told and he listened. After that, I wished to tell all the people but he showed me otherwise. He said, "Truth is a hard deer to hunt. If you eat too much truth at once, you may die of the truth. It was not idly that our fathers forbade the Dead Places." He was right — it is better the truth should come little by little. I have learned that, being a priest. Perhaps, in the old days, they ate knowledge too fast.

Nevertheless, we make a beginning. It is not for the metal alone we go to the Dead Places now — there are the books and the writings. They are hard to learn. And the magic tools are broken — but we can look at them and wonder. At least, we make a beginning. And, when I am chief priest we shall go beyond the great river. We shall go to the Place of the Gods — the place newyork — not one man but a company. We shall look for the images of the gods and find the god ASHING and the others — the gods Licoln and Biltmore and Moses. But they were men who built the city, not gods or demons. They were men. I remember the dead man's face. They were men who were here before us. We must build again.

QUESTIONS

1. Explain the significance of the title.
2. Discuss the theory that both great poets and scientists possess great vision.
3. Why was the east forbidden territory?
4. What is the setting of the story and why is the author vague as to the time?
5. Describe briefly the chief character.
6. What does the author mean by "the Place of the Gods" and "the Great Burning"?
7. How did the narrator learn that he was destined to become a priest?
8. What did John mean by "the old books"?
9. Into what type of civilization was the supposed narrator born?
10. What was John's strong dream and what did it signify?
11. What signs made John think that he should travel east?
12. Describe the Place of the Gods as John first saw it from a distance.
13. When and why did John chant his death song?
14. How did John finally reach the Place of the Gods?
15. What do UBTREAS and ASHING really stand for?
16. What dangers did John meet in the city?
17. Describe the room in which John spent the night.
18. Describe in detail John's vision.
19. What tremendously important discovery did John make the next morning? Explain clearly why this is very important to the story.

20. What did John mean by saying, "Perhaps, in the old days, they ate knowledge too fast"? Do you agree? Discuss.

21. *Word Study.* — What do the following words mean as they are used in the story: *chant* (n. and v.), *spell* (n.)? Why, in your opinion, is the vocabulary unusually simple and easy? Discuss.

Problem: LESSON OR MORAL

1. What, in your opinion, was the purpose of Mr. Benét in writing the story?

2. What is the chief lesson that the story teaches?

3. Do you believe a "Great Burning" is probable? Why or why not?

4. After a great world holocaust, do you believe man would be reduced to a simple, primitive civilization? Discuss.

5. What did John mean by stating, "We must build again"? Do you believe this would be possible? Discuss.

PART II
EARLIER TYPES OF FICTION

The Shepherd Boy

Aesop (Sixth Century B.C.)

> *We really know very little about Aesop, the Greek fabulist and philosopher. Tradition tells us that he was a lame Greek slave who received his freedom from his master, Iadmon, and that he traveled through Greece and Egypt, and lived for a time at the court of Croesus, King of Lydia. It is said that, accused by the Delphians of stealing a sacred vessel from the temple of Apollo, he was executed in 561 B.C.*
>
> *We may be sure now that Aesop did not tell all the fables that are ascribed to him. Many peoples have tales in which animals speak and act, and in which one animal teaches another a lesson in morals — or tales in which the same method is followed with men as the chief characters. Fables have been found in Egypt that must have been current about 1000 B.C. There are Hindu fables of which no one knows the age. There are the Buddhist "jatakas" — animal fables like most of the rest. And there are the African fables, from which come the original of the Tar-Baby story.*
>
> *Many of the so-called Aesop fables came from these sources. Many others are Greek in origin, but probably were not first told by Aesop. We do not know definitely that any one of them was originated by any one man. What we can say with certainty is that for a long time now these short, pithy little moral tales have been in our literary heritage and that they are said to have been first told by Aesop, a lame Phrygian slave, who lived about the sixth century* B.C.

ONCE upon a time there lived a shepherd boy who tended his flock on the outskirts of a neighboring village. The days were long and he found very little to amuse him. Knowing that the villagers were anxious to protect their property against the depredations of the wolves, the lad thought it would be fun to see them come running from their homes.

One day he cried "Wolf! Wolf!" at the top of his voice, and the men of the village, armed with scythes, pitchforks, and clubs, came running to the flock. When they had arrived, the boy laughed at them and explained that there were no wolves about, but that he wanted to break the monotony of his long day.

A few days later he tried the same trick again and, as it proved very successful, he employed it the third time. The men of the village, however, soon became disgusted and paid no attention to his calls.

One day a pack of ravenous wolves descended upon the flock and began killing the sheep. One huge beast made for the boy himself, and the latter cried "Wolf! Wolf!" at the top of his voice. The men of the village went peacefully about their work paying no attention at all to his frantic cries, and too late the Shepherd Boy learned:

A liar will not be believed even when he is telling the truth.

QUESTIONS
(See pages 4, 18.)

1. Is there anything funny about this story?
2. Where does the introduction of the story begin and end? Is there enough information in it? Is there any unnecessary information in it?
3. What is the climax of the fable? What events lead up to it? What is the conclusion of the story?
4. How is this fable typical?
5. *Word Study.* — What do the following words mean as they are used in the story: *depredations, ravenous?*

The Old Man, His Son, and Their Donkey

Aesop

AN OLD man and his young son were driving their donkey to a neighboring fair with the intention of selling it. As they were walking along driving the beast in front of them, they met a party of young girls.

One of them remarked to her companions: "Just look at that foolish pair! They are driving that donkey and trudging along behind him when one of them might just as well be riding."

Upon hearing these words, the old man put his son on the donkey's back and walked along beside him. They had not proceeded much further before they met a company of elderly men.

"There!" remarked one of them. "You can easily see what the world is coming to. There is no longer any respect for age. Just see that healthy young lummox perched up there on the donkey's back while his poor old father is walking along beside him."

This speech made the son feel guilty and thoughtless so he immediately climbed down and assisted his father to mount. Then they continued their journey, the father riding the donkey and the son walking beside him. Presently they met a group of peasants carrying their vegetables to market.

"Look at that old man riding so comfortably while his poor little son is both foot-sore and weary," remarked a well-to-do peasant. "The least he could do would be to move along and make a space for that little chap."

The father then changed his position and made room for the boy, who climbed up in back of him. Shortly after this, they met a group of middle-aged women.

"It's a shame," remarked one kindly woman, "the way these men treat their poor beasts. That poor donkey is carrying a double load. It seems to me that those two lazy persons ought to be carrying the donkey instead of making him carry them."

Father and son dismounted with alacrity and tying the donkey's legs together, they thrust a heavy pole between them and shouldered the load. While they were crossing a bridge on the outskirts of the town, the donkey, not enjoying the situation, kicked so hard that he tumbled off the pole, fell in the river and was drowned. Sadder but wiser the old man and his son returned home, firmly convinced of the truth: *Try to please everyone, and you will succeed in pleasing no one.*

QUESTIONS
(See pages 4, 18.)

1. Who are the chief characters in the fable? Have they any special traits that set them apart from other persons? Which of their character traits are necessary to the story?

2. Is this an interesting story? Explain. Is it funny? Is it a study of interesting characters? Does it present a setting? What is the purpose of the story?

3. Do you think this is a typical fable? Explain. How does it differ from some other fables?

The Good Samaritan

Saint Luke (First Century, A.D.)

Saint Luke, whose name was probably Lucanus, is
believed to have been a native of Antioch, the capital of Syria.
By profession he was a physician (Saint Paul calls him "most
dear physician"), and he may have studied medicine at the well-
known school of Tarsus, the rival of Alexandria and Athens.
The apostle traveled much as an evangelist, doubtless as the
companion of Saint Paul. Tradition tells us that he died at
the age of seventy-four in the city of Bithynia (probably another
name of Boeotia).

Saint Luke is believed to have written the Book of Luke and
the Acts of the Apostles. He was the most literary of New Testament writers and had a marvelous command of the Greek language,
in which these books were originally written.

The parable is another very old and very popular form of
narrative. Like the fable, it is a moral tale; unlike the fable it
has not usually an expressed moral. Both of the following parables
come from the Book of Luke, and they should be immediately
familiar to all.

A CERTAIN man went down from Jerusalem to
Jericho, and fell among thieves, which stripped him of his
raiment, and wounded him, and departed, leaving him half
dead.

And by chance there came down a certain priest that way:
and when he saw him, he passed by on the other side.

And likewise a Levite, when he was at the place, came and
looked on him, and passed by on the other side.

But a certain Samaritan, as he journeyed, came where he
was: and when he saw him, he had compassion on him.

And went to him, and bound up his wounds, pouring in oil and wine, and set him on his own beast, and brought him to an inn, and took care of him.

And on the morrow when he departed, he took out two pence, and gave them to the host, and said unto him, "Take care of him; and whatsoever thou spendest more, when I come again, I will repay thee."

Which now of these three, thinkest thou, was neighbour unto him that fell among the thieves?

And he said, "He that shewed mercy on him." Then said Jesus unto him, "Go, and do thou likewise."

QUESTIONS
(See pages 4, 18.)

1. Do you know any more about the good Samaritan than you do about the old man and the two boys in the fables? Explain.
2. What lesson is the parable intended to teach? How is the lesson expressed?
3. Examine the structure of the parable for introduction, action leading up to the climax, climax, conclusion.
4. *Word Study.* — What do the following words mean as they are used in the story: *raiment, compassion?*

The Prodigal Son

Saint Luke

A CERTAIN man had two sons:

And the younger of them said to his father, "Father, give me the portion of goods that falleth to me." And he divided unto them his living.

And not many days after the younger son gathered all together, and took his journey into a far country, and there wasted his substance with riotous living.

And when he had spent all, there arose a mighty famine in that land; and he began to be in want.

And he went and joined himself to a citizen of that country; and he sent him into his fields to feed swine.

And he would fain have filled his belly with the husks that the swine did eat; and no man gave unto him.

And when he came to himself, he said, "How many hired servants of my father's have bread enough and to spare, and I perish with hunger!

"I will arise and go to my father, and will say unto him, 'Father, I have sinned against heaven, and before thee,

"'And am no more worthy to be called thy son: make me as one of thy hired servants.'"

And he arose, and came to his father. But when he was yet a great way off, his father saw him, and had compassion, and ran, and fell on his neck, and kissed him.

And the son said unto him, "Father, I have sinned against heaven, and in thy sight, and am no more worthy to be called thy son."

But the father said to his servants, "Bring forth the best robe, and put it on him; and put a ring on his hand, and shoes on his feet:

"And bring hither the fatted calf, and kill it; and let us eat, and be merry:

"For this my son was dead, and is alive again; he was lost, and is found." And they began to be merry.

Now his elder son was in the field: and as he came and drew nigh to the house, he heard music and dancing.

And he called one of the servants, and asked what these things meant.

And he said unto him, "Thy brother is come; and thy father hath killed the fatted calf, because he hath received him safe and sound."

And he was angry, and would not go in: therefore came his father out, and intreated him.

And he answering said to his father, "Lo, these many years do I serve thee, neither transgressed I at any time thy commandment: and yet thou never gavest me a kid, that I might make merry with my friends:

"But as soon as this thy son was come, which hath devoured thy living with harlots, thou hast killed for him the fatted calf."

And he said unto him, "Son, thou art ever with me, and all that I have is thine.

"It was meet that we should make merry, and be glad: for this thy brother was dead, and is alive again; and was lost, and is found."

QUESTIONS
(See pages 4, 18.)

1. What is this parable intended to teach? What other lesson is there in the story?

2. Compare "The Prodigal Son," as a story with "The Good Samaritan" and the two fables. Which of the four is the best story? Why do you think so?

3. This parable has been produced as a moving picture. Give your reasons for believing that it would or would not make a good picture.

4. Try to find some real characters in the fables or parables.

5. Can you find any differences between the fables and the parables?

6. *Word Study.* — What do the following words mean as they are used in the story: *substance, riotous, transgressed?*

The Three Rings

Giovanni Boccaccio (1313–1375)

Giovanni Boccaccio has probably been one of the strongest influences in the development of modern fiction. He is said to have been born in Certaldo, near Florence. He was educated for the law, but he seems to have spent most of his early manhood making verses at the Court of Naples. About 1350, Boccaccio returned to Florence and entered diplomatic service, traveling as Florentine Ambassador to Rome, Avignon, Ravenna, and Brandenburg.

At some time before his return from Naples, Boccaccio began work upon the book that has made him famous — the "Decameron." The name "Decameron" is taken from two Greek words, one meaning "ten" and the other "day." The "Decameron" is a collection of one hundred stories divided into ten groups of ten stories each. A running narrative accounts for the division and links the stories together. It tells of seven court ladies and three court gentlemen who sought refuge from the plague of 1348 in a country villa. They found little to amuse them there, and to pass the ten days of their isolation they adopted the plan of telling a story apiece each day, making a total of one hundred stories. The completion of the book required ten years of labor.

The stories contained in the "Decameron" have been used time and again as bases of plays and stories, and the "Decameron'" method of presenting the stories as part of a longer narrative is sometimes followed to this day.

"The Three Rings" is typical of the medieval tale which flourished in almost all the countries of Europe from the thirteenth century through the sixteenth. Differing from the modern short story in form and purpose, it bears a strong resemblance to the parables of the Bible. The reader might well compare "The Three Rings" with "The Good Samaritan" and "The Prodigal Son." The story itself is simple and well told, but it lacks the singleness of aim and the compactness of form of the modern short story.

410

(Filomena's Story)

SALADIN was a genius whose valor was such that not only had it raised him from a man of small means to Sultan of Babylon, but it had gained for him many victories over kings both Saracen and Christian. Having in various wars and in the exercise of his extraordinary munificences spent all his ready money, and having need for a round sum and not knowing just where he might secure it as promptly as he might wish, he suddenly thought of a rich Jew, Melchizedek by name, who lent money for interest in the town of Alexandria.

He thought the latter possessed sufficient funds to oblige him if he felt so inclined; but this Jew was so miserly that he would never have done such a thing of his own free will, and Saladin was not willing to use force. Therefore, this mighty ruler set his wits to work to devise a scheme whereby Melchizedek might be led to serve him by means of a trick of force tempered with apparent reason.

Accordingly Saladin sent for the money lender, received him familiarly, seated him by his side, and then said to him:

"Honest man, I have understood from certain acquaintances that you are a very learned man and deeply versed in matters of religion. I would indeed like to know which of the three Laws you think is the true one, the Jewish, the Saracen, or the Christian."

The Jew, who was in truth a man of learning and intelligence, saw all too well that Saladin sought to entrap him by words, so that he might fasten a quarrel upon him, and realized that it would be fatal to praise any one of the three at the expense of the others. Accordingly, after sharpening his wits, as became one who felt the need of an exceedingly diplomatic answer, he replied as follows:

"My lord, the question that you ask me is a nice one, and to acquaint you with what seems to me to be the gist of the whole matter, I would like to tell you a little story.

"Once upon a time there was a great man of much wealth, who, among other precious jewels in his treasury, had a very costly ring. Esteeming this ornament's worth and beauty and wishing to leave it in perpetuity to his descendants, he declared that the son who should, at his death, be the owner of the ring should be recognized as his true heir and be held by all the others as chief and head of the house.

"The son who finally received the ring after the death of his father made the same kind of will as his parent before him had done. Thus the ring passed from hand to hand through many generations and at last came into the possession of a man who had three fine sons, so good, virtuous, and obedient that he loved them all alike.

"The young men knew the value of the ring and each one, desiring to be the most honored among his people, besought his father, who was now an old man, to leave him the ring when he came to die.

"The father, who loved them all equally, did not know how to make a choice. He had promised the ring to each one and did not know how he could solve the riddle. Finally he had a skilled goldsmith make two rings which were so like the original that he himself scarcely knew which was the true one.

"When he came to die, he secretly gave each son a ring, and after his death, there were naturally three claimants for the estate. Each son claimed to be the chief heir, and each one produced his ring as proof of his contention. However, the rings were so much alike that the question of the inheritance was never satisfactorily settled.

"In the same way, my lord Saladin, I am forced to answer you when you ask me regarding the Three Laws. God, the Father, gave to his three peoples, the Jew, the Saracen, and the Christian, the Three Laws, just as the father gave his three sons the three rings. Quite naturally each people believes itself to have inherited the true and only gospel, but the truth of the matter has yet to be settled."

Saladin perceived that the clever Melchizedek had managed to escape the snare which had been set for him; so this mighty ruler then revealed to him his great need for funds, at the same time confessing freely the punishments he had planned for him if he had not answered so diplomatically. The Jew immediately furnished Saladin with the necessary sum, and the Sultan later repaid him for his kindness. More than this, the latter gave him many rich gifts, was friendly toward him always, and even maintained him about his own person in high and honorable station.

QUESTIONS
(See pages 6, 19.)

1. Which of the two narratives in this story seems to you the important one? Would the story of the three rings stand without the story of Saladin? Would the story of Saladin stand without the story of the three rings? Why do you think the author placed the story of the three rings within another story?
2. Find points of similarity and of difference between this story and the fables or the parables.
3. What is the purpose of this tale? Is it a theme story? Has it a moral?
4. *Word Study.* — What do the following words mean as they are used in the story: *munificence, perpetuity, contention, diplomatically?*

The Story of An Heir

(No. 123, July 21, 1711)

Joseph Addison (1672–1719)

Joseph Addison, an English essayist and poet, was born on May 1, 1672, in Milston, a small village in Wiltshire. He entered Queen's College, Oxford, at the age of fifteen, with a larger knowledge of Latin than was possessed by most university graduates. He received his degree of M.A. in 1693. It was Addison's original intention to become a clergyman, like his father, but he was dissuaded from this by a number of influential friends, who persuaded him to enter the diplomatic service instead. Addison died at the age of forty-seven and was buried in Westminster Abbey.

Addison's style is easy, polished, and graceful. Samuel Johnson wrote, "Whoever wishes to attain an English style familiar but not coarse, and elegant but not ostentatious, must give his days and nights to the volumes of Addison." Benjamin Franklin studied "The Spectator" when he was a printer in Boston and consciously imitated the style of Addison to improve his own manner of writing.

In collaboration with Richard Steele, Addison wrote "The Tatler" and "The Spectator," which were journals containing essays on the manners, foibles, and customs of the time. Some of the most famous of "The Spectator" essays are read in high schools today under the title, "The De Coverley Papers."

Essay means literally "an attempt," and is the name given to a class of writing which attempts, generally in an informal manner, to give the author's views on any subject in which he is interested. Although "The Story of an Heir" bears a certain general resemblance to the short story of today the reader should remember that the author's purpose was not to amuse the reader by telling him a story, but rather to point out a social danger and, through the story, to suggest one manner in which this danger might be avoided. The reader should notice the clear,

*lucid manner in which the essay is written and should compare
it with any one of the compact short stories of Part I.*

> Doctrina sed vim promovet insitam
> Rectique cultus pectora roborant;
>   Utcunque defecere mores,
>   Dedecorant bene nata culpæ. [1]
>   — HORACE, *Odes IV: 4, 33.*

AS I was yesterday taking the air with my friend
Sir Roger, we were met by a fresh-colored ruddy young man,
who rid by us full speed, with a couple of servants behind him.
Upon my inquiry who he was, Sir Roger told me that he was
a young gentleman of a considerable estate, who had been
educated by a tender mother, that lives not many miles from
the place where we were. She is a very good lady, says my
friend, but took so much care of her son's health that she has
made him good for nothing. She quickly found that reading
was bad for his eyes, and that writing made his head ache.
He was let loose among the woods as soon as he was able to
ride on horseback, or to carry a gun upon his shoulder. To be
brief, I found by my friend's account of him that he had got
a great stock of health, but nothing else; and that if it were
a man's business only to live, there would not be a more
accomplished young fellow in the whole country.

The truth of it is, since my residing in these parts I have
seen and heard innumerable instances of young heirs and
elder brothers who either from their own reflecting upon the
estates they are born to, and therefore thinking all other
accomplishments unnecessary, or from hearing these notions
frequently inculcated to them by the flattery of their servants
and domestics or from the same foolish thought prevailing in
those who have the care of their education, are of no manner

[1] Instruction brings to light the inborn worth
And culture of the right refines the soul;
Neglect disfigures what is good by birth
In what degree the mood forgets the goal.

of use but to keep up their families, and transmit their lands and houses in a line to posterity.

This makes me often think on a story I have heard of two friends, which I shall give my reader at large under feigned names. The moral of it may, I hope, be useful, though there are some circumstances which make it rather appear like a novel than a true story.

Eudoxus and Leontine began the world with small estates. They were both of them men of good sense and great virtue. They prosecuted their studies together in their earlier years, and entered into such a friendship as lasted to the end of their lives. Eudoxus, at his first setting out in the world, threw himself into a court, where by his natural endowments and his acquired abilities he made his way from one post to another, till at length he had raised a very considerable fortune. Leontine, on the contrary, sought all opportunities of improving his mind by study, conversation, and travel. He was not only acquainted with all the sciences, but with the most eminent professors of them throughout Europe. He knew perfectly well the interests of its princes, with the customs and fashions of their courts, and could scarce meet with the name of an extraordinary person in the Gazette whom he had not either talked to or seen. In short, he had so well mixed and digested his knowledge of men and books, that he made one of the most accomplished persons of his age. During the whole course of his studies and travels he kept up a punctual correspondence with Eudoxus, who often made himself acceptable to the principal men about court by the intelligence which he received from Leontine. When they were both turned of forty (an age in which, according to Mr. Cowley, "there is no dallying with life") they determined, pursuant to the resolution they had taken in the beginning of their lives, to retire, and pass the remainder of their days in the country. In order to do this, they both of them married much about the same time. Leontine, with his own and his wife's fortune, bought a farm of three hundred a year, which lay within the neighborhood of his friend Eudoxus, who had purchased an estate of as many thousands. They were both of them fathers about the same time, Eudoxus having a son born to him, and Leontine a daughter; but to the unspeakable grief of the latter, his young wife, in whom all his happiness was wrapt up, died in a few days after the birth of her daughter. His affliction would have been insupportable had not he been comforted by the daily visits and conversations of his friend. As they were one day talking together with their usual intimacy, Leontine considering how incapable he was of giving his daughter a proper education in his own house, and Eudoxus reflecting on the ordinary behavior of a son who knows himself to be the heir of a great estate, they both agreed upon an exchange of children, namely, that the boy should be bred up with Leontine as his son, and that the girl should live with Eudoxus as his daughter, till they were each of them arrived at years of discretion. The wife of Eudoxus, knowing that her son could not be so advantageously brought up as under the care of Leontine, and considering at the same time that he would be perpetually under her own eye, was by degrees prevailed upon to fall in with the project. She therefore took Leonilla, for that was the name of the girl, and educated her as her own daughter. The two friends on each side had wrought themselves to such an habitual tenderness for the children who were under their direction, that each of them had the real passion of a father, where the title was but imaginary. Florio, the name of the young heir that lived with Leontine, though he had all the duty and affection imaginable for his supposed parent, was taught to rejoice at the sight of Eudoxus, who visited his friend very frequently, and was dictated by his natural affection, as well as by the rules of prudence, to make himself esteemed and beloved by Florio. The boy was now old enough to know his supposed father's circumstances, and that therefore he was to make his way in the world by his own industry. This consideration grew stronger in him every day, and produced so good an effect that he applied himself with more than ordinary attention to the pursuit of everything which Leontine recommended to him. His natural abilities, which were very good, assisted by the directions of so excellent a counsellor, enabled him to make a quicker progress than ordinary through all the parts of his education. Before he was twenty years of age, having finished his studies and exercises with great applause, he was removed from the university to the inns of court, where there are very few that make themselves considerable proficients in the studies of the place who know they shall arrive at great estates without them. This was not Florio's case; he found that three hundred a year was but a poor estate for Leontine and himself to live upon, so that he studied without intermission till he gained a very good insight into the constitution and laws of his country.

I should have told my reader that whilst Florio lived at the house of his foster-father he was always an acceptable guest in the family of Eudoxus, where he became acquainted with Leonilla from her infancy. His acquaintance with her by degrees grew into love, which in a mind trained up in all the sentiments of honor and virtue became a very uneasy passion. He despaired of gaining an heiress of so great a fortune, and would rather have died than attempted it by any indirect methods. Leonilla, who was a woman of the greatest beauty joined with the greatest modesty, entertained at the same time a secret passion for Florio, but conducted herself with so much prudence that she never gave him the least intimation of it. Florio was now engaged in all those arts and improvements that are proper to raise a man's private fortune, and give him a figure in his country, but secretly tormented with that passion which burns with the greatest fury in a virtuous and noble heart, when he received a sudden summons from Leontine to repair to him into the country the next day. For it seems Eudoxus was so filled with the report of his son's reputation, that he could no longer withhold making himself known to him. The morning after his arrival at the house of his supposed father, Leontine told him that Eudoxus had something of great importance to communicate to him; upon which the good man embraced him and wept. Florio was no sooner arrived at the great house that stood in his neighbor hood, but Eudoxus took him by the hand, after the first salutes were over, and conducted him into his closet. He there opened to him the whole secret of his parentage and education, concluding after this manner: "I have no other way left of acknowledging my gratitude to Leontine, than by marrying you to his daughter. He shall not lose the pleasure of being your father by the discovery I have made to you. Leonilla, too, shall be still my daughter; her filial piety, though mis placed, has been so exemplary that it deserves the greatest reward I can confer upon it. You shall have the pleasure of seeing a great estate fall to you, which you would have lost the relish of had you known yourself born to it. Continue only to deserve it in the same manner you did before you were possessed of it. I have left your mother in the next room. Her heart yearns toward you. She is making the same discoveries to Leonilla which I have made to yourself."

Florio was so overwhelmed with this profusion of happiness that he was not able to make a reply, but threw himself down at his father's feet, and amidst a flood of tears kissed and embraced his knees, asking his blessing, and expressing in dumb show those sentiments of love, duty, and gratitude that were too big for utterance. To conclude, the happy pair were married, and half Eudoxus's estate settled upon them. Leontine and Eudoxus passed the remainder of their lives together; and received in the dutiful and affectionate behavior of Florio and Leonilla the just recompense, as well as the natural effects, of that care which they had bestowed upon them in their education.

QUESTIONS
(See pages 7, 18.)

1. Do you like or dislike this story? Why?
2. What is the purpose of the story? Does it accomplish its purpose?
3. Does the author offer a satisfactory solution to the problem he raises? Explain.

4. In what ways does this essay-story resemble the modern short story? How is it different from the modern short story? How does it differ from essays you have read?

5. Find in the story expressions that are not in use today. Compare the style of Addison with the style of any modern short-story writer.

6. *Word Study.* — What do the following words mean as they are used in the story: *inculcated, filial, discretion, intimation?*

The Belated Travelers

Washington Irving (1783–1859)

Washington Irving, sometimes called the "Father of American Literature," was born in New York City, April 3, 1783. He was named Washington after our first President, and tradition tells us that George Washington himself laid his hands in benediction upon young Irving's head. Irving attended school until he was fifteen, but he did not go to college. Instead, he studied law for a while, not because he had any special liking for it, but to please his family. In 1815 he went to England to act as foreign agent for his brothers' business. Through no fault of Irving's the firm failed shortly afterward, and he turned his attention to writing.

His decision to write was made in 1818, but before that year he had written many of the selections that afterward appeared in "The Sketch Book," published in America in 1818, and in England two years later. This volume was a huge success on both sides of the Atlantic. Two other volumes, "Bracebridge Hall" (1822) and "Tales of a Traveler" (1824), added to his rapidly growing reputation.

In 1826 Irving left England for Spain, where he wrote "Life of Columbus" (1828), "Conquest of Granada" (1829), "Companions of Columbus" (1831), "The Alhambra" (1832), and "The Legend of the Conquest of Spain" (1835). After living in America again for a few years, Irving was appointed minister to Spain, where he served with distinction. At the end of four years he returned to America, and lived quietly at his home on the Hudson, devoting his time to literary activities. His last work, a life of George Washington, was completed a few months before his death in 1859.

Irving's style is simple, lucid, and graceful. He possessed the rare gifts of abundant humor and gentle satire. His "Sketch Book" is read and enjoyed today; his "History of New York," a humorous account of the settlement and early history of that city, *supposed to have been written by one Diedrich Knickerbocker, is highly diverting. Even before the day of the "tailor-made" short story, he wrote stories which have rarely been surpassed in form. Some of them are as compact and well executed in form as any written today.*

"The Belated Travelers" is one of a series of stories in the third part of "Tales of a Traveler." The series is made up (somewhat after the fashion of the "Decameron") of tales told by various members of a group of travelers, some of whom are mentioned at the end of this story. "The Belated Travelers" is related by a character called "The Neapolitan."

Although it is not so well known as "Rip Van Winkle" or "A Legend of Sleepy Hollow," "The Belated Travelers" is an excellent example of the nineteenth-century tale. Typical of the tale, in contrast to the modern short story, is the leisurely manner in which the action proceeds. There is a certain charm in the very lack of concentration, for, to Irving, the love story, the description of the characters, and the local color seem to be almost as important as the adventures of the chief characters. A modern writer would doubtless concentrate upon the action to gain unity of effect. The resulting story would be technically correct, but would lose some of its quaint picturesqueness.

IT WAS late one evening that a carriage, drawn by mules, slowly toiled its way up one of the passes of the Apennines. It was through one of the wildest defiles, where a hamlet occurred only at distant intervals, perched on the summit of some rocky height, or the white towers of a convent peeped out from among the thick mountain foliage. The carriage was of ancient and ponderous construction. Its faded embellishments spoke of former splendor, but its crazy springs and axle-trees creaked out the tale of present decline. Within was seated a tall, thin old gentleman, in a kind of military traveling dress, and a foraging cap trimmed with fur, though the gray locks which stole from under it hinted that his fighting days were over. Beside him was a pale, beautiful girl of eighteen, dressed in something of a northern or Polish costume. One servant was seated in front — a rusty, crusty-looking fellow, with a scar across his face, an orange-tawny *schnurbart*, or pair of mustaches, bristling from under his nose, and altogether the air of an old soldier.

It was, in fact, the equipage of a Polish nobleman; a wreck of one of those princely families once of almost oriental magnificence, but broken down and impoverished by the disasters of Poland. The count, like many other generous spirits, had been found guilty of the crime of patriotism, and was, in a manner, an exile from his country. He had resided for some time in the first cities of Italy, for the education of his daughter, in whom all his cares and pleasures were now centered. He had taken her into society, where her beauty and accomplishments gained her many admirers, and had she not been the daughter of a poor, broken-down, Polish nobleman, it is more than probable many would have contended for her hand. Suddenly, however, her health became delicate and drooping, her gayety fled with the roses of her cheek, and she sank into silence and debility. The old count saw the change with the solicitude of a parent. "We must try a change of air and scene," said he; and in a few days the old family carriage was rumbling among the Apennines.

Their only attendant was the veteran Caspar, who had been born in the family, and grown rusty in its service. He had followed his master in all his fortunes, had fought by his side, had stood over him when fallen in battle, and had received, in his defense, the saber cut which added such grimness to his countenance. He was now his valet, his steward, his butler, his factotum. The only being that rivaled his master in his affections was his youthful mistress. She had grown up under his eye; he had led her by the hand when she was a child, and he now looked upon her with the fondness of a parent. Nay, he even took the freedom of a parent in giving his blunt opinion on all matters which he thought were for her good, and felt a parent's vanity at seeing her gazed at and admired.

The evening was thickening; they had been for some time passing through narrow gorges of the mountains, along the edges of a tumbling stream. The scenery was lonely and savage. The rocks often beetled over the road, with flocks of white goats browsing on their brinks, and gazing down upon the travelers. They had between two or three leagues yet to go before they could reach any village; yet the muleteer Pietro, a tippling old fellow, who had refreshed himself at the last halting place with a more than ordinary quantity of wine, sat singing and talking alternately to his mules, and suffering them to lag on at a snail's pace, in spite of the frequent entreaties of the count and maledictions of Caspar.

The clouds began to roll in heavy masses along the mountains, shrouding their summits from view. The air was damp and chilly. The count's solicitude on his daughter's account overcame his usual patience. He leaned from the carriage, and called to old Pietro in an angry tone.

"Forward!" said he. "It will be midnight before we arrive at our inn."

"Yonder it is, *signor*," said the muleteer.

"Where?" demanded the count.

"Yonder," said Pietro, pointing to a desolate pile about a quarter of a league distant.

"That the place? Why, it looks more like a ruin than an inn. I thought we were to put up for the night at a comfortable village."

Here Pietro uttered a string of piteous exclamations and ejaculations, such as are ever at the tip of the tongue of a delinquent muleteer. Such roads, and such mountains! And then his poor animals were wayworn and leg weary; they would fall lame; they would never be able to reach the village. And then what could his *Excellenza* wish for better than the inn, a perfect *castello!* — a *palazzo!* — and such people! — and such a larder! — and such beds! His *Excellenza* might fare as sumptuously and sleep as soundly there as a prince!

The count was easily persuaded, for he was anxious to get his daughter out of the night air; so in a little while the old carriage rattled and jingled into the great gateway of the inn.

The building did certainly in some measure answer the muleteer's description. It was large enough for either castle or palace, built in a strong but simple and almost rude style, with a great quantity of waste room. It had in fact been, in former times, a hunting seat of one of the Italian princes. There was space enough within its walls and outbuildings to have accommodated a little army. A scanty household seemed now to people this dreary mansion. The faces that presented themselves on the arrival of the travelers were begrimed with dirt, and scowling in their expression. They all knew old Pietro, however, and gave him a welcome as he entered, singing and talking, and almost whooping, into the gateway.

The hostess of the inn waited herself on the count and his daughter, to show them the apartments. They were conducted through a long, gloomy corridor, and then through a suite of chambers opening into each other, with lofty ceilings, and great beams extending across them. Everything, however, had a wretched, squalid look. The walls were damp and bare, excepting that here and there hung some great painting, large enough for a chapel, and blackened out of all distinction.

They chose two bedrooms, one within another, the inner one for the daughter. The bedsteads were massive and misshapen; but on examining the beds so vaunted by old Pietro, they found them stuffed with fibers of hemp knotted in great lumps. The count shrugged his shoulders, but there was no choice left.

The chilliness of the apartments crept to their bones, and they were glad to return to a common chamber, or kind of hall, where was a fire burning in a huge cavern, miscalled a chimney. A quantity of green wood, just thrown on, puffed out volumes of smoke. The room corresponded to the rest of the mansion. The floor was paved and dirty; a great oaken table stood in the center, immovable from its size and weight. The only thing that contradicted this prevalent air of indigence was the dress of the hostess. She was a slattern, of course, yet her garments, though dirty and negligent, were of costly materials. She wore several rings of great value on her fingers, and jewels in her ears, and round her neck was a string of large pearls, to which was attached a sparkling crucifix. She had the remains of beauty, yet there was something in the expression of her countenance that inspired the young lady with singular aversion. She was officious and obsequious in her attentions, and both the count and his daughter felt relieved when she consigned them to the care of a dark, sullen-looking servant maid, and went off to superintend the supper.

Caspar was indignant at the muleteer for having, either through negligence or design, subjected his master and mistress to such quarters, and vowed by his mustaches to have revenge on the old varlet the moment they were safe out from among the mountains. He kept up a continual quarrel with the sulky servant maid, which only served to increase the sinister expression with which she regarded the travelers from under her strong, dark eyebrows.

As to the count, he was a good-humored, passive traveler. Perhaps real misfortunes had subdued his spirit, and rendered him tolerant of many of those petty evils which make prosperous men miserable. He drew a large broken armchair to the fireside for his daughter, and another for himself, and seizing an enormous pair of tongs, endeavored to rearrange the wood so as to produce a blaze. His efforts, however, were only repaid by thicker puffs of smoke, which almost overcame the good gentleman's patience. He would draw back, cast a look upon his delicate daughter, then upon the cheerless, squalid apartment, and, shrugging his shoulders, would give a fresh stir to the fire.

Of all the miseries of a comfortless inn, however, there is none greater than sulky attendants. The good count for some time bore the smoke in silence, rather than address himself to the scowling servant maid. At length he was compelled to beg for drier firewood. The woman retired muttering. On reëntering the room hastily, with an armful of fagots, her foot slipped; she fell, and striking her head against the corner of a chair, cut her temple severely.

The blow stunned her for a time, and the wound bled profusely. When she recovered, she found the count's daughter administering to her wound, and binding it up with her own handkerchief. It was such an attention as any woman of ordinary feeling would have yielded; but perhaps there was something in the appearance of the lovely being who bent over her, or in the tones of her voice, that touched the heart of the woman unused to be administered to by such hands. Certain it is, she was strongly affected. She caught the delicate hand of the Polonaise, and pressed it fervently to her lips.

"May San Francisco watch over you, *signora!*" exclaimed she.

A new arrival broke the stillness of the inn. It was a Spanish princess with a numerous retinue. The courtyard was in an uproar, the house in a bustle. The landlady hurried to attend such distinguished guests, and the poor count and his daughter, and their supper, were for a moment forgotten. The veteran Caspar muttered Polish maledictions enough to agonize an Italian ear; but it was impossible to convince the hostess of the superiority of his old master and young mistress to the whole nobility of Spain.

The noise of the arrival had attracted the daughter to the window just as the newcomers had alighted. A young cavalier sprang out of the carriage and handed out the princess. The latter was a little shriveled old lady, with a face of parchment, and sparkling black eyes; she was richly and gayly dressed, and walked with the assistance of a gold-headed cane as high as herself. The young man was tall and elegantly formed. The count's daughter shrank back at the sight of him, though the deep frame of the window screened her from observation. She gave a heavy sigh as she closed the casement. What that sigh meant I cannot say. Perhaps it was at the contrast between the splendid equipage of the princess, and the crazy, rheumatic-looking old vehicle of her father, which stood hard by. Whatever might be the reason, the young lady closed the casement with a sigh. She returned to her chair; a slight shivering passed over her delicate frame; she leaned her elbow on the arm of the chair, rested her pale cheek in the palm of her hand, and looked mournfully into the fire.

The count thought she appeared paler than usual.

"Does anything ail thee, my child?" said he.

"Nothing, dear father!" replied she, laying her hand within his, and looking up smiling in his face; but as she said so, a treacherous tear rose suddenly to her eye, and she turned away her head.

"The air of the window has chilled thee," said the count fondly, "but a good night's rest will make all well again."

The supper table was at length laid, and the supper about to be served, when the hostess appeared, with her usual obsequiousness, apologizing for showing in the newcomers; but the night air was cold, and there was no other chamber in the inn with a fire in it. She had scarcely made the apology when the princess entered, leaning on the arm of the elegant young man.

The count immediately recognized her for a lady whom he had met frequently in society, both at Rome and Naples, and to whose *converzaziones*, in fact, he had been constantly invited. The cavalier, too, was her nephew and heir, who had been greatly admired in the gay circles both for his merits and prospects, and who had once been on a visit at the same time with his daughter and himself at the villa of a nobleman near Naples. Report had recently affianced him to a rich Spanish heiress.

The meeting was agreeable to both the count and the princess. The former was a gentleman of the old school, courteous in the extreme; the princess had been a belle in her youth, and a woman of fashion all her life, and liked to be attended to.

The young man approached the daughter and began something of a complimentary observation, but his manner was embarrassed, and his compliment ended in an indistinct murmur, while the daughter bowed without looking up, moved her lips without articulating a word, and sank again into her chair, where she sat gazing into the fire, with a thousand varying expressions passing over her countenance.

This singular greeting of the young people was not perceived by the old ones, who were occupied at the time with their own courteous salutations. It was arranged that they should sup together, and as the princess traveled with her own cook, a very tolerable supper soon smoked upon the board. This, too, was assisted by choice wines and liquors and delicate confitures brought from one of her carriages, for she was a veteran epicure, and curious in her relish for the good things of this world. She was, in fact, a vivacious little old lady, who mingled the woman of dissipation with the devotee. She was actually on her way to Loretto to expiate a long life of gallantries and peccadillos by a rich offering at the hole shrine. She was, to be sure, rather a luxurious penitent, and a contrast to the primitive pilgrims, with scrip, and staff, and cockleshell; but then it would be unreasonable to expect such self-denial from people of fashion, and there was not a doubt of the ample efficacy of the rich crucifixes, and golden vessels and jeweled ornaments, which she was bearing to the treasury of the blessed Virgin.

The princess and the count chatted much during supper about the scenes and society in which they had mingled, and did not notice that they had all the conversation to themselves; the young people were silent and constrained. The daughter ate nothing, in spite of the politeness of the princess, who continually pressed her to taste of one or other of the delicacies. The count shook his head.

"She is not well this evening," said he; "I thought she would have fainted just now as she was looking out of the window at your carriage on its arrival."

A crimson glow flushed to the very temples of the daughter; but she leaned over her plate, and her tresses cast a shade over he countenance.

When supper was over, they drew their chairs about the great fireplace. The flame and smoke had subsided, and a heap of glowing embers diffused a grateful warmth. A guitar, which had been brought from the count's carriage, leaned against the wall; the princess perceived it. "Can we not have a little music before parting for the night?" demanded she.

The count was proud of his daughter's accomplishment, and joined in the request. The young man made an effort of politeness, and taking up the guitar, presented it, though in an embarrassed manner, to the fair musician. She would have declined it, but was too much confused to do so; indeed, she was so nervous and agitated that she dared not trust her voice to make an excuse. She touched the instrument with a faltering hand, and, after preluding a little, accompanied herself in several Polish airs. Her father's eyes glistened as he sat gazing on her. Even the crusty Caspar lingered in the room, partly through a fondness for the music of his native country, but chiefly through his pride in the musician. Indeed the melody of the voice and the delicacy of the touch were enough to have charmed more fastidious ears. The little princess nodded her head and tapped her hand to the music, though exceedingly out of time, while the nephew sat buried in profound contemplation of a black picture on the opposite wall.

"And now," said the count, patting her cheek fondly, "one more favor. Let the princess hear that little Spanish air you were so fond of. You can't think," added he, "what a proficiency she has made in your language, though she has been a sad girl, and neglected it of late."

The color flushed the pale cheek of the daughter. She hesitated, murmured something, but with sudden effort collected herself, struck the guitar boldly, and began. It was a Spanish romance, with something of love and melancholy in it. She gave the first stanza with great expression, for the tremulous, melting tones of her voice went to the heart; but her articulation failed, her lips quivered, the song died away, and she burst into tears.

The count folded her tenderly in his arms. "Thou art not well, my child," said he, "and I am tasking thee cruelly. Retire to thy chamber, and God bless thee!" She bowed to the company without raising her eyes, and glided out of the room.

The count shook his head as the door closed. "Something is the matter with that child," said he, "which I cannot divine. She has lost all health and spirits lately. She was always a tender flower, and I had much pains to rear her. Excuse a father's foolishness," continued he, "but I have seen much trouble in my family, and this poor girl is all that is now left to me, and she used to be so lively ——"

"Maybe she's in love," said the little princess, with a shrewd nod of the head.

"Impossible!" replied the good count, artlessly. "She has never mentioned a word of such a thing to me." How little did the worthy gentleman dream of the thousand cares and griefs and mighty love concerns which agitate a virgin heart, and which a timid girl scarcely breathes unto herself!

The nephew of the princess rose abruptly and walked about the room.

When she found herself alone in her chamber, the feelings of the young lady, so long restrained, broke forth with violence. She opened the casement, that the cool air might blow upon her throbbing temples. Perhaps there was some little pride or pique mingled with her emotions, though her gentle nature did not seem calculated to harbor any such angry inmate.

"He saw me weep," said she, with a sudden mantling of her cheek and a swelling of the throat, "but no matter, no matter!"

And so saying she threw her white arms across the window frame, buried her face in them, and abandoned herself to an agony of tears. She remained lost in a reverie until the sound of her father's and Caspar's voice in the adjoining room gave token that the party had retired for the night. The lights gleaming from window to window showed that they were conducting the princess to her apartments, which were in the opposite wing of the inn, and she distinctly saw the figure of the nephew as he passed one of the casements.

She heaved a deep, heart-drawn sigh, and was about to close the lattice, when her attention was caught by words spoken below her window by two persons who had just turned an angle of the building.

"But what will become of the poor young lady?" said a voice, which she recognized for that of the servant woman.

"Pooh! she must take her chance," was the reply from old Pietro.

"But cannot she be spared?" asked the other entreatingly; "she's so kind-hearted!"

"*Cospetto!* what has got into thee?" replied the other petulantly; "would you mar the whole business for the sake of a silly girl?" By this time they had got so far from the window that the Polonaise could hear nothing further. There was something in this fragment of conversation calculated to alarm. Did it relate to herself, and if so, what was this impending danger from which it was entreated that she might be spared? She was several times on the point of tapping at her father's door, to tell him what she had heard, but she might have been mistaken; she might have heard indistinctly; the conversation might have alluded to someone else; at any rate, it was too indefinite to lead to any conclusion. While in this state of irresolution, she was startled by a low knock against the wainscot in a remote part of her gloomy chamber. On holding up the light, she beheld a small door there which she had not before remarked. It was bolted on the inside. She advanced, and demanded who knocked, and was answered in the voice of the female domestic. On opening the door, the woman stood before it, pale and agitated. She entered softly, laying her finger on her lips as in sign of caution and secrecy.

"Fly!" said she; "leave this house instantly, or you are lost."

The young lady, trembling with alarm, demanded an explanation.

"I have not time," replied the woman, "I dare not — I shall be missed if I linger here; but fly instantly, or you are lost."

"And leave my father?"

"Where is he?"

"In the adjoining chamber."

"Call him, then, but lose no time."

The young lady knocked at her father's door. He was not yet retired to bed. She hurried into his room, and told him of the fearful warnings she had received. The count returned with her into the chamber, followed by Caspar. His questions soon drew the truth out of the embarrassed answers of the woman. The inn was beset by robbers. They were to be introduced after midnight, when the attendants of the princess and the rest of the travelers were sleeping and would be an easy prey.

"But we can barricade the inn; we can defend ourselves," said the count.

"What! when the people of the inn are in league with the banditti?"

"How, then, are we to escape? Can we not order out the carriage and depart?"

"*San Francisco!* for what? To give the alarm that the plot is discovered? That would make the robbers desperate, and bring them on you at once. They have had notice of the rich booty in the inn, and will not easily let it escape them."

"But how else are we to get off?"

"There is a horse behind the inn," said the woman, "from which the man has just dismounted who has been to summon the aid of part of the band at a distance."

"One horse, and there are three of us!" said the count.

"And the Spanish princess," cried the daughter anxiously. "How can she be extricated from the danger?"

"*Diavolo!* what is she to me?" said the woman, in sudden passion. "It is *you* I come to save, and you will betray me, and we shall all be lost. Hark!" continued she, "I am called — I shall be discovered — one word more. This door leads by a staircase to the courtyard. Under the shed, in the rear of the yard, is a small door leading out to the fields. You will find a horse there. Mount it; make a circuit under the shadow of a ridge of rocks that you will see; proceed cautiously and quietly until you cross a brook, and find yourself on the road just where there are three white crosses nailed against a tree; then put your horse to his speed, and make the best of your way to the village. But recollect, my life is in your hands. Say nothing of what you have heard or seen, whatever may happen at this inn."

The woman hurried away. A short and agitated consultation took place between the count, his daughter, and the veteran Caspar. The young lady seemed to have lost all apprehension for herself in her solicitude for the safety of the princess. "To fly in selfish silence, and leave her to be massacred!" A shuddering seized her at the very thought. The gallantry of the count, too, revolted at the idea. He could not consent to turn his back upon a party of helpless travelers, and leave them in ignorance of the danger which hung over them.

"But what is to become of the young lady," said Caspar, "if the alarm is given and the inn thrown in a tumult? What may happen to her in a chance medley affray?"

Here the feelings of the father were aroused; he looked upon his lovely, helpless child, and trembled at the chance of her falling into the hands of ruffians.

The daughter, however, thought nothing of herself. "The princess! the princess! only let the princess know her danger!" She was willing to share it with her.

At length Caspar interfered, with the zeal of a faithful old servant. No time was to be lost; the first thing was to get the young lady out of danger. "Mount the horse," said he to the count, "take her behind you, and fly! Make for the village, rouse the inhabitants, and send assistance. Leave me here to give the alarm to the princess and her people. I am an old soldier and I think we shall be able to stand siege until you send us aid."

The daughter would again have insisted on staying with the princess.

"For what?" said old Caspar bluntly. "You could do no good; you would be in the way; we would have to take care of you instead of ourselves."

There was no answering these objections; the count seized his pistols, and taking his daughter under his arm, moved toward the staircase. The young lady paused, stepped back, and said, faltering with agitation, "There is a young cavalier with the princess — her nephew; perhaps he may ———"

"I understand you, mademoiselle," replied old Caspar, with a significant nod; "not a hair of his head shall suffer harm if I can help it."

The young lady blushed deeper than ever; she had not anticipated being so thoroughly-understood by the blunt old servant.

"That is not what I mean," said she, hesitating. She would have added something, or made some explanation, but the moments were precious and her father hurried her away.

They found their way through the courtyard to the small postern gate, where the horse stood fastened to a ring in the wall. The count mounted, took his daughter behind him, and they proceeded as quietly as possible in the direction which the woman had pointed out. Many a fearful and anxious look did the daughter cast back upon the gloomy pile; the lights which had feebly twinkled through the dusky casements were one by one disappearing, a sign that the inmates were gradually sinking to repose, and she trembled with impatience lest succor should not arrive until that repose had been fatally interrupted.

They passed silently and safely along the skirts of the rocks, protected from observation by their overhanging shadows. They crossed the brook, and reached the place where three white crosses nailed against a tree told of some murder that had been committed there. Just as they had reached this ill-omened spot they beheld several men in the gloom coming down a craggy defile among the rocks.

"Who goes there?" exclaimed a voice. The count put spurs to his horse, but one of the men sprang forward and seized the bridle. The horse started back and reared, and had not the young lady clung to her father she would have been thrown off. The count leaned forward, put a pistol to the very head of the ruffian, and fired. The latter fell dead. The horse sprang forward. Two or three shots were fired, which whistled by the fugitives, but only served to augment their speed. They reached the village in safety.

The whole place was soon roused; but such was the awe in which the banditti were held that the inhabitants shrunk at the idea of encountering them. A desperate band had for some time infested that pass through the mountains, and the inn had long been suspected of being one of those horrible places where the unsuspicious wayfarer is entrapped and silently disposed of. The rich ornaments worn by the slattern hostess of the inn had excited heavy suspicions. Several instances had occurred of small parties of travelers disappearing mysteriously on that road, who, it was supposed at first, had been carried off by the robbers for the purpose of ransom, but who had never been heard of more. Such were the tales buzzed in the ears of the count by the villagers, as he endeavored to rouse them to the rescue of the princess and her train from their perilous situation. The daughter seconded the exertions of her father with all the eloquence of prayers, and tears, and beauty. Every moment that elapsed increased her anxiety until it became agonizing. Fortunately there was a body of gendarmes resting at the village. A number of the young villagers volunteered to accompany them, and the little army was put in motion. The count, having deposited his daughter in a place of safety, was too much of the old soldier not to hasten to the scene of danger. It would be difficult to paint the anxious agitation of the young lady while awaiting the result.

The party arrived at the inn just in time. The robbers, finding their plans discovered and the travelers prepared for their reception, had become open and furious in their attack. The princess's party had barricaded themselves in one suite of apartments, and repulsed the robbers from the doors and windows. Casper had shown the generalship of a veteran, and the nephew of the princess, the dashing valor of a young soldier. Their ammunition, however, was nearly exhausted, and they would have found it difficult to hold out much longer, when a discharge from the musketry of the gendarmes gave them the joyful tiding of succor.

A fierce fight ensued, for part of the robbers were surprised in the inn, and had to stand siege in their turn, while their comrades made desperate attempts to relieve them from under cover of the neighboring rocks and thickets.

I cannot pretend to give a minute account of the fight, as I have heard it related in a variety of ways. Suffice it to say, the robbers were defeated, several of them killed and several taken prisoners, which last, together with the people of the inn, were either executed or sent to the galleys.

I picked up these particulars in the course of a journey which I made some time after the event had taken place. I passed by the very inn. It was then dismantled, excepting one wing, in which a body of gendarmes was stationed. They pointed out to me the shot holes in the window frames, the walls, and the panels of the doors. There were a number of withered limbs dangling from the branches of a neighboring tree, and blackening in the air, which I was told were the limbs of the robbers who had been slain and the culprits who had been executed. The whole place had a dismal, wild, forlorn look.

"Were any of the princess's party killed?" inquired the Englishman.

"As far as I can recollect, there were two or three."

"Not the nephew, I trust?" said the fair Venetian.

"Oh, no; he hastened with the count to relieve the anxiety of the daughter by the assurances of victory. The young lady had been sustained through the interval of suspense by the very intensity of her feelings. The moment she saw her father returning in safety, accompanied by the nephew of the princess, she uttered a cry of rapture, and fainted. Happily, however, she soon recovered, and, what is more, was married shortly afterwards to the young cavalier, and the whole party accompanied the old princess in her pilgrimage to Loretto, where her votive offerings may still be seen in the treasury of the Santa Casa."

QUESTIONS
(See pages 8, 19.)

1. At what point in this story does the action begin? What is the climax of the story? Explain why you think so. Does the action lead steadily up to the climax? What information is contained in the conclusion of the story?

2. State the plot of the story in as few words as possible. What part of the story is not really essential to the plot? Does it add anything to the story?

3. How does this tale differ from the typical short story?

4. *Word Study.* — What do the following words mean as they are used in the story: *embellishment, foraging, impoverished, debility, solicitude, malediction, votive?*

David Swan *

Nathaniel Hawthorne (*1804–1864*)

When Nathaniel Hawthorne was four years old, his father, a Salem sea captain, died in a foreign port. The captain's death must have caused great sorrow to his widow, for she promptly shut herself up in her Salem house with her two daughters and her little son. All four of them lived there for years in the deepest gloom.

The aloof atmosphere of Hawthorne's early home becomes important to us when we try to understand his later life. He went to Bowdoin College where he at once gained a reputation for courtesy and for unusual reserve. During his college days, he made a few friends, among whom was Franklin Pierce, later President of the United States. Immediately after college, Hawthorne returned to his solitude. Living in retirement again, he read and wrote — and felt himself neglected when magazine editors returned his stories.

Finally, his seclusion was modified to some extent by his marriage. The necessity for earning money presented itself. Friends obtained his appointment to a political job in the Boston Customs House, which he soon lost through the operation of the Spoils System. This experience was repeated shortly afterward in the Salem Customs House.

Hawthorne had succeeded, meanwhile, in selling some stories and in building the beginnings of a reputation for himself. After the Salem disaster, he wrote and published "The Scarlet Letter," which at once fixed for him a real place in the public estimation. The effect upon Hawthorne was immediately apparent. He settled to his work and wrote several other books, among them "The House of the Seven Gables."

Then he was called upon to write the campaign biography of his friend, Franklin Pierce, who had just been nominated for

* Used by permission of and by arrangement with Houghton Mifflin Company.

the Presidency. In 1853, after Pierce's election, Hawthorne was appointed consul to Liverpool, England, and his most important work as a writer was over. He did not stop writing entirely, however. In 1856 he went to Italy to live, and four years later he returned to this country. Upon his return, he retired again — not so completely this time — to Concord, Massachusetts, where he spent his remaining four years happily enough.

"David Swan," which Hawthorne calls "a fantasy," lacks much of the actual somberness of many of his stories; it contains, however, the dreamy, contemplative touch that is one of the real marks of Hawthorne's peculiar genius. It contains, too, a suggestion of Hawthorne's intense interest in moral values, an interest that is at once apparent to any reader of his novels.

WE CAN be but partially acquainted even with the events which actually influence our course through life, and our final destiny. There are innumerable other events, if such they may be called, which come close upon us, yet pass away without actual results, or even betraying their near approach, by the reflection of any light or shadow across our minds. Could we know all the vicissitudes of our fortunes, life would be too full of hope and fear, exultation or disappointment, to afford us a single hour of true serenity. This idea may be illustrated by a page from the secret of David Swan.

We have nothing to do with David until we find him, at the age of twenty, on the highroad from his native place to the city of Boston, where his uncle, a small dealer in the grocery line, was to take him behind the counter. Be it enough to say that he was a native of New Hampshire, born of respectable parents, and had received an ordinary school education, with a classic finish by a year at Gilmanton Academy. After journeying on foot from sunrise till nearly noon of a summer's day, his weariness and the increasing heat determined him to sit down in the first convenient shade, and await the coming up of the stage-coach. As if planted on purpose for him, there soon appeared a little tuft of maples, with a delightful recess in the midst, and such a fresh bubbling spring, that it seemed never to have sparkled for any wayfarer but David Swan. Virgin or not, he kissed it with his thirsty lips, and then flung himself along the brink, pillowing his head upon some shirts and a pair of pantaloons, tied up in a striped cotton handkerchief. The sunbeams could not reach him; the dust did not yet rise from the road after the heavy rain of yesterday; and his grassy lair suited the young man better than a bed of down. The spring murmured drowsily beside him; the branches waved dreamily across the blue sky overhead; and a deep sleep, perchance hiding dreams within its depths, fell upon David Swan. But we are to relate events which he did not dream of.

While he lay sound asleep in the shade, other people were wide awake, and passed to and fro, afoot, on horseback, and in all sorts of vehicles, along the sunny road by his bedchamber. Some looked neither to the right hand nor the left, and knew not that he was there; some merely glanced that way, without admitting the slumberer among their busy thoughts; some laughed to see how soundly he slept; and several, whose hearts were brimming full of scorn, ejected their venomous superfluity on David Swan. A middle-aged widow, when nobody else was near, thrust her head a little way into the recess, and vowed that the young fellow looked charming in his sleep. A temperance lecturer saw him, and wrought poor David into the texture of his evening's discourse, as an awful instance of dead drunkenness by the roadside. But censure, praise, merriment, scorn, and indifference were all one, or rather all nothing, to David Swan.

He had slept only a few moments when a brown carriage, drawn by a handsome pair of horses, bowled easily along, and was brought to a standstill nearly in front of David's resting-place. A linchpin had fallen out, and permitted one of the wheels to slide off. The damage was slight, and occasioned merely a momentary alarm to an elderly merchant and his wife, who were returning to Boston in the carriage. While the coachman and a servant were replacing the wheel, the lady and gentleman sheltered themselves beneath the maple-trees, and there espied the bubbling fountain, and David Swan asleep beside it. Impressed with the awe which the humblest sleeper usually sheds around him, the merchant trod as lightly as the gout would allow; and his spouse took good heed not to rustle her silk gown, lest David should start up all of a sudden.

"How soundly he sleeps!" whispered the old gentleman. "From what a depth he draws that easy breath! Such sleep as that, brought on without an opiate, would be worth more to me than half my income; for it would suppose health and an untroubled mind."

"And youth, besides," said the lady. "Healthy and quiet age does not sleep thus. Our slumber is no more like his than our wakefulness."

The longer they looked the more did this elderly couple feel interested in the unknown youth, to whom the wayside and the maple shade were as a secret chamber, with the rich gloom of damask curtains brooding over him. Perceiving that a stray sunbeam glimmered down upon his face, the lady contrived to twist a branch aside, so as to intercept it. And having done this little act of kindness, she began to feel like a mother to him.

"Providence seems to have laid him here," whispered she to her husband, "and to have brought us hither to find him, after our disappointment in our cousin's son. Methinks I can see a likeness to our departed Henry. Shall we waken him?"

"To what purpose?" said the merchant, hesitating. "We know nothing of the youth's character."

"That open countenance!" replied his wife, in the same hushed voice, yet earnestly. "This innocent sleep!"

While these whispers were passing, the sleeper's heart did not throb, nor his breath become agitated, nor his features betray the least token of interest. Yet Fortune was bending over him, just ready to let fall a burthen of gold. The old merchant had lost his only son, and had no heir to his wealth, except a distant relative, with whose conduct he was dissatisfied. In such cases, people sometimes do stranger things than to act the magician, and awaken a young man to splendor, who fell asleep in poverty.

"Shall we not waken him?" repeated the lady, persuasively.

"The coach is ready, sir," said the servant, behind.

The old couple started, reddened, and hurried away, mutually wondering that they should ever have dreamed of doing anything so very ridiculous. The merchant threw himself back in the carriage, and occupied his mind with the plan of a magnificent asylum for unfortunate men of business. Meanwhile, David Swan enjoyed his nap.

The carriage could not have gone above a mile or two, when a pretty young girl came along with a tripping pace, which showed precisely how her little heart was dancing in her bosom. Perhaps it was this merry kind of motion that caused — is there any harm in saying it? — her garter to slip its knot. Conscious that the silken girth, if silk it were, was relaxing its hold, she turned aside into the shelter of the maple-trees, and there found a young man asleep by the spring! Blushing as red as any rose, that she should have intruded into a gentleman's bedchamber, and for such a purpose, too, she was about to make her escape on tiptoe. But there was peril near the sleeper. A monster of a bee had been wandering overhead — buzz, buzz, buzz — now among the leaves, now flashing through the strips of sunshine, and now lost in the dark shade, till finally he appeared to be settling on the eyelid of David Swan. The sting of a bee is sometimes deadly. As free-hearted as she was innocent, the girl attacked the intruder with her handkerchief, brushed him soundly, and drove him from the maple shade. How sweet a picture! This good deed accomplished, with quickened breath, and a deeper blush, she stole a glance at the youthful stranger, for whom she had been battling with a dragon in the air.

"He is handsome!" thought she, and blushed redder yet.

How could it be that no dream of bliss grew so strong within him, that, shattered by its very strength, it should part asunder and allow him to perceive the girl among its phantoms? Why, at least, did no smile of welcome brighten upon his face? She was come, the maid whose soul, according to the old and beautiful idea, had been severed from his own, and whom, in all his vague but passionate desires, he yearned to meet. Her only could he love with a perfect love — him only could she receive into the depths of her heart — and now her image was faintly blushing in the fountain by his side; should it pass away, its happy luster would never gleam upon his life again.

"How sound he sleeps!" murmured the girl.

She departed, but did not trip along the road so lightly as when she came.

Now, this girl's father was a thriving country merchant in the neighborhood, and happened, at that identical time, to be looking out for just such a young man as David Swan. Had David formed a wayside acquaintance with the daughter, he would have become the father's clerk, and all else in natural succession. So here, again, had good fortune — the best of fortunes — stolen so near that her garments brushed against him, and he knew nothing of the matter.

The girl was hardly out of sight when two men turned aside beneath the maple shade. Both had dark faces, set off by cloth caps, which were drawn down aslant over their brows. Their dresses were shabby, yet had a certain smartness. These were a couple of rascals, who got their living by whatever the devil sent them, and now, in the interim of other business, had staked the joint profits of their next piece of villainy on a game of cards, which was to have been decided here under the trees. But finding David asleep by the spring one of the rogues whispered to his fellow —

"Hist! — Do you see that bundle under his head!"

The other villain nodded, winked, and leered.

"I'll bet you a horn of brandy," said the first, "that the chap has either a pocketbook or a snug little hoard of small change stowed away amongst his shirts. And if not there, we shall find it in his pantaloons' pocket."

"But how if he wakes?" said the other.

His companion thrust aside his waistcoat, pointed to the handle of a dirk, and nodded.

"So be it!" muttered the second villain.

They approached the unconscious David, and, while one pointed the dagger toward his heart, the other began to search the bundle beneath his head. Their two faces, grim, wrinkled and ghastly with guilt and fear, bent over their victim, looking horrible enough to be mistaken for fiends, should he suddenly awake. Nay, had the villains glanced aside into the spring, even they would hardly have known themselves, as reflected there. But David Swan had never worn a more tranquil aspect, even when asleep on his mother's breast.

"I must take away the bundle," whispered one.

"If he stirs, I'll strike," muttered the other.

But, at this moment, a dog, scenting along the ground, came in beneath the maple-trees, and gazed alternately at each of these wicked men, and then at the quiet sleeper. He then lapped out of the fountain.

"Pshaw!" said one villain. "We can do nothing now. The dog's master must be close behind."

"Let's take a drink, and be off," said the other.

The man with the dagger thrust back the weapon into his bosom, and drew forth a pocket-pistol, but not of that kind which kills by a single discharge. It was a flask of liquor, with a block-tin tumbler screwed upon the mouth. Each drank a comfortable dram, and left the spot, with so many jests and such laughter at their unaccomplished wickedness that they might be said to have gone on their way rejoicing. In a few hours they had forgotten the whole affair, nor once imagined that the recording angel had written down the crime of murder against their souls in letters as durable as eternity. As for David Swan, he still slept quietly, neither conscious of the shadow of death when it hung over him, nor of the glow of renewed life when that shadow was withdrawn.

He slept, but no longer so quietly as at first. An hour's repose had snatched from his elastic frame the weariness with which many hours of toil had burthened it. Now he stirred — now moved his lips, without a sound — now talked in an inward tone to the noonday specters of his dream. But a noise of wheels came rattling louder and louder along the road, until it dashed through the dispersing mist of David's slumber — and there was the stagecoach. He started up, with all his ideas about him.

"Halloo, driver! — Take a passenger?" shouted he.

"Room on top!" answered the driver.

Up mounted David, and bowled away merrily toward Boston, without so much as a parting glance at the fountain of dreamlike vicissitude. He knew not that a phantom of Wealth had thrown a golden hue upon its waters — nor that one of Love had sighed softly to their murmur — nor that one of Death had threatened to crimson them with his blood — all in the brief hour since he lay down to sleep. Sleeping or waking, we hear not the airy footsteps of the strange things that almost happen. Does it not argue a superintending Providence, that, while viewless and unexpected events thrust themselves continually athwart our path, there should still be regularity enough in mortal life to render foresight even partially available?

QUESTIONS
(See pages 8–9.)

1. What is the theme of this story? Do you agree with it?
2. Is the story interesting aside from its theme? Has it any interesting characters? Is David Swan a real character?
3. What actually happened to David Swan in this story? Which was the most important of the impending events in this story?
4. Can you think of any other important possible fate that might have been added to this story? Explain.
5. What is the plot of this story? What is its setting?
6. *Word Study.* — What do the following words mean as they are used in the story: *vicissitude, venomous, superfluity, villainy?*

The Tell-Tale Heart *

Edgar Allan Poe (1809–1849)

Edgar Allan Poe came of a good Maryland family. His father and mother were actors, members of a wandering troupe of players. Edgar was born in 1809 at Boston, where the actors happened to be playing. Two years later, in Richmond, Virginia, both parents died and their children were separated by adoption. Edgar fell into the hands of John Allan, a merchant of Richmond, who gave him an education.

Poe went to the University of Virginia where he acquired gambling debts and a reputation for drunkenness. Mr. Allan removed him from the University and tried to put him into his counting house. There was a quarrel, and the boy went North and joined the army. About the same time (he was eighteen), Poe published his first book, "Tamerlane and Other Poems."

After Poe had been two years in the army, Mr. Allan found him again and helped him obtain an appointment to the Academy at West Point. Poe soon tired of the Academy, and began deliberately to accumulate enough demerits to cause his dismissal. The task was not difficult. Mr. Allan then definitely disowned him, and the young man faced the world with no money, no friends, a talent amounting to genius, and a large collection of bad habits.

For the rest of his life he depended upon his writing for his living. He contributed stories, poems, and literary criticism to several magazines before his ability was recognized; then he became an editor. For years he worked on magazines in Baltimore, in Philadelphia, and finally in New York. Everywhere his story was the same; he would work for a while and then his irregular habits and his dissatisfaction with the world would cause him to lose his job.

In the meanwhile, he had married a thirteen-year-old cousin, Virginia Clemm, to whom he was devoted. In 1847, she died in

* First published in *The Pioneer*, January, 1843.

their poverty-stricken home in Fordham. Two years later, when he was completing arrangements for another marriage, he paid a visit to Baltimore. He was found unconscious on the streets of that city and removed to a hospital, where he died.

Poe is famous for his poetry as well as for his prose. All of you have probably read "The Bells," "Annabel Lee," and "The Raven"; some of you may have read others of his poems and some of his short stories, especially "The Gold Bug" and "The Pit and the Pendulum."

The importance of Poe's contribution to the development of the short story is generally recognized. It was he who, in a magazine criticism of Hawthorne's "Twice-Told Tales," first formulated a theory of technique for the short story. It was he, again, who gave us almost perfect specimens of that technique. And, finally, it was he who invented and perfected that peculiarly modern type of fiction, the detective story.

Poe's work is exceptionally vivid and imaginative. His stories are romances in that they deal with improbable, if not quite impossible, situations. But in spite of his departure from the realities of life, he still must put his own personality into his stories; we find them colored by his gloomy introspection, his morbid temperament, and his grim appreciation of the horrible.

It is interesting to compare his style with the genial and leisurely style of Washington Irving and the no less imaginative but more gentle and reserved style of Nathaniel Hawthorne.

"The Tell-Tale Heart" is a fine example of Poe's peculiar method of obtaining a single effect. The story has been classed by one critic as one of the fifteen greatest stories in the world.

TRUE! — nervous — very, very dreadfully nervous I had been and am! but why *will* you say that I am mad? The disease had sharpened my senses — not destroyed — not dulled them. Above all was the sense of hearing acute. I heard all things in the heaven and in the earth. I heard many things in hell. How, then, am I mad? Hearken! and observe how healthily — how calmly I can tell you the whole story.

It is impossible to say how first the idea entered my brain; but once conceived, it haunted me day and night. Object there was none. Passion there was none. I loved the old man. He had never wronged me. He had never given me insult. For his gold I had no desire. I think it was his eye! yes, it was this! One of his eyes resembled that of a vulture — a pale blue eye, with a film over it. Whenever it fell upon me, my blood ran cold; and so by degrees — very gradually — I made up my mind to take the life of the old man, and thus rid myself of the eye for ever.

Now this is the point. You fancy me mad. Madmen know nothing. But you should have seen *me*. You should have seen how wisely I proceeded — with what caution — with what foresight — with what dissimulation I went to work!

I was never kinder to the old man than during the whole week before I killed him. And every night, about midnight, I turned the latch of his door and opened it — oh, so gently! And then, when I had made an opening sufficient for my head, I put in a dark lantern, all closed, closed, so that no light shone out, and then I thrust in my head. Oh, you would have laughed to see how cunningly I thrust it in! I moved it slowly — very, very slowly, so that I might not disturb the old man's sleep. It took me an hour to place my whole head within the opening so far that I could see him as he lay upon his bed. Ha! — would a madman have been so wise as this? And then, when my head was well in the room, I undid the lantern cautiously — oh, so cautiously — cautiously (for the hinges creaked) — I undid it just so much that a single thin ray fell upon the vulture eye. And this I did for seven long nights — every night just at midnight — but I found the eye always closed; and so it was impossible to do the work; for it was not the old man who vexed me, but his Evil Eye. And every morning, when the day broke, I went boldly into the chamber, and spoke courageously to him, calling him by name in a hearty tone, and inquiring how he had passed the night. So you see he would have been a very profound old man, indeed, to suspect that every night, just at twelve, I looked in upon him while he slept.

Upon the eighth night I was more than usually cautious in

opening the door. A watch's minute hand moves more quickly than did mine. Never before that night had I *felt* the extent of my own powers — of my sagacity. I could scarcely contain my feelings of triumph. To think that there I was, opening the door, little by little, and he not even to dream of my secret deeds or thoughts. I fairly chuckled at the idea; and perhaps he heard me; for he moved on the bed suddenly, as if startled. Now you may think that I drew back — but no. His room was as black as pitch with the thick darkness, (for the shutters were close fastened, through fear of robbers,) and so I knew that he could not see the opening of the door, and I kept pushing it on steadily, steadily.

I had my head in, and was about to open the lantern, when my thumb slipped upon the tin fastening, and the old man sprang up in the bed, crying out — "Who's there?"

I kept quite still and said nothing. For a whole hour I did not move a muscle, and in the meantime I did not hear him lie down. He was still sitting up in the bed listening — just as I have done, night after night, hearkening to the death watches in the wall.

Presently I heard a slight groan, and I knew it was the groan of mortal terror. It was not a groan of pain or of grief — oh, no! — it was the low stifled sound that arises from the bottom of the soul when overcharged with awe. I knew the sound well. Many a night, just at midnight, when all the world slept, it has welled up from my own bosom, deepening, with its dreadful echo, the terrors that distracted me. I say I knew it well. I knew what the old man felt, and pitied him, although I chuckled at heart. I knew that he had been lying awake ever since the first slight noise, when he had turned in the bed. His fears had been ever since growing upon him. He had been trying to fancy them causeless, but could not. He had been saying to himself — "It is nothing but the wind in the chimney — it is only a mouse crossing the floor," or "It is merely a cricket which has made a single chirp." Yes, he had been trying to comfort himself with these suppositions; but he had found all in vain. *All in vain;* because Death, in approaching him, had stalked with his black shadow before him, and enveloped the victim. And it was the mournful influence of the unperceived shadow that caused him to feel — although he neither saw nor heard — to *feel* the presence of my head within the room.

When I had waited a long time, very patiently, without hearing him lie down, I resolved to open a little — a very, very little crevice in the lantern. So I opened it — you cannot imagine now stealthily, stealthily — until, at length, a single dim ray, like the thread of the spider, shot from out the crevice and fell upon the vulture eye.

It was open — wide, wide open — and I grew furious as I gazed upon it. I saw it with perfect distinctness — all a dull blue, with a hideous veil over it that chilled the very marrow in my bones; but I could see nothing else of the old man's face or person: for I had directed the ray, as if by instinct, precisely upon the damned spot.

And now have I not told you that what you mistake for madness is but over-acuteness of the senses? — now, I say, there came to my ears a low, dull, quick sound, such as a watch makes when enveloped in cotton. I knew *that* sound well, too. It was the beating of the old man's heart. It increased my fury, as the beating of a drum stimulates the soldier into courage.

But even yet I refrained and kept still. I scarcely breathed. I held the lantern motionless. I tried how steadily I could maintain the ray upon the eye. Meantime the hellish tattoo of the heart increased. It grew quicker and quicker, and louder and louder every instant. The old man's terror *must* have been extreme! It grew louder, I say, louder every moment! — do you mark me well? I have told you that I am nervous: so I am. And now at the dead hour of the night, amid the dreadful silence of that old house, so strange a noise as this excited me to uncontrollable terror. Yet, for some minutes longer I refrained and stood still. But the beating grew louder, louder! I thought the heart must burst. And now a new anxiety seized me — the sound would be heard by a neighbor! The old man's hour had come! With a loud yell, I threw open the lantern and leaped into the room. He shrieked once — once only. In an instant I dragged him to the floor, and pulled the heavy bed over him. I then smiled gaily, to find the deed so far done. But, for many minutes, the heart beat on with a muffled sound. This, however, did not vex me; it would not be heard through the wall. At length it ceased. The old man was dead. I removed the bed and examined the corpse. Yes, he was stone, stone dead. I placed my hand upon the heart and held it there many minutes. There was no pulsation. He was stone dead. His eye would trouble me no more.

If still you think me mad, you will think so no longer when I describe the wise precautions I took for the concealment of the body. The night waned, and I worked hastily, but in silence. First of all I dismembered the corpse. I cut off the head and the arms and the legs.

I then took up three planks from the flooring of the chamber, and deposited all between the scantlings. I then replaced the boards so cleverly, so cunningly, that no human eye — not even *his* — could have detected anything wrong. There was nothing to wash out — no stain of any kind — no blood-spot whatever. I had been too wary for that. A tub had caught all — ha! ha!

When I had made an end of these labors, it was four o'clock — still dark as midnight. As the bell sounded the hour, there came a knocking at the street door. I went down to open it with a light heart — for what had I *now* to fear? There entered three men, who introduced themselves, with perfect suavity, as officers of the police. A shriek had been heard by a neighbor during the night; suspicion of foul play had been aroused; information had been lodged at the police office, and they (the officers) had been deputed to search the premises.

I smiled — for *what* had I to fear? I bade the gentlemen welcome. The shriek, I said, was my own in a dream. The old man, I mentioned, was absent in the country. I took my visitors all over the house. I bade them search — search *well*. I led them, at length, to *his* chamber. I showed them his

treasures, secure, undisturbed. In the enthusiasm of my confidence, I brought chairs into the room, and desired them
here to rest from their fatigues, while I myself, in the wild
audacity of my perfect triumph, placed my own seat upon
the very spot beneath which reposed the corpse of the victim.

The officers were satisfied. My *manner* had convinced them.
I was singularly at ease. They sat, and while I answered
cheerily, they chatted familiar things. But, ere long, I felt
myself getting pale and wished them gone. My head ached,
and I fancied a ringing in my ears: but still they sat and still
chatted. The ringing became more distinct: it continued and
became more distinct: I talked more freely to get rid of the
feeling: but it continued and gained definitiveness — until, at
length, I found that the noise was *not* within my ears.

No doubt I now grew *very* pale; but I talked more fluently,
and with a heightened voice. Yet the sound increased — and
what could I do? It was *a low, dull, quick sound — much such
a sound as a watch makes when enveloped in cotton.* I gasped
for breath — and yet the officers heard it not. I talked more
quickly — more vehemently; but the noise steadily increased.
I arose and argued about trifles, in a high key and with violent
gesticulations, but the noise steadily increased. Why *would*
they not be gone? I paced the floor to and fro with heavy
strides, as if excited to fury by the observation of the men —
but the noise steadily increased. O God! what *could* I do? I
foamed — I raved — I swore! I swung the chair upon which
I had been sitting, and grated it upon the boards, but the
noise arose over all and continually increased. It grew louder
— louder — *louder!* And still the men chatted pleasantly, and
smiled. Was it possible they heard not? Almighty God! — no,
no! They heard! — they suspected! — they *knew!* — they
were making a *mockery* of my horror! — this I thought, and
this I think. But anything was better than this agony! Anything was more tolerable than this derision! I could bear those
hypocritical smiles no longer! I felt that I must scream or
die! — and now — again — hark! louder! louder! louder!
louder! — "Villains!" I shrieked, "dissemble no more! I ad-

mit the deed! — tear up the planks! — here, here! — it is the
beating of his hideous heart!''

QUESTIONS
(See pages 8, 9, 27.)

1. Who tells this story? What, then, is the point of view? Could anybody else have told the story? Why did not Poe write as the all-
   knowing author?

2. What is the story about — the murder of an old man, or the mental
   condition of the murderer? Give reasons for your belief.

3. How does Poe establish in your mind the belief that the murderer
   was insane?

4. Re-read Poe's statement about unity of effect. (See page 9.) Can
   you find anything in this story that belies the statement?

5. Compare this story with ''The Damned Thing'' by Ambrose Bierce.
   Which is the better story? Which gives the more unified effect? Try
   to find out why.

6. Which is more like the early forms of short narrative, ''David Swan''
   or ''The Tell-Tale Heart''? Which story do you enjoy more? Why?

7. If you were to arrange the stories in Part II, without regard to time,
   in the order of their development toward the modern short-story
   form, what would your order of arrangement be?

8. *Word Study.* — What do the following words mean as they are used
   in the story: *dissimulation, suavity, audacity, hypocritical?*

Bibliography and Reading Lists

It is hoped that the following references may prove to be helpful to both teachers and students. The lists are, of course, far from being anything at all like a short-story index and are to be considered as offering reading suggestions. While a few of the books mentioned may be out of print at present, the editor has attempted to select titles which are still available.

SOME MAGAZINES CONTAINING SHORT STORIES

Adventure Magazine
American Girl (Girl Scouts)
American Legion
Argosy
Atlantic Monthly
Boys' Life
Co-ed
Columbia
Cosmopolitan
Ellery Queen's Mystery Magazine
Everywoman's Family Circle Magazine
Good Housekeeping
Harper's Bazaar
Harper's Magazine
Ladies' Home Journal
Mademoiselle
McCall's
Redbook
Saturday Evening Post
Seventeen
The New Yorker
This Week
Vogue
Woman's Day

YEARBOOKS OF THE SHORT STORY

O. Henry Memorial Award Prize Stories Brickell and Engle (eds.)
Best American Short Stories M. Foley (ed.)
Saturday Evening Post Stories

SHORT STORY INDEXES

Index to Short Stories Ina Ren Eyck Firkin
The Standard Index of Short Stories 1900–1914 Francis J. Hannigan
Short Story Index (60,000 stories) Cook and Monroe

SOME SHORT STORY COLLECTIONS

Abbott, E. H. (ed.) *But Once a Year, Christmas Stories*
Andrews, R. C. (ed.) *My Favorite Stories of the Great Outdoors*
Aymar, G. C. (ed.) *Treasury of Sea Stories*

Baldwin, C. S. (ed.) *American Short Stories*

Bates, S. C. (ed.) *Twentieth Century Short Stories*

Becker, M. L. (ed.) *Golden Tales of Our America; Growing Up with America*, etc. (See other collections by the same editor.)

Becker and Lehman (eds.) *Under Twenty*

Benét, S. V. *Thirteen O'Clock; Tales Before Midnight*, etc.

Benjamin and Hargreaves (eds.) *Great English Short Stories*

Blaustein, P. M. and A. P. (eds.) *Doctors' Choice*

Boyle, K. *Thirty Stories*

Bradford, R. *Let the Band Play Dixie*

Buck, P. *The First Wife and Other Stories*

Burnet, W. (ed.) *Time to Be Young*

Cavanah and Weir (eds.) *Treasury of Dog Stories; Twenty-four Horses*

Cerf and Moriarty (eds.) *Anthology of Famous British Stories*

Certner and Henry (eds.) *Short Stories for Our Times*

Chesterton, G. K. *Father Brown Omnibus* (See individual collections of Father Brown stories.)

Clark and Lieber *Great Short Stories of the World*

Cobb, I. S. *Old Judge Priest; This Man's World*, etc.

Cohen, O. R. *Epic Peters, Pullman Porter; Polished Ebony; Come Seven*, etc.

Colter, J. R. (ed.) *Omnibus of Adventure; Omnibus of Romance*

Conklin, G. *Best of Science Fiction*

Cook, D. C. (ed.) *Best Detective Stories of 1957*, etc.

Cooper, P. (ed.) *Famous Dog Stories*

Cournos, J. (ed.) *American Short Stories of the Nineteenth Century*

Costain and Beecroft (eds.) *Stories to Remember* (two volumes)

Dahl, R. *Someone Like You; Over to You*

Daly, M. (ed.) *My Favorite Stories*

Davenport, B. (ed.) *Ghostly Tales to Be Told*

Day, A. C. (ed.) *Greatest American Short Stories*

Doyle, A. C. *Book of Sherlock Holmes; The Maracot Deep and Other Stories* (See other volumes of short stories by Doyle.)

Eaton, H. T. (ed.) *Short Stories*

Edmonds, W. D. *Mostly Canallers*

Fenner, P. R. (ed.) *Cowboys, Cowboys, Cowboys; Dogs, Dogs, Dogs*, etc. (See other collections by the same editor; there are many.)

Fenton, C. (ed.) *Best Short Stories of World War II*

Ferber, E. *Mother Knows Best*, etc.

Fisher, D. C. *Four Square*, etc.

Fox, J. Jr. *Christmas Eve on Lonesome*

French, J. L. (ed.) *Great Detective Stories of the World*

Gale, Z. *Bridal Pond*, etc.
Galsworthy, J. *Caravan*
Garland, H. *Main-Traveled Roads*
Garrity, D. A. (ed.) *Forty-four Irish Short Stories*
Gaster, T. H. (ed.) *The Oldest Stories in the World*
Goodman, J. A. (ed.) *Fireside Book of Dog Stories*
Gordimer, N. *The Soft Voice of the Serpent*
Gray, C. W. (ed.) *Deep Waters*

Hanson, H. (ed.) *First-Prize Stories from the O. Henry Memorial Awards*
Harte, B. (See Complete Works.)
Havighurst, W. (ed.) *Masters of the Modern Short Story*
Hawthorne, N. *Twice-told Tales*, etc.
Haycraft, H. (ed.) *Boys' Book of Great Detective Stories*
Henry, O. (See Complete Works or individual volumes.)
Herzberg, M. (ed.) *Treasure Chest of Sea Stories*
Hibbard, C. A. *Stories of the Old South*

Jacobs, W. W. *Night Watches; Deep Waters*, etc.
Jaffe and Scott (eds.) *Study in the Short Story*
Jessup, A. (ed.) *American Humorous Short Stories; Little French Master-
     pieces*
Joseph, M. *Best Cat Stories*

Kipling, R. *Jungle Book; Plain Tales from the Hills*, etc.
Knight, R. A. (ed.) *It Might Be You*
Kuebler, H. (ed.) *The Treasury of Science Fiction*

Lardner, R. *Round Up; The Big Town*, etc.
Lieber and Williams (eds.) *Great Short Stories of All Nations*
London, J. *Sundog Trail and Other Stories*
Long, R. (ed.) *Twenty Best Stories*

Marshall, E. *The Heart of Little Shikara and Other Stories*
Melville and Hargreaves (eds.) *Great French Short Stories*
Mikels, R. *Short Stories for High School Courses*
Morley, C. *Tales from a Rolltop Desk*
Morrow, H. *The Lincoln Stories*
Munroe, H. *The Short Stories of Saki*

Nash, O. (ed.) *I Couldn't Help Laughing*
Nason, L. H. *The Incomplete Mariner*
Neale, A. (ed.) *The Great Weird Stories*

O'Connor, F. *Traveller's Samples; Bones of Contention*
Overton, G. (ed.) *The World's One Hundred Best Short Stories*
Owen, F. (ed.) *Teen-age Baseball Stories; Teen-age Football Stories*, etc.
     (See other titles on this series.)

Persky, L. (ed.) *Adventures in Sport*
Poe, E. A. See Collected Works or individual volumes.
Posselt, E. (ed.) *World's Greatest Christmas Stories*

Queen, E. (ed.) *Queen's Awards*

Rawlings, M. K. *When the Whipperwill*
Rinehart, M. R. *Best of Tish*, etc.
Runyan, D. *Blue Plate Special*, etc.
Rhys and Dawson Scott (eds.) *Twenty-six Adventure Stories*

Sabatini, R. *Historical Nights*
Sayers, D. (ed.) *Omnibus of Crime*
Schweikert, H. C. (ed.) *Short Stories; French Short Stories; Russian Short Stories*
Sloane, W. (ed.) *Stories for Tomorrow*
Steele, W. D. *Best Stories; Storm; Land's End*, etc.
Stuart, Jesse *Tales from the Plum Grove Hills*

Tarkington, B. *Penrod; Penrod and Sam; Little Orvie*, etc.
Terhune, A. P. *Lad: a Dog; Buff, a Collie*, etc.

Van Buren and Bemis (eds.) *Father in Modern Story; Mother in Modern Story*

Wharton, E. *Certain People*
Wilson, D. (ed.) *Family Christmas Book*

INEXPENSIVE PAPERBACK SHORT-STORY COLLECTIONS

Benét, S. V. *The Stephen Vincent Benét Pocketbook*
Bowen, E. *Short Stories of Katherine Mansfield*
Brunini and Connolly (eds.) *Stories of Our Century by Catholic Authors*

Cather, W. *Five Stories*
Cerf, B. (ed.) *Famous Ghost Stories; Great Modern Short Stories*
Crane, M. (ed.) *Fifty Great Short Stories*

Foley, M. (ed.) *Best American Short Stories* — 1953, 1955, 1956
Foote, S. *The Night Before Chancellorville and Other Stories*

Gordimer, N. *The Soft Voice of the Serpent and Other Stories*

Hanson, H. (ed.) *Pocket Book of O. Henry*

Isherwood, C. (ed.) *Great English Short Stories*

Kauffman, S. (ed.) *Great Dog Stories*
Kipling, R. *Great Short Stories*

London, J. *The Seed of McCoy and Other Stories*

Stegner, W. and M. (eds.) *Great American Short Stories*
Stern, P. Van Doren (ed.) *Modern American Short Stories*
Stevenson, R. L. *Great Short Stories*

West, R. B. *The Short Story in America*
 (For additional titles, consult the latest catalog of Paperbooks, New York 16, New York.)

A FEW BOOKS ABOUT WRITING THE SHORT STORY

Allen, W. E. *The Writer on His Art*

Baker, D. *How to Be an Author*
Brande, D. *Becoming a Writer*
Burack, A. *Writer's Handbook*

Glicksberg, C. I. *Creative Writing; Writing the Short Story*

Hull, H. *Writer's Book*

Lait, J. *Practical Guide to Successful Writing*
Leggett and Others *Handbook for Writers*
Lewis, C. *Writing for Young Children*

Neal, H. E. *Writing and Selling Fact and Fiction*

Robinson, M. L. *Writing for Young People*

Swallow, A. *The Beginning Writer*

SOME MAGAZINES DEVOTED TO WRITING

The Author and Journalist
The Writer
The Writer's Digest
(*The Writer's Yearbook* is published annually by
The Writer's Digest.)

Stories to Read